WADE PRICE TR...

THE WORLD OF WADE

and

THE WORLD OF WADE BOOK 2

First Edition

by IAN WARNER and MIKE POSGAY

---

*This book is dedicated to the memory
of four Wade collectors and enthusiasts
who were of so much help
to us in the past.*

*H. Straker Carryer
John Feist
Alec McCullough
and
Richard Melia*

CONTENTS

Outside Front Cover Descriptions:

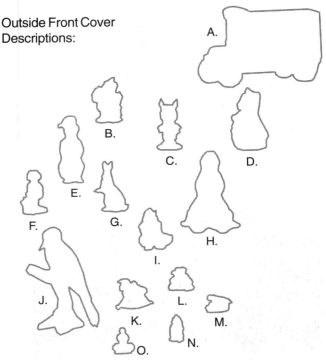

A. Jim Beam Van Money Box *(See Nos. 332 and 333 of WPT.)*

B. Burglar *(See No. 31 of WPT.)*

C. Scrappy Doo *(See No. 113 of WPT.)*

D. Felicity Squirrel *(See Nos. 76 and 77 of WPT.)*

E. Hamm's Beer Bear *(See Nos. 82, 83 and 84 of WPT.)*

F. Flo *(See Nos. 70 and 71 of WPT.)*

G. Grey-Haired Rabbit *(See No. 101 of WPT.)*

H. Arthur Hare *(See Nos. 74 and 78 of WPT.)*

I. Prisoner *(See No. 35 of WPT.)*

J. Woodpecker *(See No. 25 of WPT.)*

K. Rocking Horse *(See No. 52 of WPT.)*

L. Bear Ambitions *(See No. 90 of WPT.)*

M. Human Cannonball *(See No. 50 of WPT.)*

N. Clown *(See No. 46 of WPT.)*

O. Strongman *(See No. 49 of WPT.)*

Inside Back Cover Descriptions:

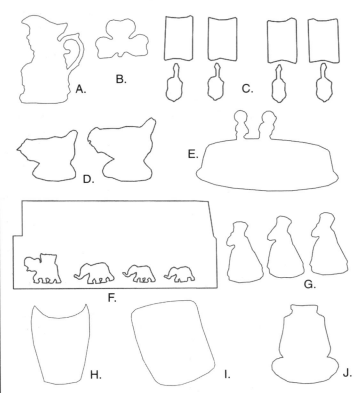

A. Highwayman *(See No. 16 Fig. 125 pg. 198 of The W of W.)*

B. Wade (Ireland) Ltd. "Shamrock" Advertising Sign

C. Set of Teenage Pottery Pins *(See Fig. 48 pg. 142 of The W of W2.)*

D. Reproduction "Madam Mim" (left) and Original "Madam Mim" (right)

E. Bandstand for the Robertson "Gollies"

F. The Elephant Train complete with original packaging *(See Fig. 30 pg. 31 of The W of W2.)*

G. Queen of Hearts *(See Fig. 48 pg. 99 of The W of W.)*

H. "Fantasia" Vase *(See Fig. 102 pg 140 of The W of W.)*

I. "Fantasia" Tray *(See Fig. 102 pg. 140 of The W of W.)*

J. Lighter and Ashtray by Wade (Ireland) Ltd.

INTRODUCTION

With the continuing popularity and success of *The World of Wade* and *The World of Wade Book 2*, the authors and publisher decided that a comprehensive price guide would help satisfy the many requests for items not priced in either of the books. As discussed with numerous collectors at the first U.K. Wade Fair in Birmingham (September 1994) *Wade Price Trends - First Edition* is the result of these discussions. One major request was that the prices be listed in both U.K. pounds and American dollars.

As you will see, *Wade Price Trends* is divided into three sections:

1.) A new text and color section illustrating items produced by the Pottery after the publication of *The World of Wade Book 2* along with additional, original research;

2.) Suggested Prices to *The World of Wade*; and

3.) Suggested Prices to *The World of Wade Book 2*.

Collectors will notice that items shown in the illustrations of trade literature, which were given figure numbers and not priced in the original editions, are now listed. Where sets are incomplete in the color sections, we have listed the missing items below the numbered items that appear in the color section. We have also cross referenced as many items as possible.

The handy backstamp section has been included in this book along with a number of additional marks. Most notable of these additions are a number of the earlier Wade & Co. backstamps from the late nineteenth century. A number of Wade products bearing these earlier backstamps appear in the color section. We also note an extremely rare, molded backstamp utilizing the word Burslem. To date, to our knowledge this is the first Wade-Burslem mark.

The special backstamp section has also been extended to include some of the more recent marks used for the limited editions made by Wade in the past few years.

A few years ago, Mike and I were introduced to Wharton Lang, son of Faust Lang. Many interesting discussions ensued after our first meeting. We are passing onto readers some background history of the famous, late 1930's, Wade modeller. Wharton Lang also supplied us with a number of interesting photographs, some of which we are reproducing in this book. These photographs illustrate the many talents of this designer but are not necessarily examples of his work for Wade. They are reproduced here to give the reader a better insight into the world of this designer.

In the mid-1980's, Iris and Straker Carryer were most helpful and encouraging in sharing their memories of the days of Wade (Ireland) Ltd. Recently, Iris Carryer has been sharing with us, more of her memories of her early years in Burslem. Iris has a superb sense of humour and her recollections of her grandparents and her father, the late Sir George Wade, have given us numerous occasions for a "good laugh."

The Wade family's deep interest and understanding of ceramics continue with Iris and Straker's daughter Felicity Graham and her husband, who now live in Northern Ireland. Amongst Felicity's many talents is her ability to produce delightful drawings and sketches. Iris has kindly given us permission to reproduce one of these drawings in this book. The drawing reproduced below was originally one of many used to illustrate a review of Iris' memories of her years in Burslem which included numerous amusing anecdotes of her maternal grandmother and life as a young girl, with "Pa." It illustrates Iris, as a young girl, with her maternal grandfather making her first impressions in clay.

THE METHOD OF ESTABLISHING SUGGESTED PRICES

The suggested prices in the *Wade Price Trends* are derived from prices submitted to us by our panel of advisers and contributors from both the United Kingdom and the United States of America. Prices also taken into consideration are those sent to us by a number of collectors and from prices achieved at various specialty auctions.

It must be pointed out that the prices quoted are average prices taken from all those that were submitted to us. These prices do not reflect specials e.g. factory, store outlets, show specials, etc. The price survey also netted some surprises which is attributed to the popularity or lack thereof an item in a particular country. From the prices quoted to us, we found that it is often a case of items in the U.S.A. being less popular than similar items in the U.K. or vice versa.

Remember, this is a suggested price guide only. Prices suggested are not to be interpreted literally as final dealer prices; rather it is an indication of the range around which collectors might expect to pay.

WHAT TO LOOK FOR WHILST PURCHASING WADE ITEMS FOR PERSONAL COLLECTIONS

All prices are for items in excellent condition. We prefer not to use the overworked expression "mint," as this would refer only to unused items still contained in original unopened packaging. Of course, it is also possible for the so-called "mint" items to be damaged between final glazing and the original packaging.

The 1930's cellulose-finished Wade figures are very collectable but collectors should pay prices related to the amount of flaking and repainting on any particular piece. The Wade flowers are also another area for collectors to use caution. We have yet to see one Wade flower without some sort of minor damage. Nowadays, rarer items have often been repaired. It is the duty of the vendor to explain this to a potential customer. Well-repaired and restored pieces are quite desirable but should not command the price for a similar item in excellent, unrestored condition.

It is advisable for collectors to remember a few tips when looking for Wade at flea markets, car boot sales, etc. It is often quite an exciting experience to find unusual or rare Wade items at the types of locations listed above. To avoid disappointment when unpacking a "find" on arriving home, bear in mind the few following suggestions:

1) check for defects such as flaking, chips— either minor or extensive. It is amazing how easy it is to overlook damage of many sorts on dirty, unwashed items.

2) If, by any chance, there are two items on a table, compare them for any damage, missing glaze, flaking etc. If there are rare or unusual items in large numbers, beware of fakes and reproductions!

3) Always buy what you really want and at prices that are realistic and also at prices to suit your pocketbook. As a collector, do not buy purely for investment. Prices have been rising speedily for the past few years, but this does not mean they will rise indefinitely.

ABBREVIATIONS

N P A	—	No Price Available
The W of W	—	The World of Wade
The W of W2	—	The World of Wade Book 2
WPT	—	Wade Price Trends
I.A.J.B.B.S.C.	—	International Association of Jim Beam Bottle and Specialties Clubs
T.O.I.W.C.C.	—	The Official International Wade Collectors Club
h., l., w.,		Refers to measurements: h.= High; l.= Long; w.= Wide

A WORD OF THANKS TO OUR PANEL OF ADVISERS AND CONTRIBUTORS

Finally, we most sincerely thank our panel of advisors for the long hours they all spent filling in the very lengthy questionnaire we sent to them. Without your help, we would not have been able to suggest prices for over 3,000 Wade items. Thank you all!

IMPORTANT

We encourage collectors to submit photographs of items which have not appeared in either *The World of Wade*, *The World of Wade Book 2* or *The Wade Price Trends*. To contact the authors please write to:

P.O. Box 93022
499 Main Street South
Brampton, Ontario
Canada L6Y 4V8

ACKNOWLEDGMENTS

Our grateful thanks go to the following for their generous help and contributions to this book.

JOYCE ADAMS, Wiltshire, England

CARYL ALCOCK, Wade Ceramics Limited, England

RALPH BROUGH, Wade Ceramics Limited, England

DAPHNE CARE, Cornwall, England

DAVID CHOWN, West Sussex, England

PETER CHISHOLM, Perthshire, England

ELIZABETH AND JOHN CLARKE, Middlesex, England

BARBARA COOKSEY, Shropshire, England

ELAINE AND ADRIAN CRUMPTON, Buckinghamshire, England

JOY DAMSELL, Wade Ceramics Limited, England

RON DANNER, New Hampshire, U.S.A.

DEREK L. J. DAWE, Staffordshire, England

ALAN DIXON, Ringtons Limited, England

GERRY J. DOUTRE, President, Redco Foods, Inc., U.S.A.

TOM FISH AND SHANNON MCCANDLISH, Oregon, U.S.A.

NANCY FRONCZAK, Illinois, U.S.A.

PEGGY GAMBLE, West Yorkshire, England

VERONICA GARSIDE, Wiltshire, England

ROBERT GLADSTONE, *Antique and Collectibles Trader*, Canada

EDITH HACKING, Ontario, Canada

ADELE HALL, Wade Ceramics Limited, England

BETTY AND DENNIS HANNIGAN, Pennsylvania, U.S.A.

CHARLES HARLAN, Washington, U.S.A.

TONY HEMMINGS, Wade Ceramics, England

PEGGY S. JOHNSON, Illinois, U.S.A.

HARRIET AND BRUCE KELLMAN, New York, U.S.A.

ESTHER KRAMER, Pennsylvania, U.S.A.

DAVE LEE, England

GRAHAM LISTER, Lister Art Books, England

HEATHER AND WILLIAM MACARTHUR, Ontario, Canada

LAWRENCE MARTIN, Wiltshire, England

MICHELLE MARTIN, Wiltshire, England

MAUREEN MASSEY, Wade Ceramics, England

DAVID AND LYNNE MAUND, Hampshire, England

DENISE MELIA, Pennsylvania, U.S.A.

CAROL AND JOHN MURDOCK, Colorado, U.S.A.

VALERIE MOODY, Colorado, U.S.A.

KEN AND MARGARET NEATE, Oxfordshire, England

MOLLY NEWMAN, Oregon, U.S.A.

SHAWN PATTERSON, Ontario, Canada

MARY I. REGISTER, Administrative Assistant, Redco Foods, Inc., U.S.A.

WILLIAM L. READ, Oregon, U.S.A.

CYNTHIA RISDON, Wade Ceramics, England

MRS. J.M. ROWLES, Greater Manchester, England

RUSSELL SCHOOLEY, West Sussex, England

SHARON SHAPIRO, Connecticut, U.S.A.

MARY ANN AND ROBERT SLOAN, Oregon, U.S.A.

LIBUSE AND STEVE SMYKAL, Ontario, Canada

DAVID SPAID, California, U.S.A.

GAIL SPENCE, Antique Diary, U.K.

SHIRLEY SUMBLES, Indiana, U.S.A.

ALAN AND BETTY TAYLOR, Staffordshire, England

RONA TRAINOR, Florida, U.S.A.

MURIEL TROUTON, Seagoe Ceramics Limited, Northern Ireland

KIM WEBB, Wade Ceramics, England

JEREMY AND ANABELLE WADE, Shropshire, England

TERRY WASSELL, Wales

MAUREEN WIGHTON, Ontario, Canada

JENNY WRIGHT, Wade Ceramics Limited, England

JO-ANN YADROW, Oregon, U.S.A.

We would like to thank Wharton Lang for the time he took from his busy schedule to talk with us about his father and for his permission to quote from an article by H. L. Weaver.

A special thank you to Warren and Marylin Shaver for bringing to our attention the rare Snow White, Doc and Sneezy brooches.

We thank the helpful staff of Antique Publications, especially David E. Richardson, D. Thomas O'Connor and James S. Measell for their understanding, advice and continued interest in our books. We also thank Elliott Graham for his patience during the hectic color photography sessions and Terry Richards Nutter for all her hard work (as recorded on film), patience and her willingness to understand the many demands we made upon her.

Additional black & white and color photography by Mike Posgay and Ian Warner.

DIRECTORY OF CONTRIBUTORS

ELIZABETH CLARKE
Middlesex, England
Tel. & Fax 01895 230 261
Specializing in Wade and other collectables. Regular exhibitor at fairs throughout England

DAVID CHOWN & RUSSELL SCHOOLEY
C&S COLLECTABLES AT SPOONERS
15 High Street
Arundel, West Sussex, England BN18 9AD
Tel. 01903 884388 • Fax 01243 867046
Specializing in Wade, Beswick, Royal Doulton & Pendelfin; Mail order, specialty fairs and at the above address during regular store hours

CAROLE MURDOCK & VALERIE MOODY
COLLECTOR'S CORNER
8199 Pierson Ct., Arvada, CO. U.S.A. 80005
Tel. (303) 421-9655 (Carole)
Tel. (303) 424-4401 (Valerie) • Fax (303) 421-0317
Specializing in Wade; Mail order, specialty & antique shows and at the above address by prior arrangement.

Collector's Corner also publishes a Wade newsletter: The Wade Watch. Edited by Carole Murdock & Valerie Moody. Available at the above address.

ELAINE AND ADRIAN CRUMPTON
Buckinghamshire, England
Tel. 01908 310608
Specializing in Wade; Mail order and specialty fairs

PAT AND GARY KEENAN
KEENAN ANTIQUES
P.O.Box 111, Dover, PA 17315 U.S.A.
Tel. (717) 292-4820 • Fax (717) 292-4664
Specializing in Wade; Mail order, specialty fairs

HARRIET AND BRUCE KELLMAN
New York, U.S.A.
Tel. (914) 476-1451
Specializing in Wade, Shelley and Head Vase Planters; Antique and Collectables shows in the north/east U.S.A.

DAVID AND LYNNE MAUND
Hampshire, England
Tel. 01703 695506 • Fax 01703 696036
Specializing in Wade, Royal Doulton and Spode decanters and mini liquor bottles.

ROBERT AND MARY ANN SLOAN
P.O. Box 187
Toledo, OR 97391 U.S.A.
Tel. (541) 336-2444
Specializing in Wade Mail Order and specialty fairs

ALAN AND BETTY TAYLOR
The Potteries Centre, Unit 40F
Newcastle Business Centre, Winpenny Road
Newcastle-under-Lyme, Staffordshire
England ST5 7RH
Tel. 01782 565378
Specializing in Wade; Mail order, antique fairs and at the above address by prior arrangement

Alan and Betty Taylor also publish a quarterly newsletter—The Jolly Potter. The newsletter is available from the above address.

THE OFFICIAL INTERNATIONAL WADE
COLLECTORS CLUB
Wade Ceramics Limited, Royal Victoria Pottery
Westport Road, Burslem, Stoke-on-Trent
Staffordshire, England ST6 4AG
Tel. 01782 588400 (UK) • 44 1782 58840 (Int'l)
Fax. 01782 813663 (UK) • 44 1782 813663 (Int'l)

Membership in the club entitles members to a quarterly newsletter—The Magazine, and a free figurine when membership is opened or renewed. There are also a number of limited edition pieces made available each year to members only.

JOANN YADRO
P.O.Box 2143
White Salmon, WA 98672 U.S.A.
Tel. (509) 493-3484 • Fax (509) 493-9233
Specializing in old and rare Wade; Mail order and Palmer Wirf (America's largest antique & collectables show) Expo Center, Portland Oregon.

DESIGNERS AND MODELLERS

FAUST LANG (1882 - 1973)
Wood Sculptor and designer

Faust Lang at Work

Due to the extraordinary success of the Wade Figures designed by Jessica Van Hallen from the early 1930's through to the start of World War II, The Wade Potteries engaged the services of Faust Lang, a well known German wood carver who had taken up residence in England. He was to design a series of animal and bird figures to complement the Van Hallen figures. The animal figures were to be quality pieces with multi-colored, under glaze finishes. Unfortunately, due to the onset of the war, the run of the Faust Lang animal figures was relatively short. Today, when found, the Lang figures command hefty prices.

In 1887, in Oberammergau, Germany, a son was born to a successful wood sculptor one Andreas Lang. This son, Faustinus Emmanuel Lang was soon to follow in his father's footsteps as a wood carver. About three and one half years after the child's birth, his mother was surprised to find her young son happily hammering away at a piece of wood in his father's studio. This interest proved to be a lasting one and by the time young Faust Lang reached the age of seven, the elder Lang began giving his son regular instructions and guidance in the art of wood carving. These sessions took place each evening after young Faust returned from school.

The town of Oberammergau is famous for the Passion Play and in 1890, at the age of three, young Faust was chosen as one of the players. In 1900, Faust Lang once again appeared in the Passion Play, this time as second violin in the musical section of the play. In the 1910 version of the play, the younger Lang was a tenor in the choir and his father took the part of St. Peter. Both the younger and elder Langs were to repeat their performances in the next Passion Play. The year 1930 was the fifth and final time Faust Lang would appear in the play, again singing tenor.

In or around 1900, Faust Lang developed a strong interest in the sport of skiing. This interest was encouraged by Lang's father who soon started to design and make skis for himself and all members of his family. Faust Lang was far too eager to wait for his father to finish all the skis so he made his own. The younger Lang's first effort on the slopes was not a success and he ended up on his face.

By 1922, Faust Lang had developed into an excellent and experienced skier and was chosen to be a member of the Bavarian relay team for the Winter Olympic Games held in nearby Garmisch-Partenkirchen. For his efforts, Lang was awarded a bronze medal when his relay team placed third.

In 1911, Faust Lang married an English girl he

Wharton Lang, Mike Posgay and Ian Warner

Above: Wood carving in progress of a Stoat by Faust Lang

Left: A wood carving by Faust Lang

Above: Wood carving of a woodpecker by Faust Lang;
Right: The Ballerina — wood carving by Faust Lang

Faust Lang (left) and Wharton Lang (right)

had first met in 1909 when she was a visitor to Oberammergau. In 1925, they had a son, Wharton Lang who, like his father and grandfather before him, was to carry on the family tradition of wood carving.

Due to the unstable German political scene of the 1930's, Faust Lang decided to move his family to the English countryside and the homeland of his wife. The family first settled in the county of Wiltshire in 1933 but in 1934, Lang established his own studio in North Cornwall. At this time, Faust Lang began instructing his son Wharton in the art of painting and drawing and later in the art of wood carving.

It was around this time that Faust Lang began a series of wood carvings that were to be used as models for the pottery figures made by The George Wade Pottery. A number of these figures are illustrated in Fig. 7 and Fig.8 in *The World of Wade*. The original models for these figures were first carved in wood by Faust Lang and then transposed to a clay mould form by Wade modellers.

Carvings by Lang were exhibited at the Royal Academy in 1945 and 1946 resulting in much wider recognition of the artist. One commission which

brought Lang even further recognition was for a plaque depicting the Castle of Mey for Queen Elizabeth, the Queen Mother. One of Lang's most successful and exciting carvings was that of a female skater simply titled "The Skater," which was stolen from his studio and has never been recovered.

The carvings executed by Faust Lang over his long career ranged from figures of peasants in the Bavarian tradition to leaping horses, deer and weasels to full size religious carvings. Some of his most exciting carvings were "The Skater," The Bavarian Dancers" and "the Ballet Dancer." These carvings showed Lang's complete understanding of the human body and his ability to depict the flow of the figures' clothing and bodies as if in actual motion.

Faust Lang died on February 18, 1973, after a long and full life. Today his son, Wharton Lang, a successful wood sculptor in his own right, continues the family tradition at his studio in Cornwall. Wharton Lang specializes in creatures of the sea and sea birds, many of which have been displayed at galleries around the country.

WADE POTTERIES MARKS & BACKSTAMPS

WADE & CO.

Mark Type 04
1893
Ink Stamp

Mark Type 03
1899
Ink Stamp

Mark Type 02
1900
Ink Stamp

Mark Type 01
1901
Ink Stamp

Wades'

England

Mark Type 0
Late 1900s - Mid 1920s
Ink Stamp

WADES
ENGLAND

Mark Type 1
Mid 1920s - 1927
Ink Stamp

WADES ORCADIA WARE
BRITISH MADE

Mark Type 1A
Mid 1920s - 1927
Ink Stamp

WADE HEATH & CO. LTD.

WADEHEATH
ENGLAND

Mark Type 2
1928 - 1937
Ink Stamp

WADEHEATH ORCADIA WARE
BRITISH MADE

Mark Type 2A
1928 - 1934
Ink Stamp

Mark Type 2B
1934 - Late 1930s
Ink Stamp

Mark Type 2C
Mid 1930s - Late 1930s
Ink Stamp

Mark Type 2D
1934 - Late 1930s
Ink Stamp

WADEHEATH **B** ENGLAND

Mark Type 3
1939 - 1942
Ink Stamp

Flaxman Ware Hand Made Pottery
BY WADEHEATH ENGLAND

Mark Type 4
Circa 1936
Ink Stamp

Wadeheath
Ware
England

Mark Type 5
Circa 1937
Ink Stamp

FLAXMAN WADE HEATH ENGLAND

Mark Type 6
Circa 1937 - 1938
Ink Stamp

WADE HEATH ENGLAND

Mark Type 7
Circa 1938 - 1950
Ink Stamp

WADE HEATH ENGLAND **A**

Mark Type 7A
1942 - Mid 1940s
Ink Stamp

WADE HEATH ENGLAND **J**

Mark Type 7B
Circa 1945 (?)
Ink Stamp

WADE HEATH ENGLAND

Mark Type 8
Circa 1938 - 1950
Ink Stamp

WADE HEATH ENGLAND **A**

Mark Type 8A
Circa 1942 - Late 1940s
Ink Stamp

"GOTHIC"
WADE HEATH ENGLAND

Mark Type 9
Circa Late 1930s - 1950
Ink Stamp

WADE ENGLAND

Mark Type 10
Circa Late 1940s
Ink Stamp

WADE
MADE IN ENGLAND

Mark Type 10A
Late 1940's
Ink Stamp

WADE
ENGLAND
A

Mark Type 10B
Circa 1945 - Late 1940's
Ink Stamp

WADE
ENGLAND
"GOTHIC"

Mark Type 11
Circa 1948-1954
Ink Stamp

Mark Type 11A
1947 - Mid 1950's
Transfer

Mark Type 12
Circa 1950-1955
Ink Stamp

Mark Type 12A
Circa Mid 1950's - Late 1950's
Ink Stamp

Mark Type 12B
Circa Mid 1950's - Late 1950's
Ink Stamp

Mark Type 12C
Circa Late 1950's
Ink Stamp

Mark Type 13
Circa 1947-Early 1950's
Ink Stamp

WADE
ENGLAND

Mark Type 14
Circa 1947-Early 1950's
Ink Stamp

Mark Type 15
Circa 1947-1953
Ink Stamp

WADE
MADE IN
ENGLAND
HAND PAINTED

Mark Type 16
Circa 1953+
Transfer

Mark Type 17
Circa 1953+
Transfer

Mark Type 17A
1953 - Early 1960's
Ink Stamp

Mark Type 18
Circa 1953+
Transfer

Mark Type 18A
Circa Mid 1950's - 1960's
Transfer

Mark Type 18B
Circa Mid 1950's - 1960's
Transfer

Mark Type 18C
Circa Mid 1950's
Ink & Transfer

WADE
ENGLAND

Mark Type 19
Circa 1953+
Transfer
(George Wade & Son Ltd.
Also Used This Mark
From Circa 1953 On.)

Mark Type 19A
Late 1950's
Transfer

Mark Type 19B
1956 - Early 1960's
Transfer

Mark Type 19C
Circa 1956 - Early 1960's
Transfer

Mark Type 20
1985+
Transfer

GEORGE WADE & SON LTD.

Mark Type 20A
1931 - Mid 1930's
Ink Stamp

Mark Type 21
Circa Early 1930's-Late 1930's
Ink Stamp

Mark Type 21A
Late 1930's
Ink Stamp

WADE

MADE IN ENGLAND

Mark Type 22
Circa Early 1930's-Late 1930's
Hand Painted Ink

Mark Type 23
Circa 1939
Ink Stamp

Mark Type 23A
1947+
Ink Stamp

WADE
Porcelain
made in England

Mark Type 24
1958+
Molded

WADE
PORCELAIN
MADE IN ENGLAND

Mark Type 25
1957-1981
Molded

WADE
MADE IN
ENGLAND

Mark Type 26
1959+
Molded

WADE
MADE IN ENGLAND

Mark Type 27
1958+
Molded

GENUINE
WADE
PORCELAIN

Mark Type 27A
Mid 1980's
Transfer

WADE CERAMICS LTD.

Mark Type 27B
1990+
Transfer

WADE (IRELAND) LTD.

Mark Type 27C
Circa 1950+
Ink Stamp

Mark Type 28
1953+
Impressed

Mark Type 29
Mid 1954+
Impressed

Mark Type 30
Mid 1954
Transfer

Mark Type 31
Mid 1950's+
Molded

Mark Type 32
1955
Impressed

Mark Type 32A
Circa - Early 1960's - 1967
Transfer

Mark Type 32B
Circa Early 1960's - 1967
Transfer

Mark Type 33
1962
Molded

Mark Type 33A
1962
Moulded

Mark Type 34
Mid 1960's
Molded

Mark Type 35
1970
Impressed

Mark Type 36
1973
Impressed

WADE
IRELAND

Mark Type 37
1970+
Transfer

MADE IN
IRELAND
BY
WADE

Mark Type 38
Mid 1970's
Impressed

Mark Type 39
1965-1968
Impressed

Mark Type 40
1977+
Molded

Mark Type 41
1980+
Molded
&
Transfer

Mark Type 41A
1991
Ink Stamp

WADE HEATH & CO. LTD.
&
REGINALD CORFIELD (SALES) LTD.

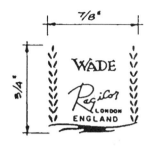

Mark Type 42
1950-1957
Transfer

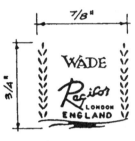

Mark Type 43
1957-1966
Transfer

(NOTE: MARK 43 SIMILAR TO
MARK 42 BUT HEAVIER
LETTERING.)

WADE
Regicor
HAND PAINTED
IN STAFFORDSHIRE
ENGLAND

Mark Type 43A
Circa Early - Mid 1960's
Transfer

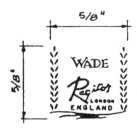

Mark Type 44
1962-1968
Transfer

Mark Type 45
1968-1970
Transfer

WADE (PDM) LTD.

Mark Type 46
1970-1980
Transfer

Mark Type 47
1980+
Transfer

Mark Type 48
1980
Transfer

Mark Type 49
1990+
Transfer

SPECIAL BACKSTAMPS

S 1

S 2

S 3

S 4

S 5

S 6

S 7

S 14

S 21

ARABIA
DESIGN
Myrna
ENGLAND

S 8

S 15

S 22

A limited edition of this
Traditional Cider Mug
was reproduced for
Taunton Cider by
Wade Potteries - Staffordshire.

S 9

S 16

S 10

The Belfry Hotel
HANDFORTH, WILMSLOW
Tel . 061-437 0511/6

The Stanncylands Hotel
Wilmslow, Cheshire
Tel . 0625 525225

S 17

S 23

S 11

S 18

Rose
WADE
ENGLAND

S 24

S 12

Orchard
WADE
ENGLAND

S 25

1886-1986

S 13

S 19

Lady Clare

S 20

S 26

500 pairs of these traditional Cider Mugs were reproduced in miniature by Wade Potteries for the TAUNTON CIDER COMPANY 1981

S 27

One of 65 mugs presented in recognition of outstanding devotion to duty at the 1982 TAUNTON CIDER WASSAIL

S 32

WILTON CASTLE
WILTON
CLEVELAND

S 37

A limited edition of 4000 produced for the TAUNTON CIDER COMPANY by Wade Heath Potteries, Staffordshire, in the year of 1981

S 28

500 pairs of these traditional Cider Mugs were reproduced in miniature by Wade Potteries for the TAUNTON CIDER COMPANY 1982

S 33

S 38

500 of these traditional Cider Mugs were reproduced by Wade Potteries for the TAUNTON CIDER COMPANY 1989

S 29

One of 160 mugs presented in recognition of outstanding devotion to duty at Taunton Cider's first OPEN DAY 5th May 1986

S 34

S 39

S 30

A limited number of these traditional Cider Mugs were reproduced by Wade Potteries for the TAUNTON CIDER COMPANY

S 35

Valor

A LIMITED EDITION OF 1000

by

WADE

S 40

Produced exclusively for the Taunton Cider Company by Wade Potteries of Staffordshire

S 31

BOSTON TEA PARTIES
1773 – 1774
DAVISON NEWMAN
& CO. LTD.
ESTABLISHED 1650
CITY OF LONDON
SHIPPERS OF BAWSTONABA TEA

S 36

S 41

S42

**HOUSE OF STRAW
1995**

S46

S43

S47

Whimbles
by
WADE

S48

S44

S49

S45

S50

The Hallen Plaque. Measures 7"w. x 9½" h. with an inscription on the back reading:
Henry Hallen made this picture at Red Street Old Works May 14, 1831.
John Hallen

TEXT TO COLOR PLATES

MISCELLANEOUS FIGURINES, BIRDS AND ANIMALS

		U.S. $	British £
No. 1.	PAN — measures 8^1/$_4$" high and has Mark Type 21 on the back.	1025.00	550.00
No. 2.	PAN — measures 8^1/$_4$" high and has Mark Type 21 on the back.	1025.00	550.00
No. 3.	DYLLIS — measures 7" high and has Mark Type 21 on the back.	1025.00	550.00
No. 4.	FROLIC — measures 8^1/$_4$" high and has Mark Type 21 on the back.	780.00	450.00
No. 5.	SONIA — measures 9^1/$_2$" high and has Mark Type 21 on the back.	780.00	450.00
No. 6.	ALFIE and PEGGY — measures 6" high and has Mark Type 21 on the base.	350.00	175.00
No. 7.	ANTON — measures 5^3/$_4$" high and has Mark Type 21 on the base.	290.00	160.00
No. 8.	GLORIA — measures 5^3/$_4$" high and has Mark Type 21 on the back.	300.00	160.00
No. 9.	ANITA — measures 6^3/$_4$" high and has Mark Type 21 on the back.	285.00	150.00
No. 10.	THE SWAN PRINCESS — measures 8^1/$_4$" high and has Mark Type 21A on the base along with the name of the figure.	1050.00	500.00
No. 11.	PEX FAIRY (1948 - 1950) — measures 2^3/$_8$" high and has a paper label reading: Made in Ireland by Wade Co. Armagh.	500.00	250.00
No. 12.	PEX FAIRY (1948 - 1950) — measures 2^3/$_8$" high and has a paper label reading: Made in Ireland by Wade Co. Armagh.	500.00	250.00
No. 13.	"CARNIVAL" FIGURE LAMP— measures 7" high (figure only) and has Mark Type 21A on the back.	300.00	175.00
No. 14.	SITTING PUP — measures 4" high and has Mark Type 6 on the base.	125.00	95.00
No. 15.	OPEN MOUTHED DUCKLING — measures 3^3/$_4$" high and has Mark type 6 on the base along with an impressed Mold Mark No. 334.	120.00	90.00
No. 16.	MICKEY MOUSE — measures 3^3/$_4$" high and is unmarked.	1050.00	650.00

SNOW WHITE AND THE SEVEN DWARFS BROOCHES LATE 1930'S

It is only recently that the three brooches illustrated surfaced and until the 1996 Beam/Wade Fair held in Seattle, WA, these three were the only ones known to exist. At the Seattle Fair two brooches (Doc and Sleepy) were offered for sale. These brooches have an unusual molded Wade Burslem mark on the back. To date this is the first time that an item has surfaced with such a mark. Due to the rarity of these items the prices given here are preliminary estimates based on the two brooches in Seattle, bearing in mind that those sold were missing the actual metal clasp which we feel is an important, integral part of the brooch. Another factor in pricing is the condition of the finish. The five items we have seen are all cellulose finished and all had a certain amount of flaking.

		U.S. $	British £
No. 17.	"SNOW WHITE" BROOCH measures 1^3/$_8$" h. x 1^1/$_{16}$" w. and is mold marked on the back: WADE BURSLEM ENGLAND "Snow White" Made in England.	1000.00	680.00
No. 18.	"DOC" BROOCH — measures 1^3/$_8$" h. x 3^1/$_4$" w. and is mold marked on the back:"Doc" Made in England WADE BURSLEM ENGLAND.	800.00	550.00
No. 19.	"SLEEPY" BROOCH — measures 1^1/$_2$" h. x ^{5}/$_8$" w. and is mold marked on the back: "Sleepy" Made in England WADE BURSLEM.	800.00	550.00

MR. PUNCH 1996

The figure of Mr. Punch illustrated is the first figure in an exciting new series entitled Punch and Judy. Mr. Punch is being produced in a limited number of 2000 pieces.

Punch was commissioned by Peggy Gamble and Sue Styles. It might be of interest to collectors to know that both, Peggy and Sue are breeders and judges of corgies - note the backstamp. The figurine was modelled by Ken Holmes.

		U.S. $	British £
No. 20.	MR. PUNCH — measures 6¹/₄" high and has special Mark Type S49 on the base.	75.00	41.00

CHILD STUDIES — 1962

		U.S. $	British £
No. 21.	BOY wearing English National Costume — (decorated) measures 4³/₄" high	480.00	325.00
No. 22.	GIRL wearing Irish National Costume — (decorated) measures 4¹/₂" high	480.00	325.00
	GIRL wearing Irish National Costume — (undecorated) measures 4¹/₂" high	380.00	275.00
No. 23.	BOY wearing Scottish National Costume — (decorated) measures 4³/₄" high	480.00	325.00
	BOY wearing Scottish National Costume — (undecorated) measures 4³/₄" high	380.00	275.00

WADE FIGURES AND BIRDS

		U.S. $	British £
No. 24.	ZENA (underglaze) — measures 8⁷/₈" high and has Mark Type 21A on the base.	660.00	400.00
No. 25.	WOODPECKER — measures 6³/₄" high and has Mark Type 10 on the base.	620.00	350.00

WADE LIMITED EDITIONS 1993 - 1996

		U.S. $	British £
No. 26.	WELCOME HOME — measures 4" h. x 4³/₄" l. and is marked WADE Limited Editions "Welcome Home." Modelled by Ken Holmes. This figure was limited to 2500 pieces.	60.00	40.00
No. 27.	FIRESIDE FRIEND — measures 3¹/₂" h. x 3¹/₂" w. and is marked WADE Limited Editions "Fireside Friend." Modelled by Ken Holmes. This figure was limited to 2500 pieces.	60.00	40.00
No. 28.	TOGETHERNESS — measures 4¹/₂" h. x 3³/₄" w. and is marked WADE Limited Editions "Togetherness." Modelled by Ken Holmes. This figure was limited to 2500 pieces.	60.00	40.00

		U.S. $	British £
No. 29.	SNOWMAN — measures 5" high and is marked Christmas 1994 Wade Made in England on the base. This figure was limited to 1500 pieces.	85.00	50.00
No. 30.	SNOW WOMAN — measures 4⁷/₈" high and is marked Christmas 1995 Wade Made in England on the base. This figure was limited to 1500 pieces.	50.00	30.00

WADE LIMITED EDITIONS COMMISSIONED BY ELAINE AND ADRIAN CRUMPTON

		U.S. $	British £
No. 31.	BURGLAR — measures 3¹/₄" high and is mold marked "Wade" on the base. This figure was issued in a limited number of 2000 pieces.	50.00	45.00
No. 32.	POLICEMAN (without a painted face) — measures 3⁵/₈" high and is mold marked: 'Wade' on the base. This figurine was issued in a limited number of 400 pieces.	80.00	60.00
No. 33.	POLICEMAN (with a painted face) — measures 3⁵/₈" high and is mold marked 'Wade' on the base. This figurine was issued in a limited number of 1600 pieces. NOTE: Fake models of the Policeman with a painted face have appeared on the secondary market. The major differences are: (1) a black or light blue uniform instead of the cobalt blue of the legitimate issue. (2) a yellow badge instead of white/silver and (3) none of the buttons are painted.	55.00	38.00
No. 34.	LAWYER/BARRISTER — measures 3" high and has a transfer mark on the base — WADE Made in England. This figurine was issued in a limited number of 2000 pieces.	50.00	30.00
No. 35.	PRISONER — measures 2³/₄" high and is mold marked 'Wade' on the base. This figurine was issued in a limited number of 2000 pieces.	50.00	22.00
	PRISONER (with Brown Hair)	85.00	38.00

U.S.A. RED ROSE TEA PROMOTION 1993 & 1996

In 1983, Redco Foods, Inc., the distributors of Red Rose Tea in the U.S., introduced their first series of miniature porcelain premiums to be packaged in boxes of 100 tea bags. This series consisted of 15 figurines (See Nos. 226 - 240. pg. 42 of *The W of W*) selected from the Wade retail line of the 1971-1984 "Whimsies." This series was discontinued in 1985 after receiving a very positive reception from the public.

Due to the overwhelming response, a second series was introduced in 1985 which also consisted of 15 figurines (See Nos. 241 - 255. pg. 42 of *The W of W*), again selected from the "Whimsies" retail line. In 1990, five additional figurines (See Nos. 298-16 - 298-19 pg. 60 of *The W of W2*) were added to the set. This second series of twenty figurines is due to be withdrawn from circulation sometime in 1996.

The third series of Red Rose Tea premiums was introduced in 1993 and initially consisted of 10 circus figurines. The figurines chosen were similar in design to those used for the 1978-1979 series of Tom Smith Party Cracker figurines but with minor color modifications.

The circus figurines were included in boxes of 48 tea bags and, until 1996, ran concurrently alongside the second series of animal figurines packaged in the boxes of 100 tea bags. When the animal series is discontinued, the circus figurines will be packaged in both boxes of 48 and 100 tea bags.

In 1996, five completely new figurines were designed and produced by Wade for the Red Rose Tea series of circus figurines. The current set of fifteen figurines is illustrated in the color section of this book and described below.

		U.S. $	British £
No. 36.	MALE MONKEY (MACAQUE)— measures 1⁵/₈" high and is mold marked WADE ENGLAND. *(See also No.264-1 pg.43 of The W of W)*	5.00	4.00
No. 37.	POODLE — measures 1³/₄" high and is mold marked WADE ENGLAND. *(See also No.264-2 pg.43 of The W of W)*	5.00	4.00
No. 38.	SEAL— measures 1⁵/₈" high and is mold marked WADE ENGLAND. *(See also No.264-3 pg.43 of The W of W)*	5.00	4.00
No. 39.	FEMALE MONKEY (MACAQUE) — measures 1¹/₂" h. and is mold marked WADE ENGLAND. *(See also No.264-4 pg.43 of The W of W)*	5.00	8.00
No. 40.	HORSE — measures 1³/₄" high and is mold marked WADE ENGLAND. *(See also No.264-5 pg.43 of The W of W)*	10.00	3.00
No. 41.	BEAR— measures 1³/₁₆" high and is mold marked WADE ENGLAND. *(See also No.264-6 pg.43 of The W of W)*	10.00	4.00

		U.S. $	British £
No. 42.	TIGER— measures 1⁵/₈" high and is mold marked WADE ENGLAND. *(See also No.264-7 pg.43 of The W of W)*	10.00	3.00
No. 43.	ELEPHANT— measures 1¹/₄" high and is mold marked WADE ENGLAND. *(See also No.264-8 pg.43 of The W of W)*	14.00	3.50
No. 44.	LION — measures 1⁵/₈" high and is mold marked WADE ENGLAND. *(See also No.264-9 pg.43 of The W of W)*	5.00	4.00
No. 45.	ELEPHANT— measures 1³/₁₆" high and is mold marked WADE ENGLAND. *(See also No.264-10 pg.43 of The W of W)*	14.00	3.50
No. 46.	CLOWN WITH DRUM— measures 1⁵/₈" high and is mold marked WADE ENG.	3.00	5.00
No. 47.	CLOWN WITH PIE— measures 1¹/₂" high and is mold marked WADE ENG.	3.00	5.00
No. 48.	RINGMASTER— measures 1³/₄" high and is mold marked WADE ENG.	3.00	5.00
No. 49.	STRONGMAN— measures 1¹/₂" high and is mold marked WADE ENGLAND.	3.00	5.00
No. 50.	HUMAN CANNONBALL— measures 1¹/₈" h. x 1⁵/₈" l. and is mold marked WADE ENGLAND.	3.00	5.00

WADE LIMITED EDITIONS COMMISSIONED BY KEENAN ANTIQUES

		U.S. $	British £
No. 51.	SANTA CLAUS AND SLEIGH (1994)— measures 1¹/₂" h. x 2¹/₈" l. and has Mark Type 26 (transfer) on the base.	25.00	18.00
No. 52.	ROCKING HORSE (1995) — measures 2¹/₄" h. x 2¹/₂" l. and has Mark Type 26 (transfer) on the base.	25.00	18.00

TOM SMITH & CO. LTD. PARTY CRACKERS

SNOW ANIMAL SET 1994 - 1995

For the 1994 - 1995 Snow Animal set the eight original figurines used in the 1992 -1993 Snow Animal set were used once again but with the addition of two new figurines as listed below. For the eight original figurines see Nos.300-1 to 300-8 pg.61 of *The W of W2*.

		U.S. $	British £
No. 53.	WHALE — measures $^7/_8$" h. x $1^1/_4$" l. and is mold marked WADE ENGLAND on the base.	6.00	3.00
No. 54.	GOOSE — measures $1^3/_8$" h. x 1" l. and is mold marked WADE ENGLAND on the base.	6.00	3.00

NURSERY SET 1994 - 1995

No. 55.	LITTLE BO-PEEP — measures $1^3/_4$" high and is mold marked WADE ENGLAND on the base.	6.00	3.00
No. 56.	LITTLE JACK HORNER — measures $1^3/_8$" high and is mold marked WADE ENGLAND on the base.	6.00	3.00
No. 57.	BOY BLUE — measures $1^3/_4$" high and is mold marked WADE ENGLAND on the base.	6.00	3.00
No. 58.	QUEEN OF HEARTS — measures $1^3/_4$" high and is mold marked WADE ENGLAND on the base.	6.00	3.00
No. 59.	CAT AND THE FIDDLE — measures $1^7/_8$" high and is mold marked WADE ENGLAND on the base.	6.00	3.00
No. 60.	RIDE A COCK HORSE — measures $1^1/_2$" high and is mold marked WADE ENG. on the base.	6.00	3.00
No. 61.	HUMPTY DUMPTY — measures $1^1/_2$" high and is mold marked WADE ENGLAND on the back.	6.00	3.00
No. 62.	HICKORY DICKORY DOCK — measures $1^3/_4$" high and is mold marked WADE ENGLAND on the base.	6.00	3.00
No. 63.	TOM THE PIPER'S SON — measures $1^5/_8$" high and is mold marked WADE ENGLAND on the base.	6.00	3.00
No. 64.	DOCTOR FOSTER — measures $1^3/_4$" high and is mold marked WADE ENGLAND on the base.	6.00	3.00

THE ALPHABET TRAIN 1958 - 1959

The engine is approximately 1" h. x 2" l. and the cars are $^3/_4$" h. x 1" long. A complete set consists of one engine and six cars.

		U.S. $	British £
No. 65.	ALPHABET TRAIN (complete)	550.00	400.00

WADE LIMITED EDITIONS COMMISSIONED BY C&S COLLECTABLES

C&S Collectables is owned and operated by David Chown and Russell Schooley out of their Antique/Collectables store — "Spooners" in Arundel, England.

No.66.	HOLLY HEDGEHOG MUG — measures $3^3/_4$" high and was issued for the second Wade Fair in June 1995 held in Birmingham, England.	25.00	10.00
No.67.	HOLLY HEDGEHOG THIMBLE — measures $1^1/_8$" high and has Mark Type 26 (transfer) on the back. This thimble was issued for the second Wade Fair in June 1995 held in Birmingham, England.	8.00	3.00
No.68.	ANDY CAPP with cigarette (1994) — measures 3" high and has Mark Type 27B on the base along with the wording: 1994 ©MIRROR GROUP NEWSPAPERS LTD. C&S COLLECTABLES. Only 110 Andy Capp figurines with the cigarette were issued.	125.00	125.00
No.69.	ANDY CAPP without cigarette (1994) — measures 3" high and has Mark Type 27B on the base along with the wording: 1994 ©MIRROR GROUP NEWSPAPERS LTD. C&S COLLECTABLES. There were 1900 Andy Capp figurines produced without the cigarette.	25.00	50.00
No.70.	FLO without cigarette (1995) — measures 3" high and has Mark Type 27B on the base along with the wording: 1995 ©MIRROR GROUP NEWSPAPERS LTD. C&S COLLECTABLES. There were 1900 FLO figurines produced without the cigarette.	25.00	20.00
No.71.	FLO with cigarette (1995) — measures 3" high and has Mark Type 27B on the base along with the wording: 1995 ©MIRROR GROUP NEWSPAPERS LTD. C&S COLLECTABLES. There were only 120 FLO figurines produced with the cigarette.	100.00	110.00

	U.S. $	British £
No.72. FELICITY SQUIRREL THIMBLE — measures 1¹/₈" high and has Mark Type 26 (transfer) on the back. This thimble was issued for the Wade Fair in April 1996 held in Birmingham, England.	8.00	3.00
No.73. FELICITY SQUIRREL MUG — measures 3³/₄" high and was issued for the Wade Fair in April 1996 held in Birmingham, England.	25.00	10.00
No.74. ARTHUR HARE (1993) — measures 5¹/₄" high and is marked: ARTHUR HARE ©C&S Collectables Wade England. 1650 pieces were produced.	55.00	30.00
No.75. HOLLY HEDGEHOG (1994) — measures 3¹/₂" high and is marked: HOLLY HEDGEHOG © C&S Collectables WADE ENGLAND. 2000 pieces were produced.	45.00	30.00
No.76. FELICITY SQUIRREL (1995) — measures 4¹/₄" high and is marked: FELICITY SQUIRREL 1250 Limited Edition C&S Collectables ©1995 Arthur Hare Productions Wade England. Of the 1250 figurines 250 were marked with the name Collector's Corner replacing the name C&S Collectables.	45.00	25.00
No.77. FELICITY SQUIRREL (1995) — measures 4¹/₄" high and is marked: FELICITY SQUIRREL 1250 Limited Edition C&S Collectables ©1995 Arthur Hare Productions Wade England. Of the 1250 figurines 250 figurines were produced with the red glaze and with the Wade England logo on the base. Of the 250 red glazed figures 6 were issued with the Collector's Corner logo. The prices quoted exclude the six squirrels with the Collector's Corner logo.	45.00	30.00
No.78. ARTHUR HARE (1993) — measures 5¹/₄" high and is marked: ARTHUR HARE ©C&S Collectables Wade England. 2000 pieces were produced. Out of the 2000 pieces, there were 350 figurines produced in this color.	80.00	65.00

"DISNEYS" 1961 — 1965

	U.S. $	British £
No. 79. AM — measures 6⁵/₈" high and is marked Wade Porcelain Copyright Walt Disney Productions. Made in England.	200.00	120.00
No. 80. JOCK — measures 4" high and is marked Wade Porcelain Copyright Walt Disney Productions. Made in England.	475.00	310.00
No. 81. DACHIE — measures 5" high and is marked Wade Porcelain Copyright Walt Disney Productions. Made in England.	475.00	310.00

WADE LIMITED EDITIONS COMMISSIONED BY SILVER STATE SPECIALITIES

	U.S. $	British £
No. 82. HAMM'S BEAR "SANTA'S HELPER" 1995 — measures 4⁷/₈" high and is marked 1995 Wade SSS. There were 2000 pieces produced in the black color.	55.00	35.00
No. 83. HAMM'S BEAR "SANTA'S HELPER" 1996 — measures 4⁷/₈" high and is marked SSS Wade 1996 Original 1950's Hamm's Bear. There were only 1200 pieces produced in the brown color of which 840 pieces were designated for the U.S. market and 360 for the U.K. market.	55.00	35.00
No. 84. HAMM'S BEAR "SEATTLE 1996" — measures 5" high and is marked SSS Wade 1996. There were 2000 pieces issued in the black color.	55.00	35.00

WADE LIMITED EDITIONS 1995

After forming the Official International Wade Collectors Club in 1994 the club's first limited edition offer to members only was a set of four figurines based upon the children's story "Three Little Pigs." The figures were issued quarterly along with the quarterly magazine.

	U.S. $	British £
No. 85. HOUSE OF STRAW (1995) — measures 4⁷/₈" high and is marked, on the base, with the Wade Collectors Club logo along with the name of the figure.	70.00	50.00
No. 86. HOUSE OF WOOD (1995) — measures 4⁵/₈" high and is marked, on the base, with the Wade Collectors Club logo along with the name of the figure.	60.00	40.00

	U.S. $	British £
No. 87. HOUSE OF BRICK (1995)	60.00	40.00

— measures 5¹/₈" high and is marked, on the base, with the Wade Collectors Club logo along with the name of the figure.

No. 88. THE BIG BAD WOLF (1995) 60.00 40.00
— measures 5¹/₂" high and is marked, on the base, with the Wade Collectors Club logo along with the name of the figure.

BEAR AMBITIONS 1995

A set of six die pressed miniature teddy bear figurines produced in a single glaze. Each figurine has its own distinctive decoration signifying the artistic talent or hobby of the particular bear. All figurines are mold marked WADE ENG. on the back.

No. 89.	ADMIRAL SAM — measures 1⁵/₈" high	3.50	2.00
No. 90.	ARTISTIC EDWARD — measures 1¹/₂" high	3.50	2.00
No. 91.	BEATRICE THE BALLERINA — measures 1³/₄" high	3.50	2.00
No. 92.	ALEX THE AVIATOR — measures 1⁵/₈" high	3.50	2.00
No. 93.	MUSICAL MARCO — measures 1⁵/₈" high	3.50	2.00
No. 94.	LOCOMOTIVE JOE — measures 1⁵/₈" high	3.50	2.00

ICI MAN CIRCA LATE 1960'S

No. 95.	ICI MAN — measures 8¹/₄" high and is mold marked Wade England ICI Atromid S.	NPA	NPA
No. 96.	ICI MAN — measures 3¹/₈" high and is mold marked Atromidin Wade England ICI.	65.00	40.00
No. 97.	ICI MAN — measures 8¹/₄" high and is mold marked Atromidin Wade England ICI.	NPA	NPA

KOALA BEAR 1978 - CIRCA 1980

This figure, shown to us at the Wade Fair in Birmingham, has been identified as part of the Animal Figures set produced by Wade (Ireland) Ltd. in the late 1970's. The complete set consisted of Walrus, Polar Bear, Koala Bear, Rhino, Elephant and Lion. (For additional information and an illustration of the Walrus see text and Fig. 175 pg. 225 of *The W of W2*).

No. 98.	KOALA BEAR — measures 7" high and is unmarked.	645.00	375.00

WADE LIMITED EDITIONS 1994 - 1995

	U.S. $	British £
No. 99. "BURSLEM"	75.00	45.00

THE FACTORY CAT (1994/5) — measures 3¹/₄" high and is mold marked Wade on the base. This figurine was a free gift for every new member of the OIWCC who joined the club in the first year of its existence.

WADE LIMITED EDITIONS COMMISSIONED BY U.K. FAIRS LTD. 1994

No. 100. SPANIEL DOG (1994) — 120.00 70.00
measures 3" high and is mold marked WADE on the base. This figurine was limited to an issue of 1000 pieces and sold to the first thousand attendees at the first Wade Fair held in Birmingham, U.K. in September 1994. A numbered Certificate of Authenticity accompanied each figurine.

No. 101. GREY HAIRED RABBIT 95.00 55.00
(1995) — measures 3¹/₂" high and is mold marked WADE on the base. This figurine was limited to an issue of 1000 pieces and sold to the first thousand attendees at the second Wade Fair held in Birmingham, U.K. in June 1995. A numbered Certificate of Authenticity accompanied each figurine.

WADE LIMITED EDITIONS 1995 - 1996

No. 102. CHRISTMAS PUPPY 35.00 15.00
(1995/6) — measures 2¹/₄" h. x 3" l. and is mold marked WADE on the base. This figurine was a free gift for every new member of the OIWCC who joined the club in the second year of its existence.

THE ELEPHANT TRAIN 1956

No. 103. ELEPHANT TRAIN — 900.00 400.00
A set of five elephant figures, graduated in size. The price quoted is for a full set.

MONEY BOXES 1994

A set of four single glazed money boxes representative of various farmyard animals. Each money box is mold marked WADE ENGLAND on the base.

No. 104.	RABBIT MONEY BOX — measures 6³/₄" high	20.00	14.00
No. 105.	PIG MONEY BOX — measures 4¹/₂" high	20.00	14.00

	U.S. $	British £
No.106. FROG MONEY BOX — measures 5" high	20.00	14.00
No.107. COW MONEY BOX — measures 6" high	20.00	14.00

WADE LIMITED EDITIONS COMMISSIONED BY ROBERT WILLIAMSON 1995

No.108. "BLOW-UP" GINGERBREAD MAN — measures 4¹/₄" high and is mold marked WADE on the base. — 50.00 — 30.00

WADE LIMITED EDITIONS COMMISSIONED BY U.K. FAIRS LTD. 1996

No.109. "SMILING FROG" — 75.00 — 40.00 measures 2¹/₄" high and is mold marked WADE on the base. This limited issue of 1250 pieces was produced for the April 1996 Wade Fair in Birmingham, England.

WADE LIMITED EDITIONS 1996

No.110. SEATTLE "WESTIE" 1996 — 30.00 — 20.00 measures 3" high and has a transfer mark SEATTLE 1996 along with the OIWCC logo. This figure was produced in the amount of 3000 pieces for sale in Seattle. Any unsold pieces were to be offered to members of the OIWCC on a first come/first served basis.

WADE LIMITED EDITIONS COMMISSIONED BY MARGARET STRICKLAND 1994

No.111. POLACANTHUS MONEY 80.00 — 45.00 BOX (1994) — measures 3¹/₈" h. x 7³/₄" l. and has a transfer mark WADE surrounded by an outline drawing of the Isle of Wight. This money box was issued in a limited number of 2000 pieces. The design of this money box is based on the skeleton of a dinosaur uncovered on the Isle of Wight.

WADE LIMITED EDITIONS COMMISSIONED BY G & G COLLECTABLES 1994 - 1995

No.112. SCOOBY DOO (1994) — 75.00 — 40.00 measures 5¹/₈" high and is transfer marked on the base: ©H/B Inc SCOOBY DOO Limited Edition of 2000 G&G Collectable WADE England. Each piece is individually numbered.

	U.S. $	British £
No.113. SCRAPPY DOO (1995) — measures 3¹/₂" high and is transfer marked on the base: ©H/B Inc SCRAPPY DOOLimited Edition of 2000 G&G Collectable WADE England. Each piece is individually numbered.	75.00	40.00

MISCELLANEOUS ITEMS BY WADE CIRCA 1995 - 1996

No.114. NENNIE (1995) — 70.00 — 37.50 measures 4³/₄" high and is transfer marked Nennie produced exclusively for ficol by Wade. Each piece is individually numbered.

MARKS AND SPENCER'S EDWARD BEAR 1995 - 1996

This ceramic money box was made by Wade Ceramics for Marks and Spencer PLC. Each bear was originally sold packed with milk chocolate coins.

No.115. EDWARD BEAR 18.00 — 10.00 MONEY BOX — measures 6¹/₈" high and is unmarked.

MISCELLANEOUS FIGURINES LATE 1930'S - 1996

No.116. OWL — measures 850.00 — 450.00 5¹/₂" high and is marked WADE MADE IN ENGLAND 1941. OWL

No.117. HAWK — measures NPA — NPA 13¹/₂" high and is unmarked.

No.118. PIGEON — NPA — NPA measures 14³/₄" high and is unmarked. Rear view of No.119.

No.119. PIGEON — NPA — NPA measures 14³/₄" high and is unmarked. Front view of No.118.

No.120. COCKATOO — measures 825.00 — 450.00 6" high and has Mark Type 21A on the base.

No.121. GREBE — measures 950.00 — 550.00 9¹/₄" high and has Mark Type 21A on the base along with the wording: WADE ENGLAND 1939. GREBE. *(See also No. Q, Fig. 8 pg. 16 of The W of W)*

No.122. TOUCAN — 375.00 — 200.00 has Mark Type 21A on the base.

		U.S. $	British £
No.123.	DOUBLE BUDGERIGARS — measures 7⁵/₈" high and has Mark Type 21 on the base along with the wording: WADE ENGLAND 1941. BUDGERIGARS	825.00	450.00
No.124.	CROUCHING MONKEY — measures 2¹/₂" high and is ink stamped WADE MADE IN ENGLAND on the base. *(See also No. 25, Fig.5 pg. 14 of The W of W)*	180.00	130.00
No.125.	DOUGAL (1995) — measures 3¹/₄" h. x 6" l. and is transfer marked: CAMTRAKS' Childhood Favourites No.1 Dougal by Wade ©Serge Danot/AB Productions. Licensed by Link Licensing Ltd. This figurine was produced in a limited number of 2000 pieces.	50.00	30.00

WADE LIMITED EDITIONS 1996

		U.S. $	British £
No.126.	MUMMY BEAR (1996) — measures 4" high and has transfer mark MUMMY BEAR 1996 on the base along with the OIWCC logo. This figurine was produced in a limited number of 1500 pieces.	35.00	17.50

May Issue	August Issue	Christmas Issue
NUMBER TWO **Daddy Bear**	NUMBER THREE **Goldilocks**	NUMBER FOUR **Baby Bear**

FIG. 1. *Illustration of future issues in the "Three Bear" Series*

PLAQUES AND MEDALLIONS EARLY 1960'S

It is believed that these plaques were produced by Wade for an outside company which subsequently applied the plaques to various shaped pin boxes (see also Nos. 805 and 806 pg.86 of *The W of W2*). A number of these plaques were amended at the time of firing to be used as pendants.

		U.S. $	British £
No.127.	PLAQUE — measures 3¹/₄" in dia. and is unmarked.	45.00	20.00

		U.S. $	British £
No.128.	PLAQUE — measures 3³/₈ x 2³/₄" and is unmarked.	45.00	20.00
No.129.	MEDALLION — measures 2³/₄" x 2" and is unmarked.	30.00	15.00
No.130.	MEDALLION — measures 2³/₈" x 1³/₄" and is unmarked.	30.00	15.00
No.131.	PLAQUE — measures 2¹/₂" x 2" and is unmarked.	30.00	15.00
No.132.	MEDALLION — measures 2³/₈" x 1³/₄" and is unmarked.	30.00	15.00
No.133.	MEDALLION — measures 2¹/₈ " x 1¹/₂" and is unmarked.	30.00	15.00

EXPERIMENTAL ITEMS AND PROTOTYPES CIRCA EARLY 1960'S — EARLY 1996

		U.S. $	British £
No.134.	PORSCHE — measures ¹/₂" h. x 2¹/₂" l. and is unmarked. This was a "one off" experimental prototype.	NPA	NPA
No.135.	PORSCHE — measures ¹/₂" h. x 2¹/₂" l. and is unmarked. This was a "one off" experimental prototype.	NPA	NPA
No.136.	DACHSHUND — measures 2¹/₄" h. x 3¹/₂" long and is unmarked. This was a "one off" experimental prototype.	NPA	NPA
No.137.	BEATLES PLAQUE — George Harrison, measures 2¹/₂" dia. and is unmarked.	NPA	NPA
No.138.	BEATLES PLAQUE — John Lennon, measures 2¹/₂" dia. and is unmarked.	NPA	NPA
No.139.	BEATLES PLAQUE — Ringo Starr, measures 2¹/₄" dia. and is unmarked.	NPA	NPA
No.140.	BEATLES PLAQUE — Paul McCartney, measures 2¹/₄" dia. and is unmarked.	NPA	NPA
No.141.	COCKATOO — measures 4¹/₂" high and is signed B. Harper. It is possible that this small cockatoo was designed for a projected series of three size containers as in the Penguin spirit container series.	NPA	NPA

		U.S. $	British £
No.142.	DROOPY JNR. — measures 2^1/$_4$" high and is unmarked. This is a slip-cast prototype version of the figurine used in the T.V. Pets series. *(See also No.65 pg.35 of The W of W)*	NPA	NPA
No.143.	BORIS— measures 2^3/$_8$" high and is unmarked. This is a slip-cast prototype version of the figurine used for the early 1960's Disney series.	NPA	NPA
No.144.	ZEBRA— measures 1^5/$_8$" high and is unmarked. This is a slip-cast prototype which did not go into production.	NPA	NPA
No.145.	COCKATOO — measures 5" high and is unmarked. This spirit container is a production model which is shown here to illustrate the difference in size between it and No.141 described above. *(See also No.72 pg.35 of The W of W)*	120.00	80.00
No.146.	THE SHERIFF OF NOTTINGHAM — measures 2" high and is unmarked. This is a slip-cast prototype of the fourth figurine in the Sherwood Forest series.	NPA	NPA
No.147.	SHERIFF OF NOTTINGHAM — measures 2" high and is unmarked. This is a slip-cast prototype of the fourth figurine in the Sherwood Forest series.	NPA	NPA
No.148.	TEENAGE POTTERY (early 1960's) — measures 2^3/$_4$" x 1^3/$_4$" and is unmarked. This prototype cameo of Frankie Vaughan did not go into production.	NPA	NPA
No.149.	THE BREWMASTER— measures 5^1/$_4$" high and is unmarked. This is a undecorated version of the figure illustrated as item No.150.	NPA	NPA
No.150.	THE BREWMASTER— measures 5^1/$_4$" high and has Mark Type 43 on the base. This ornamental advertising item was produced in the early 1960's for Flowers Beer.	320.00	175.00

MISCELLANEOUS TABLEWARE
MID 1930'S - EARLY 1990'S

		U.S. $	British £
No.151.	STORAGE JAR —- measures 5^1/$_4$" h. x 4^3/$_{16}$"dia. and has Mark Type 19 on the base.	30.00	15.00
No.152.	CAVIAR JAR (1970) — measures 5^1/$_2$" high and is transfer marked: W. G. White, London, Wade Porcelain Co. Armagh. This jar was produced in three sizes: 2 oz., 4 oz. and 8 oz.	30.00	15.00
No.153.	WATER JUG — measures 6^7/$_{16}$" high and has Mark Type 1 on the base along with a molded mark ENGLAND and Pattern No.6078.	100.00	60.00
No.154.	VASE — measures 12" h. x 6^1/$_2$" dia. and has Mark Type 4 on the base along with the impressed shape No.21/12 and Pattern No.143.	160.00	80.00
No.155.	WATER JUG— measures 6^3/$_{16}$" high and has Mark Type 1 on the base along with the letter "B" and Pattern No.6163.	100.00	60.00
FIG.2.	"S" SHAPE ASHTRAY WITH RABBIT — measures 4" x 4^1/$_4$" and is marked Wade Made in England.	130.00	80.00

Fig. 2

		U.S. $	British £
No.156.	FLOWER BOWL— measures 5^1/$_4$" h. x 8^1/$_4$" dia. and has Mark Type 2 on the base along with the impressed Shape No.129.	200.00	90.00
No.157.	SUGAR BOWL— measures 2^1/$_8$" h. x 4" dia. and has Mark Type 33A on the base.	25.00	10.00
No.158.	TEAPOT— measures 6^1/$_4$" high and has Mark Type 33 on the base. *(See also Fig.164 pg.220 of The W of W2)*	80.00	35.00
No.159.	CREAMER— measures 3^1/$_2$" high and has Mark Type 33A on the base.	25.00	10.00

BALLYFREE FARMS POTTERY 1974 - 1975

This Ballyfree Breakfast set was designed by Kilkenny Design Workshops and produced by Wade (Ireland) Ltd. The distribution of these items was based on the submission of a certain number of tokens per item. The finished glaze of the items in these sets was similar to the "amber glaze" of the "Countryware" line produced in 1973-1984, also designed by Kilkenny Design Workshops. *(See No.696 - 699 pg.64 of The W of W)*

In 1974 the following items were made available:

    SALT AND PEPPER SET
    SINGLE EGG CODDLER
    LARGE MUG

In 1975 the following items were made available:

MUG	SINGLE EGG CUP
PLATE	DOUBLE EGG CUPS
CEREAL BOWL	JUG

An advertisement for Ballyfree Farms Breakfast Sets.

We'd like to break it gently...

. . . to Ballyfree Pottery collectors, that we're having to raise the number of tokens you need to collect each item in the Breakfast Set. This is due to the rapidly increasing cost of producing our high quality pottery, specially designed for us by Kilkenny Design Workshops and made in porcelain by Wades.

Remember, the unique Ballyfree pottery is still obtained FREE by saving the pottery tokens which appear on all Ballyfree egg boxes. All you have to do is continue enjoying those full-flavoured, nutritious Ballyfree Browns!

30 tokens
60 tokens
28 tokens
20 tokens
20 tokens
20 tokens

Mug	30 tokens
Plates	20 tokens
Cereal Bowls	28 tokens
Single Egg Cup	20 tokens
Double Egg Cups	20 tokens
Jug	60 tokens

New values apply from May 20th.
On the other side of this leaflet comes the good news — three super new items to add to the range, available from mid-May onwards.

"The great free offer goes on — until May 1975 at least so there's no need to rush!"

Super new Ballyfree Pottery!

You'll love these new items to add to the Ballyfree Breakfast Set — a big-daddy mug, a salt & pepper set, and an egg coddler. *

All you have to do to collect these and the other items in the range is save the tokens from every Ballyfree egg box. (You'll find them on Ballyfree Scotch Eggs and Take 'n Bake and Turkeys too). Then take them to your nearest Collection Centre for the free items of your choice.

45 tokens
45 tokens
55 tokens

Salt & Pepper sets	55 tokens
Egg Coddler	45 tokens
Large Mug	45 tokens

* available from May 20th 1974.

BALLYFREE COLLECTION CENTRES
1. 61 Lower Baggot Street, Dublin 2. Mondays only. 9.30 — 12 noon : 1.15 — 5.15 p.m.
2. 143 Lower Drumcondra Road, Dublin 9. Tuesdays only. 9.30 — 12 noon : 1.15 — 5.15 p.m.
3. 68 Convent Road, Dun Laoghaire, County Dublin. Tuesdays only. 11 a.m. — 1 p.m. : 2 — 5 p.m.
4. Ballyfree Farms, Glenealy, County Wicklow. Saturdays only. 9.30 a.m. — 12.30 p.m.

GUARANTEE
Don't forget — genuine Ballyfree Browns are GUARANTEED to be of the highest quality.

Ballyfree Farms
Glenealy, County Wicklow.

	U.S. $	British £
FIG.3. DOUBLE EGG CUPS	25.00	15.00

(See Fig.4 for molded mark on the base)

Fig. 3

Fig. 4

FIG. 4. *Molded Mark on base of Double Egg Cups.*

MISCELLANEOUS TABLEWARE
MID 1930'S - EARLY 1990'S CONT'D.

No.160. TANKARD — measures 5" high and has Mark Type 19 on the base. — 30.00 — 12.00

No.161. COVERED SUGAR — measures 4⁷/₈" high to top of finial and is mold marked: Irish Porcelain, Wade Ireland Design by D.G. Nelson. — 75.00 — 35.00

No.162. FLOWER JUG — measures 9" high and has Mark Type 7 on the base. — 80.00 — 55.00

No.163. EMPRESS LAMP — measures 8¹/₂" high and has a mark type similar to Mark Type 18 but with the word EMPRESS replacing the word FESTIVAL. — 75.00 — 40.00

	U.S. $	British £

No.164. PRESERVE JAR — measures 4" high and has Mark Type 7 on the base. — 30.00 — 15.00

No.165. CHEMISTS JAR — measures 4³/₈" high and is transfer marked: Made in Ireland by Wade Co. Armagh. (Not shown is the lid to this jar). — 30.00 — 15.00

No.166. TEAPOT "STRAWBERRY" PATTERN — measures 6¹/₄" high and has special Mark Type S11 on the base. — 35.00 — 18.00

No.167. MUG "STRAWBERRY" PATTERN — measures 4¹/₈" high and has special Mark Type S11 on the base. — 12.00 — 6.00

No.168. TEA CADDY — measures 3³/₄" high and has Mark Type 20 on the base. — 65.00 — 30.00

No.169. CUP AND SAUCER — the cup measures 2³/₄" high and the saucer measures 5¹/₂" dia. Both items have Mark Type 18C on the base along with the Pattern Number 6024. — 20.00 — 10.00

No.170. BREAD AND BUTTER PLATE "HARLECH" — measures 6³/₄" dia. and is marked WADE HARLECH. — 15.00 — 8.00

No.171. DESSERT PLATE "HARLECH" — measures 9" dia. and is marked WADE HARLECH. — 10.00 — 5.00

No.172. SOUP BOWL AND PLATE "HARLECH" — the soup bowl measures 1³/₄" h. x 9" dia. and the plate measures 6¹/₄" dia. Both items are marked WADE HARLECH. — 25.00 — 15.00

No.173. CUP AND SAUCER "HARLECH" — the cup measures 2³/₄" high and the saucer measures 5¹/₂" dia. Both items are marked WADE HARLECH. — 20.00 — 10.00

No.174. CUP AND SANDWICH PLATE — the cup measures 2³/₄" high and the plate measures 10¹/₂" dia. Both items have Mark Type 17 on the base. — 35.00 — 18.00

No.175. BOWL "WALT DISNEY" — measures 6¹/₂" dia. and has Mark Type 8A on the base. — 130.00 — 85.00

No.176. FRUIT BOWL — measures approx. 11" long and has Mark Type 16 on the base. This copper lustre dish is from the same set as item No.897 pg.89 of *The W of W2*. This implies that sets were produced both in copper lustre and silver finishes. — 35.00 — 20.00

		U.S. $	British £

No.177. PLATE "WALT DISNEY"— measures 6¼" dia. and has Mark Type 8A on the base. — 100.00 — 50.00

No.178. PLATE "PRIMROSE" — measures 6⅜" dia. and has Mark Type 8A on the base. — 25.00 — 12.00

No.179. EGG CUP — measures 1½" high and is marked: WADE 8 on the base. — 15.00 — 6.00

No.180. BOWL — measures 1⁷⁄₁₆" h. x 6½" dia. and is marked WADE on the base. — 10.00 — 5.00

No.181. BOWL — measures 2½" h. x 8¾" dia. and has Mark Type 10B on the base. — 25.00 — 10.00

No.182. PLATE — measures 5⅝" dia. and has Mark Type 8A on the base. — 20.00 — 10.00

No.183. SALT SHAKER "REGAL GREEN" — measures 2⅜" high and is unmarked. — 30.00 — 15.00

No.184. MUSTARD POT "REGAL GREEN" — measures 2¼" high and has Mark Type 17 on the base. — 35.00 — 20.00

No.185. BOWL — measures 3¼" h. x 7⅞" dia. and has Mark Type 6 on the base. — 100.00 — 55.00

FIG. 5. BARGE POSY BOWL (early 1970'S) — measures 8" long and is mold marked Wade England. The side of the cabin has the name John Wilson and the actual barge is called Heron. — 30.00 — 20.00

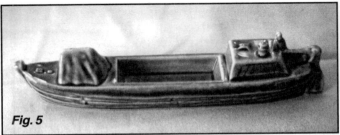

Fig. 5

No.186. PRESERVE JAR — measures 4⅛" high to top of finial and has Mark Type 20 on the base. — 30.00 — 15.00

No.187. PRESERVE JAR — measures 4" high and has Mark Type 2 on the base. — 35.00 — 20.00

		U.S. $	British £

No.188. "SPUTNIK" MONEY BOX — (1993) measures 4¼" high and is unmarked. This money box, referred to by Wade Ceramics as Sputnik, was commissioned by MacMillan Davies Brunning Ltd. on behalf of the Scarborough Building Society. The money boxes were offered to young customers opening their first account. These money boxes were known by the Scarborough Building Society as "YOUNG SUPER SAVER MONEY BOX." The original color of the money boxes was a white face with a blue hat. The item illustrated has an applied, red enamel mouth. This was added sometime after the item left the premises of the Scarborough Building Society. — 110.00 — 50.00

No.189. BUTTER DISH — the lid measures 3" to the top of finial and is unmarked. The base measures 6¾" l. x 4⅝" w. and has Mark Type 20 on the base. — 50.00 — 28.00

No.190. BUNNY MUG — measures 4¼" high and is marked: GENUINE WADE on the base. — 15.00 — 5.00

No.191. "ROLL OUT THE BARREL" TANKARD — measures 5¾" high and is unmarked. This item has the unusual green glaze rather than the more common brown glaze. *(See also No.444 pg.67 of The W of W2)* — 150.00 — 80.00

FIG.6. "FALSTAFF" COVERED DISH — measures approximately 2½" high and is marked Wade Falstaff on the base. The metal lid was applied after the item left the potteries. — 35.00 — 20.00

Fig. 6

	U.S. $	British £

FIG.7. "FALSTAFF" COVERED   45.00   25.00
DISH — measures approximately
4" high and is marked Wade Falstaff on the
base. The metal lid was applied after the
item left the potteries.

Fig. 7

FLOWER JUGS AND MUGS LATE 1920'S - 1995

No.192. FLOWER JUG   50.00   25.00
"ORANGE GROVE" — measures
7¹/₂" high and has special Mark Type S41
on the base.

No.193. FLOWER JUG   50.00   25.00
"SUNBURST" — measures
7¹/₂" high and has special Mark Type
S42 on the base.

No.194. FLOWER JUG —   120.00   75.00
measures 8³/₄" high and has
Mark Type 2 on the base along with
decoration No.3765 and an impressed
shape No. "Castile 15."

	U.S. $	British £

No.195. FLOWER JUG   50.00   25.00
"JAPANESE GARDEN" — measures
7⁵/₈" high and has special Mark Type
S43 on the base. A variation of this jug was
also available as a Japanese Humidifies
or Wall Pocket.

No.196. FLOWER JUG   50.00   25.00
"PARADISE" — measures
6³/₄" high and has special Mark Type
S44 on the base.

No.197. MUG — measures   40.00   25.00
4³/₈" high and has Mark Type "0"
on the base. This mug is a companion
piece to the water jug shown as item
No.562 pg.73 of *The W of W2.*

No.198. HALF PINT TANKARD   25.00   12.00
— measures 3³/₄" high and
has Mark Type 19B on the
base. This Veteran Car Tankard
has an unusual cobalt blue glaze rather
than the more traditional brown glaze
used for the Veteran Car series.

No.199. FLOWER JUG   50.00   25.00
"NOUVELLE" — measures
6³/₄" high and has special Mark Type
S45 on the base.

MISCELLANEOUS ITEMS 1920'S - 1995

No.200. ASHTON & HAYES   35.00   15.00
CANISTER — measures
7³/₄" high and has Mark Type 27B
on the base.

No.201. "NORDICA" CUP   10.00   4.00
AND SAUCER — the cup measures
2" h. x 2¹/₂" dia. and the saucer measures
4³/₄" dia. This cup and saucer was part of a
tableware range made for a major Swedish
department store. All items in this set are
marked Rorstrand Sweden.

No.202. "NORDICA" COFFEE POT   30.00   10.00
— measures 7" high to the top of the finial
and is marked Rorstrand Sweden on the base.

No.203. EGG CUP — measures   15.00   6.00
1¹/₂" h. x 2¹/₄" dia. at the top.
This egg cup was part of a tableware
range made for a major Swedish department
store. All items in this set are marked
Rorstrand Sweden.

	U.S. $	British £

No.204. VASE — measures 30.00 12.00
$7^3/\text{s}$" high and has Mark Type 28 on the base.

No.205. WALL TILE — this fragment NPA NPA
of hand decorated wall tile was made by A. J.
Wade & Co. and was salvaged from an office
once occupied by the late Sir George Wade.

No.206. SUGAR BOWL — measures 8.00 4.00
3" h. x $3^1/4$" dia. and has Mark
Type 27B on the base.

No.207. CREAMER — measures 18.00 5.00
$3^3/4$" high and has Mark Type
27B on the base.

No.208. PIN BADGE "MIKE" NPA NPA
(1996) — measures $1^3/\text{s}$" dia.
and has an impressed mark S52/5S
on the back.

No.209. PIN BADGE "IAN" NPA NPA
(1996) measures $1^3/\text{s}$" dia. and
has an impressed mark S52/5S on the back.
Item Nos.208 and 209 are two of six pin
badges made especially for the participants
at the Wade Booth at the 1996 Seattle
Beam/Wade Fair. The additional names are:
Adele, Jenny, Kim and Molly.

No.210. PHARMACEUTICAL 30.00 15.00
CONTAINER — measures
$1^1/2$" high and is marked WADE ENGLAND
B1. The quality of this porcelain piece is
very fine and delicate. To date only one
other similar piece has surfaced. This
second item is similar to a small mixing
bowl with the addition of a spout.

No.211. WADE CERAMICS SIGN — 25.00 12.00
measures $2^1/2$" x $3^3/4$" and
is unmarked on the back.

No.212. FAUCET CAP "COLD" — NPA NPA
measures 1" dia. and has an
impressed mark: 1" on the back.

No.213. FAUCET CAP "HOT" — NPA NPA
measures 1" dia. and has an
impressed mark: 1" on the back.

No.214. KEY HOLE COVERS — 15.00 8.00
each measures $2^1/4$" long and each has an
impressed mark: S103/3 on the back.

No.215. TETLEY TEA 30.00 25.00
SALT SHAKER —
measures 4" high and is marked:
Wade England ©Tetley G.B. Limited 1996.

	U.S. $	British £

No.216. TETLEY TEA 30.00 25.00
PEPPER SHAKER — measures
$3^1/4$" high and is marked:
Wade England ©Tetley G.B. Limited 1996.

No.217. GAFFER MONEY BOX — 60.00 50.00
measures 6" high and is marked:
An Original Design for Tetley G.B. by Wade
England © Tetley G.B. Limited 1996.

No.218. MINIATURE MUG — 7.00 5.00
measures $1^1/4$" high and has a transfer
mark similar to Mark Type 27 on the base.
This mug was commissioned by Keenan
Antiques and was first made available at
the Seattle Fair in 1996. This item was
made in a limited number of 500 pieces.

No.219. WHIMBLE "BETTY BOOP" 8.00 3.00
— measures $1^1/\text{s}$" high and has
special Mark Type S48 on the back. There
was a limited issue of 500 pieces for this
item which was commissioned by C&S
Collectables in 1996.

No.220. WHIMBLE " SPOONERS" 8.00 3.00
(1996) — measures $1^1/\text{s}$" high and has a
special Mark Type S48 on the back. There
was a limited issue of 1000 pieces of this
Wimble which is based on the store front of
C&S Collectables.

No.221. WHIMBLE "SEATTLE 1996" 8.00 3.00
— measures $1^1/\text{s}$" high and has a
special Mark Type S48 on the back.
C&S Collectables commissioned Wade
Ceramics to make 500 pieces to celebrate
the first Beam/Wade Fair held in 1996 in
Seattle, WA.

No.222. WHIMBLE "INTERNATIONAL 8.00 3.00
WADE COLLECTORS CLUB" —
measures $1^1/\text{s}$" high and has a special Mark
Type S48 on the back. C&S Collectables
commissioned Wade Ceramics, in 1996,
to produce 1000 pieces illustrating the
club logo.

No.223. DECANTER SET 275.00 185.00
(circa mid 1950's). The decanter
measures $8^1/2$" high and has Mark Type 29
on the base. Each miniature goblet
measures $2^1/2$" high and has Mark Type 28
on the base. The suggested price given is
for the complete set (decanter/stopper and
six goblets).

MISCELLANEOUS FLOWER JUGS, VASES AND TEAPOTS EARLY 1900 - LATE 1930'S

		U.S. $	British £
No.224.	VASE — measures 7¹/₈" high and has Mark Type 2 on the base.	50.00	35.00
No.225.	VASE — measures 7¹/₂" high and has Mark Type 2 on the base.	75.00	50.00
No.226.	FLOWER JUG — measures 8³/₄" high and has Mark Type 4 on the base along with shape No.90 and decoration No.142(8).	100.00	60.00
No.227.	FLOWER JUG — measures 7¹/₂" high and has Mark Type 2 on the base along with shape No.127.	90.00	50.00
No.228.	FLOWER JUG — measures 8³/₄" high and has Mark Type 4 on the base along with shape No.13L.	80.00	55.00
No.229.	FLOWER JUG — measures 8³/₄" high and has Mark Type 7 on the base along with shape No.148 and decoration No.4292.	30.00	25.00
No.230.	FLOWER JUG — measures 6¹/₂" high and has Mark Type 2 on the base along with decoration No.3494.	60.00	35.00
No.231.	FLOWER JUG — measures 8⁷/₈" high and has Mark Type 4 on the base along with shape No.133 and decoration No.5084.	80.00	55.00
No.232.	MINIATURE VASE — measures 3³/₄" high and has Mark Type 6 on the base. *(See also No.611 pg.75 of The W of W2)*	55.00	30.00
No.233.	MINIATURE VASE — measures 4" high and has Mark Type 6 on the base.	55.00	30.00
No.234.	MINIATURE VASE — measures 4" high and has Mark Type 6 on the base.	55.00	30.00
No.235.	COFFEE POT — measures 8" high and has Mark Type 2 on the base.	100.00	40.00
No.236.	HOT WATER POT — measures 5¹/₂" high and has Mark Type "0" on the base. *(See also No.567 pg.58 of The W of W and Nos.658 and 671 pg.78 of The W of W2)*	75.00	40.00
No.237.	TEA & WATER POT STAND — measures 8¹/₄" l. x 7" w. and has Mark Type "0" on the base. *(See also No.566 pg.58 of The W of W and Nos.659 and 672 pg.78 of The W of W2)*	30.00	20.00

		U.S. $	British £
No.238.	TEAPOT — measures 5¹/₂" high and has Mark Type "0" on the base. *(See also No.568 pg.58 of The W of W and No.657 pg.78 of The W of W2)*	75.00	40.00
No.239.	TEAPOT "Bee" shape — measures 6¹/₄" high and has Mark Type 8A (with the letter "J" instead of "A") on the base.	120.00	65.00
No.240.	FLOWER JUG — measures 6³/₄" high and has Mark Type 6 on the base along with shape No.150.	90.00	70.00
No.241.	FLOWER JUG — measures 4" high and has Mark Type 6 on the base. *(See also Nos.558 and 559 pg.72 of The W of W2)*	65.00	50.00
No.242.	TEAPOT — decoration No.1629, measures 5³/₄" high and has Mark Type 2 on the base. *(See also Nos.812, 813 and 814 pg. 87 of The W of W)*	110.00	55.00

BEAR AMBITIONS TEAPOTS 1994 - 1995

The teapots Nos. 243 - 248 are referred to as Bear Ambitions teapots and were designed by Judith Wootton. Each teapot has a special backstamp noting the name of the character featured on the teapot along with a brief outline of the character's artistic or mechanical abilities. Each base is also marked WADE.

		U.S. $	British £
No.243.	"LOCOMOTIVE JOE" TEAPOT — measures 6¹/₂" high	35.00	20.00
No.244.	"ARTISTIC EDWARD" TEAPOT — measures 6¹/₂" high	35.00	20.00
No.245.	"MUSICAL MARCO" TEAPOT — measures 6¹/₂" high	35.00	20.00
No.246.	"ALEX THE AVIATOR" TEAPOT — measures 6¹/₂" high	35.00	20.00
No.247.	"ADMIRAL SAM" TEAPOT — measures 6¹/₂" high	35.00	20.00
No.248.	"BEATRICE THE BALLERINA" TEAPOT — measures 6¹/₂" high	35.00	20.00

LONDON LIFE TEAPOTS 1994 - 1995

Teapots Nos.249 - 251 feature typical scenes from London. The teapots were designed by Barbara Cooksey and each teapot has a special backstamp reading: WADE London Life Made in England designed by Barbara Cooksey.

		U.S. $	British £
No.249.	"THE GUARDS" TEAPOT — measures 6³/₄" high	35.00	20.00
No.250.	"THE CAPITAL" TEAPOT — measures 6³/₄" high	35.00	20.00

	U.S. $	British £
No.251. "ON PARADE" TEAPOT — measures 6³/₄" high	35.00	20.00

MISCELLANEOUS TEAPOTS AND JUGS LATE 1880'S - 1994

No.252. "FESTIVE" TEAPOT — 35.00   10.00
measures 6" high and has Mark Type 27B on
the base. This teapot was made for Boots
Drug Stores for Christmas 1993.

No.253. "FESTIVE" TEAPOT — 35.00   10.00
measures 6" high and has Mark Type 27B on
the base. This teapot was made for Boots
Drug Stores for Christmas 1993.

No.254. "POPPY" TEAPOT — 25.00   15.00
measures 6¹/₂" high and has
Mark Type 27B on the base. This teapot was
produced in the early 1990's and replaced an
earlier poppy teapot shown as item No.558
pg.58 of *The W of W*.

No.255. "POPPY" TEAPOT — 20.00   12.00
measures 5¹/₂" high and has Mark Type 27B
on the base. This teapot was produced in the
early 1990's and replaced an earlier poppy
teapot shown as item No.558 pg.58 of
The W of W.

No.256. "OLD ENGLISH CASTLE" 120.00   65.00
TEAPOT — measures 5" high and has Mark
Type 7 on the base along with a mold
mark:OLD ENGLISH CASTLE MADE IN
ENGLAND.

No.257. "BRITANNIA" TEAPOT 200.00   120.00
(1901)— measures 6¹/₂" high and has
Mark Type "01" on the base along with the
registration No. 369349.

No.258. "EXCELSOR" JUG (1893) 100.00   60.00
— measures 6³/₄" high and has
Mark Type "04" on the base along with the
registration No.220194 Patent 544.

No.259. "EUREKA" JUG (1896) — 100.00   60.00
measures 7¹/₄" high and has the wording:
EUREKA Rd282788 V818 on the base.

No.260. TEAPOT — measures 120.00   65.00
5¹/₂" high and has Mark Type 1 on the base.

No.261. TEAPOT — 120.00   65.00
measures 5¹/₄" high and has
Mark Type 1 on the base.

No.262. "ACME" JUG (1899) — 100.00   60.00
measures 7¹/₄" high and has Mark Type "03"
on the base along with the registration
No.343857.

	U.S. $	British £
No.263. "CADROON" TEAPOT (1900) — measures 6³/₄" high and has Mark Type "02" on the base along with the registration No.355036.	120.00	65.00

BRITISH HOME STORES LATE 1980'S - 1994

No.264. TABLE LAMP — 75.00   30.00
measures 11¹/₄" high and is unmarked.

No.265. TABLE LAMP — 70.00   30.00
measures 11¹/₄" high and is unmarked.

No.266. "BON APPETIT" OPEN 10.00   3.00
SUGAR — measures 3¹/₂" h. x 3³/₄" dia.
and is marked: BhS Bon Appetite Tableware
Made in Britain.

No.267. "BON APPETIT" CREAMER 10.00   3.00
— measures 3⁷/₈" high and is marked:
BhS Bon Appetite Tableware Made in
Britain.

No.268. "BON APPETIT" UTENSIL 20.00   5.00
JAR — measures 6¹/₈" h. x 4" dia. and is
marked: BhS Bon Appetite Tableware Made
in Britain.

No.269. SOUP BOWL — 10.00   5.00
measures 6¹/₂" dia. and is marked
MADE IN BRITAIN. This bowl was part of a
tableware set known as Country Garland.

No.270. GRAVY BOAT AND DISH — 20.00   10.00
the boat measures 4" to top
of spout and is marked: BhS Country
Garland Tableware Made in Britain. The dish
measures 6¹/₂" dia. and is unmarked.

No.271. OPEN SUGAR — 10.00   3.50
measures 2⁷/₈" high and is
marked: BhS Strawberry Tableware
Made in Britain.

No.272. CREAMER — 10.00   3.50
measures 3⁷/₈" high and is
marked: BhS Strawberry Tableware
Made in Britain.

No.273. GRAVY BOAT AND DISH — 20.00   10.00
the boat measures 3¹/₈" h. x 7" overall
spout and handle and is marked on the
base: BhS Priory Tableware Made in Britain.
The plate measures 5¹/₈" x 7" and is
unmarked.

BOOTS THE CHEMISTS 1995 - 1996

No.274. "NOSTALGIA" WATER 25.00   15.00
PITCHER — measures 8¹/₄" high and is
marked: Boots the Chemists on the base.

	U.S. $	British £

No.275. "NOSTALGIA" BOWL — 15.00 10.00
measures 2³/₄" h. x 10¹/₄" dia.
and is unmarked. This is a companion
piece to item No.274.

No.276. TOOTHBRUSH HOLDER — 8.00 5.00
measures 3¹/₂" h. x 2⁷/₈" dia.
and is marked: Boots the Chemists.

No.277. SOAP DISH — measures 18.00 12.00
3" h. x 7" l. and is unmarked.
This soap dish and the toothbrush
holder item No.276 were sold as a boxed set.

No.278. TEA CADDY — measures 18.00 10.00
6" h. to top of finial x 3¹/₄" square
and has Mark Type 27B on the base.

No.279. "H.R.H." KITTY 8.00 5.00
MESSAGE BOWL — measures
2" h. x 5" dia. and has a paper label, on the
base, reading in part: Made in U.K. Wade
Ceramics Ltd. England.

No.280. "FISHFACE" KITTY 8.00 5.00
MESSAGE BOWL — measures
2" h. x 5" dia. and has a paper label, on the
base, reading in part: Made in U.K. Wade
Ceramics Ltd. England.

No.281. SHAVING MUG — 8.00 5.00
measures 3¹/₄" high and is
marked on the base: Boots the Chemists.
The shaving mug was marketed along with a
shaving brush as a boxed set.

HARRODS KNIGHTSBRIDGE EARLY 1990'S

No.282. TEAPOT — measures 40.00 25.00
5¹/₄" high and is marked on the base:
Harrods Knightsbridge Made Exclusively
in the United Kingdom.

No.283. HARRODS DOORMAN 50.00 45.00
MONEY BOX — measures 6³/₄" high
and is marked: Harrods Knightsbridge.

No.284. HARRODS DOORMAN 35.00 25.00
SALT SHAKER — measures
4¹/₈" high and is marked: Harrods
Knightsbridge.

No.285. HARRODS DOORMAN 35.00 25.00
PEPPER SHAKER — measures
4¹/₈" high and is marked: Harrods
Knightsbridge.

No.286. HARRODS STORE 40.00 25.00
TEAPOT — measures 6¹/₄" high and is
marked on the base: Harrods Knightsbridge
Made Exclusively in the United Kingdom.

MISCELLANEOUS ITEMS MID 1990'S.

	U.S. $	British £

No.287. BOOTS VAN MONEY BOX — 50.00 45.00
measures 5¹/₄" h. x 8" long and is
unmarked.

No.288. "ENGLISH BREAKFAST" 75.00 35.00
TEA CADDY (1993) — measures
7¹/₄" high and is marked: Handcrafted and
Produced Exclusively for Williamson and
Magor by Wade Royal Victoria Pottery.
(See also Nos.788 and 789 pg.85 of The W of W2)

No.289. TETLEY VAN TEA CADDY 130.00 80.00
(1994 - 1995) — measures
5³/₈" h. x 8³/₄" long and is marked:
An original Design for Lyons Tetley by
Wade England.

RINGTONS LIMITED TEA MERCHANTS

Sam Smith, the founder of Ringtons Limited, was born in Leeds on June 22, 1872. At the early age of nine years, Sam Smith began helping out with the family expenses by taking a part time job as a butcher's boy. One year later, as a half timer, Smith joined the staff of a thriving Leeds-based tea merchant.

Not too long after starting his employment with the tea merchant, Sam Smith began impressing his employers by his enthusiasm and his capacity for hard work. Smith's first position was that of an errand boy and his friendly and capable manner soon made him an ideal candidate for the position of salesman.

By the age of thirty-five, Smith had attained a top position at his place of employment and had gained so much knowledge in the tea trading that he was looked upon as an expert in his chosen field. One aspect of the retail business that particularly interested Smith was the door to door van delivery system introduced shortly before the end of the 19th century. To Smith's active mind, this system of delivery and sales was ideal for the tea trade.

In 1907, much to the surprise of his friends and co-workers, Smith quit his job and opened his own tea trader business. Due to Smith's high regard for his former employer and also due to certain legalities, Smith opened his new business far to the north of Leeds in the city of Newcastle.

Due to a rather small initial capital investment of £250 which bought one horse, one van, various utensils and a stock of tea, Sam Smith took on , for a short while, a business partner. The partner's last name was Titterington and it was from the last few letters of this name that the title of the company originated: Ringtons.

For some time, the new business struggled mainly due to the housewives reticence to trust a new tea merchant. Very soon, however, mainly due to Smith's engaging personality, knowledge of the tea trade and steadily increasing amounts of fine quality blended tea, he gradually won over the Newcastle housewives.

Within one year, Sam Smith was the employer of four assistants and the owner of two horse-drawn vans. The business had also outgrown its original rented "lock-up" premises so relocated to an abandoned rifle range which provided the much needed extra space.

Very soon, the delivery vans, with their distinctive lettering and coloring, became a familiar sight on the streets of Newcastle. The company's reputation was keeping pace with the expanding business and the reliability and friendliness of the salesmen, not to mention the high quality of the tea, won over hundreds of new customers.

By 1914, Ringtons employed seventeen assistants and owned eleven horse-drawn delivery vans. Unfortunately, this run of expansion did not last long for it was in 1914 that the Great War began. Fifteen salesmen were called up for the war but with his usual consideration for his staff, Sam Smith promised them their jobs back as soon as the war was over.

To add more problems to running a successful enterprise with hardly any staff, the government of the day introduced rationing and conditional sales laws. These laws encouraged grocers to insist that if customers bought sugar from them, the customers would also have to buy the tea from them. This, of course, spelt disaster for Ringtons so in order to survive, the company had to resort to selling anything edible. This included all sorts of canned goods along with dried eggs and evaporated milk.

At the end of the war, Ringtons was left with only three vans on the road and the business at the very edge of extinction. However, true to his word, Smith reengaged the twelve former members of his staff who survived the war. Together, Sam Smith and his staff began to rebuild the business to its prewar glory.

With the withdrawal of the restrictive laws, Ringtons was soon doing what the firm did best—selling high quality tea. As soon as the vans were back on the Newcastle streets, the prewar customers flocked back to buy tea from the familiar vans. Very soon, the company was back on its feet doing better business than before the war.

By 1926, Ringtons had to open a new head office, also located in Newcastle. New staff was recruited by the score and new depots were opened all over the north of England. It was at this time that Ringtons first began to offer premiums to its customers, a custom which is still going strong today.

The first depot to be opened in Leeds was in 1927, followed in 1935 by a blending and packing factory. This, interestingly, was on the site of the tiny cottage in which Sam Smith had been born.

Although Ringtons first introduced motorized vans in the mid 1920's, customers preferred the horse-drawn vehicles. It was not until 1954 that all vehicles became motorized.

Sam Smith was determined that the business would remain a family business and luckily Smith's second son, Douglas, was interested in joining the company. He worked his way up from a van boy to chairman of the board. Douglas' sons also followed in their father's footsteps and worked their way up through the company to learn the business of tea merchants until they were able to join the board. Today, Sam Smith's great grandson, Nigel Smith, is managing director and the Smith family, the fourth generation, is still playing a very prominent role in the running of Ringtons.

The second World War once again brought impending doom to Ringtons. Four hundred employees were called up and the fleet of over 200 vans had to be taken off the road due to gasoline rationing. At the end of hostilities, it fell upon the younger generation to rebuild the business. Sam Smith died in 1949 in his seventy-seventh year. He left behind him a flourishing business built on his hard work, persistence and sound principles.

With the ever-increasing price of gasoline and changing public tastes, Ringtons has had to change with the times. Tea bags were eventually, and most probably reluctantly, introduced and due to increasing demand by its customers, Ringtons also began selling coffee. Premiums have also now taken an important place in the sales of Ringtons' tea and coffee. Even with the increased costs of delivery and overhead, Ringtons still insists upon giving the customers quality and value for its money.

Although premiums and incentives have been part of Ringtons' sales procedures for many years, it is only relatively recently that Wade Ceramics Limited has entered the picture. Following is a listing of items made by Wade for Ringtons over the past few years. A number of these items are also illustrated in the color section.

1982 — **RINGTONS 75 th ANNIVERSARY TEA CADDY —**
White Ringtons horse van logo surrounded by laurel leaves.

1980's — ROSE CHINTZ RANGE —
a range of items sold at various times throughout the 1980's. The line comprised of:

Single Planter

Double Planter

Photograph Frame

Bud Vase

Rose Bowl

Table Lamp

MALING REPLICAS

1987 — Small Caddy showing Castles and Bridges
(See No. 694. pg. 79 of the W of W 2)

1989 - Tall Caddy showing cathedrals
(See No. 693. pg. 79 of the W of W2)

1991 - Willow Pattern Caddy
(See Fig. 102. pg. 181 of the W of W2)

1993 - Willow Pattern Caddy
(See Fig. 103. pg. 181 of the W of W2)

1994 - Willow Pattern Jug

1996 - Willow Pattern Tea Pot

1989 - FLORAL TRELLIS RANGE —

Tea Set produced by Wade (Ireland) Ltd. The set comprised of the following:

Tea Pot
(See No. 685. pg. 79 of the W of W2)

Cup and Saucer

Milk and Sugar Set
(See Nos. 686 & 687. pg. 79 of the W of W2)

Tea Plates

WILLOW PATTERN

Starting in 1994, Ringtons commissioned Wade to produce a Willow Pattern tea set based on The Willow Pattern produced for Ringtons in the 1920's by The Maling Pottery. Although there are as many variations on the blue and white ware as there are manufacturers, the Ringtons design utilizes two figures on the bridge.

1994

Large Tea Pot, Small Tea Pot, Beakers (tall handled mugs), Coasters,

Tea Plates, Cups and Saucers, Milk and Sugar.
(See the color section of this book for some of these items.)

1995

Dinner plates, Coffee Pot and soup/cereal bowls.
(See the color section of this book)

1996

Storage Jar, Salt & Pepper, Toast Rack, Egg Cups and Butter/Cheese Dish

STREET SCENE TEAPOTS 1993-1994

Between 1992 and 1994, four teapots illustrating Ringtons delivery vans of the 1920's, 1950's, 1960's and 1980's. *(See the color section of this book.)*

STREET SCENE MUGS 1994

Sets of mugs with similar scenes to the teapots. One set of mugs consisted of two mugs featuring the vans from the 1920's and the 1950's. The second set consisted of two mugs featuring the scenes from the 1960's and the 1980's.

CHRISTMAS ITEMS 1995

For Christmas 1995, Ringtons offered their customers two items:

Street Games Wall Plates
Ringtons Delivery Van Money Box.

		U.S. $	British £
No.290.	SMALL TEAPOT — measures $5^1/2$" high and has special Mark Type S50 on the base.	50.00	20.00
No.291.	COFFEE POT — measures $9^3/4$" high and has special Mark Type S50 on the base.	55.00	30.00
No.292.	LARGE TEAPOT — measures $6^1/4$" high and has special Mark Type S50 on the base.	45.00	25.00
No.293.	SAUCER — measures $5^3/4$" dia. and has special Mark Type S50 on the base.	10.00	5.00
No.294.	BEAKER — measures 4" high and has special Mark Type S50 on the base.	25.00	10.00
No.295.	PLATE — measures $6^3/4$" dia. and has special Mark Type S50 on the base.	10.00	5.00
No.296.	OPEN SUGAR — measures 3" high and has special Mark Type S50 on the base.	14.00	8.00
No.297.	CREAMER — measures $6^1/4$" high and has special Mark Type S50 on the base.	14.00	8.00
No.298.	"STREET SCENE" TEAPOT — measures $6^1/8$" high and has a mark on the base reading: 1920's Collector Teapot Made Especially for Ringtons a Family Business Est.1907. By Wade Ceramics 1993.	40.00	25.00

	U.S. $	British £

No.299. "STREET SCENE" TEAPOT — measures 7¹/₈" high and has a mark on the base reading: 1950's Collector Teapot Made Especially for Ringtons a Family Business Est.1907. By Wade Ceramics 1993.   40.00   25.00

No.300. "STREET SCENE" TEAPOT — measures 7³/₄" high and has a mark on the base reading: 1960's Collector Teapot Made Especially for Ringtons a Family Business Est.1907. By Wade Ceramics 1994.   40.00   25.00

No.301. "STREET SCENE" TEAPOT — measures 7¹/₄" high and has a mark on the base reading: 1980's Collector Teapot Made Especially for Ringtons a Family Business Est.1907. By Wade Ceramics 1994.   40.00   25.00

No.302. MINIATURE "MALING" JUG — measures 6" high to top of finial and is marked on the base: Ringtons Limited Tea Merchants Newcastle upon Tyne. Produced by Wade Ceramics based upon an original "MALING" jug. Produced for Ringtons in the late 1920's. 1995.   50.00   20.00

No.303. RINGTONS DELIVERY VAN MONEY BOX — measures 5¹/₄" h. x 8" l. and is marked: Manufactured Especially for Ringtons Ltd. by Wade Ceramics.   65.00   50.00

No.304. "STREET GAMES" WALL PLATE — measures 10" dia. and is marked: Manufactured Exclusively for Ringtons Ltd. by Wade Ceramics.   25.00   12.00

No.305. CLOCK — measures 6¹/₄" h. x 5" w. x 2¹/₂" deep and is marked: Especially Commissioned by Ringtons Ltd. by Wade Ceramics 1992.   60.00   22.00

No.306. MINIATURE "MALING" TEAPOT (1996) — measures 4¹/₈" high and is marked : Ringtons Ltd. Tea Merchants, Algernon Road Newcastle on-Tyne, Produced by Wade Ceramics based upon an original "MALING" teapot, produced for Ringtons in the 1930's. 1996.   50.00   20.00

No.307. BUTTER DISH (1996) — measures 4" high to top of handle (incl. base).The base measures 5³/₄" w. x 8¹/₄" l. and is marked on the underside: Exclusive Willow Pattern Design specially commissioned by Ringtons Ltd. Produced by Wade Ceramics.   30.00   15.00

	U.S. $	British £

No.308. SALT AND PEPPER SHAKERS (1996) — each item measures 3¹/₂" high and each is marked: Ringtons Ltd. by Wade Ceramics. Priced individually.   10.00   6.00

No.309. TOASTRACK (1996) — measures 3" h. x 6¹/₈" l. x 3¹/₂" w. and is marked: Ringtons Produced by Wade Ceramics.   25.00   10.00

No.310. EGG CUPS (1996) — each egg cup is 2" h. x 2" dia. and each is marked on the base: Ringtons by Wade. Priced individually.   6.00   3.00

No.311. "STREET SCENE" MUG (1994) — measures 3⁵/₈" high and is marked on the base: Collectors Mug especially made for Ringtons a Family Business Est. 1907. By Wade Ceramics 1995. This mug had similar scenes as those used for the 1920s and 1950s Street Scene Teapots.   8.00   10.00

No.312. "STREET SCENE" MUG (1994) — measures 3⁵/₈" high and is marked on the base: Collectors Mug especially made for Ringtons a Family Business Est. 1907. By Wade Ceramics 1995. This mug had similar scenes as those used for the 1960's and 1980's Street Scene Teapots. There is an unexplained discrepancy in the production dates of these items.   18.00   10.00

No.313. STORAGE JAR (1996) — measures 7¹/₄" h. x 5" dia. and is marked: Exclusive Willow Pattern Design specially Commissioned by Ringtons Ltd. Produced by Wade Ceramics.   25.00   15.00

J. W. THORNTON LTD. 1993

No.314. DELIVERY VAN MONEY BOX (1993) — measures 4³/₄" h. x 8" l. and is mold marked on the base: Manufactured exclusively for J. W. Thornton Ltd. Made in England. This van money box is one of three van money boxes produce by Wade for J. W. Thornton Ltd.   60.00   50.00

THE INTERNATIONAL ASSOCIATION OF JIM BEAM BOTTLE AND SPECIALTIES CLUBS

The International Jim Beam Bottle and Specialties Club was formed in 1966 to cater to collectors of glass and ceramic decanters made by Regal China for the Jim Beam Company. The club was an instant success and clubs were formed in many parts of the United States. In 1970, due to this expansion, it was decided to form a National Association with an annual convention to be held in different cities of the U.S.A. each year. The first convention, in 1971, was held in Denver, Colorado.

When the third convention was held in Detroit, Michigan, the Association had grown to include members from not only the U.S. but also from Canada, New Zealand and Australia. It was therefore decided to revise the word "National" in the Club's title to "International."

Between 1955 and 1992, Regal China produced a variety of decorative decanters for Jim Beam such as club bottles, state bottles, sports bottles and general business bottles. From 1971 through 1992, Regal China also produced special decanters for each annual convention of the International Association.

In 1992, when Regal China closed their doors, the International Association had to look elsewhere for a source of their annual convention decanters. It was at this time that Wade Ceramics Ltd. entered the picture. Wade produced the decanter for the 1993 convention held in North Carolina and it was such a success with Jim Beam collectors that the pottery was asked to make presentations for the 1994 and 1995 conventions.

1995 saw not only the 200th anniversary of the founding of the Jim Beam Company but also the 25th anniversary of the International Association. For the 1995 convention Wade produced a ceramic 'whisky barrel' which was again a great success with collectors.

At one time, the International Association had a membership of 20,000 members from a total of 205 clubs. Although the membership has decreased somewhat over the years, it now has members from many countries other than the U.S.A. These countries include Canada, New Zealand, Australia, Japan, Germany, Mexico, England, Andorra, The Netherlands, Finland and New Guinea.

In 1995, the International Association of Jim Beam Bottle and Specialties Clubs and The International Wade Collectors Club agreed to give their members the opportunity of joining each other's association. Seattle, Washington, the city hosting the 1996 International Association's convention will see the first appearance of Wade dealers at the convention.

In 1996, the International Association of Jim Beam Bottle and Specialties Clubs commissioned Wade Ceramics to produce two water jugs based on existing blanks.

One water jug, based on a Bass shape water jug (see No.1326 pg.110 of *The W of W2*), was produced in a limited number of 186 in a blue glaze and the Jim Beam logo on both sides. This jug was given out at the 1996 Convention at the "one of a kind" contest. The procedes of this contest go to charities. The jug is marked, on the base, with the International logo and the wording : Awarded for one of a kind Charity Contest, Wade England.

The second jug, based on a Pusser water jug (see No.1189 pg.103 of *The W of W2*), was produced in a limited number of 132 in a white glaze and the Jim Beam logo appearing on both sides. This jug was given out to local clubs for making membership quotas. The jug is marked, on the base, with the International logo and the wording: Awarded for Membership Achievement, Wade England.

		U.S. $	British £
No.315.	TEAPOT — measures 8¹/₂" high to top of finial and is marked: Animated Characters Copywrite: R. Ellis 1995. All rights reserved. Exclusively Produced for the I.A.J.B.B.S.C. Limited edition 1 of 1700. By Wade.	40.00	25.00
No.316.	TEAPOT — measures 8¹/₂" high to top of finial and is marked: Animated Characters Copywrite: R. Ellis 1995. All rights reserved. Exclusively Produced for the I.A.J.B.B.S.C. Limited edition 1 of 1700. By Wade.	40.00	25.00

LIQUOR BARRELS 1995

The photography for these barrels took place at the design stage therefore some variations may exist on the production models. These barrels were produced for the 200th Anniversary of the James Beam Distillery and the 25th Anniversary of the I.A.J.B.B.S.C.

No.317.	LIQUOR BARREL (1995) — measures 6¹/₄" h. x 7¹/₄" l. and has Mark Type 27A on the base.	75.00	50.00
No.318.	LIQUOR BARREL (1995) — measures 6¹/₄" h. x 7¹/₄" l. and has Mark Type 27A on the base.	125.00	85.00
No.319.	LIQUOR BARREL (1995) — measures 6¹/₄" h. x 7¹/₄" l. and has Mark Type 27A on the base.	NPA	NPA
No.320.	LIQUOR BARREL (1995) — measures 6¹/₄" h. x 7¹/₄" l. and has Mark Type 27A on the base.	75.00	50.00
No.321.	JOHN PAUL JONES DECANTER (1993) — measures 8¹/₂" high and is back stamped with the 1993 Jim Beam Convention information along with the word - Wade. There were 450 decanters made with the cobalt blue stoppers.	65.00	45.00

FIG.8. *Top view of the stoppers for Item Nos. 322, 323, and 331.*

	U.S. $	British £
No.322. JOHN PAUL JONES FLAGON (1995) — is approximately 7" high to the top of stopper and is marked on the base: Genuine Wade Porcelain, Limited edition 900 and has the gold International logo on the top of the stopper. The production of this item with the blue neck and stopper was limited to 900 pieces.	50.00	35.00
No.323. JOHN PAUL JONES FLAGON (1995) — is approximately 7" high to the top of stopper and is marked on the base: Genuine Wade Porcelain, Limited edition 900 and has the gold International logo on the top of the stopper. The production of this item with the green neck and stopper was limited to 350 pieces.	60.00	40.00
No.324. JOHN PAUL JONES DECANTER (1993) — measures $8^1/_2$" high and is back stamped with the 1993 Jim Beam Convention information along with the word - Wade. There were 450 decanters made with the white stopper.	65.00	45.00

FIG.9.   *Base of Item Nos. 321 and 324.*

	U.S. $	British £
No.325. COOKIE JAR (1994) — measures 8" high to top of finial and is dated, on the base along with the President's signature. This item was produced for the 1994 Convention in Dallas, TX. Production was limited to 100 pieces.	50.00	35.00
No.326. SAUCER (1993) — measures $7^3/_4$" dia. and is dated on the base along with the President's signature. Production was limited to 75 pieces.	25.00	15.00
No.327. CUP (1993) — measures $3^1/_2$" h. x $4^3/_8$" dia. and is dated on the base along with the President's signature. Production was limited to 75 pieces.	35.00	25.00
No.328. TEAPOT (1995) — measures $6^1/_4$" high and is dated along with the President's signature and has the I.A.J.B.B.S.C. logo on the base as well as Mark Type 27B.	60.00	40.00

Thank You For Your Support At Our 25th Convention in 1995

FIG.10.   *Rear View of Item No. 328.*

	U.S. $	British £
No.329. TEA TIDY (1996) — measures $3^3/_4$" x $4^7/_8$" and has the I.A.J.B.B.S.C. logo as well as Mark Type 27B on the base. There were 400 items produced.	20.00	12.00
No.330. TEA TIDY (1996) — measures $3^3/_4$" x $4^7/_8$" and has the I.A.J.B.B.S.C. logo as well as Mark Type 27B on the base. There were 400 items produced.	20.00	12.00
No.331. JOHN PAUL JONES FLAGON (1995) — is approximately 7" high to the top of stopper and is marked on the base: Genuine Wade Porcelain, Limited edition 900 and has the gold International logo on the top of the stopper. The production of this item with the white neck and stopper was limited to 750 pieces.	65.00	45.00

	U.S. $	British £

No.332. VAN MONEY BOX (1996) — 95.00 65.00
measures 5^1/$_4$" h.x 8" l.
and is marked on the base: I.A.J.B.B.S.C.
26th Annual Convention July 6 -12, 1996
Seattle Washington. 1 of 305. Also included
on the base is Mark Type 27B and the
International logo.

No.333. VAN MONEY BOX (1996) — 125.00 85.00
measures 5^1/$_4$" h. x 8" l. and
is marked on the base: I.A.J.B.B.S.C.
26th Annual Convention July 6 - 12, 1996
Seattle Washington. 1 of 315. Also included
on the base is Mark Type 27B and the
International logo.

FIG. 11 "25TH ANNIVERSARY" 20.00 18.00
COASTERS (1995) — These
coasters were produced in two colors:
cobalt blue or black. There were 767 sets
(four coasters per set) produced in blue
and 758 sets (four coasters per set)
produced in black. The prices quoted are
for a set of four coasters. Each coaster
measures 3^7/$_8$" dia.

Fig. 11

DECANTERS, ASHTRAYS AND WATER JUGS

No.334. BELL'S OLD SCOTCH 490.00 285.00
WHISKY "GOLF" (1993) —
this 75cl decanter was produced for the
South African market. The price quoted is
for a full, sealed and boxed container.

No.335. DIMPLE SCOTCH 350.00 200.00
WHISKY (COAT OF ARMS) —
this 75cl bottle measures 8^1/$_4$" high
The price quoted is for a full, sealed and
boxed container.

	U.S. $	British £

No.336. DIMPLE SCOTCH 720.00 425.00
WHISKY "DRAGON" (1988) —
this 75cl bottle measures 8^1/$_4$" h.
The price quoted is for a full, sealed and
boxed container.

No.337. BELL'S OLD SCOTCH 510.00 300.00
WHISKY "HAWAII" —
this 75cl decanter measures 7^3/$_4$" h. and
has Mark Type 27B on the base.

No.338. BELL'S OLD SCOTCH 500.00 300.00
WHISKY "CURLING" (1992) —
this 75cl decanter was produced for the
South African market. The price quoted is for
a full, sealed and boxed container.

No.339. BELL'S OLD SCOTCH 450.00 260.00
WHISKY "FISHING" (1994) —
this 75cl decanter was produced for the
South African market. The price quoted is for
a full, sealed and boxed container.

No.340. TENNANTS LAGER PLATE 45.00 25.00
— measures 9^1/$_2$" dia. and
has Mark Type 43 on the base.

No.341. CARLSBERG LAGER 80.00 45.00
PILSNER ASHTRAY — measures
5^1/$_4$" dia. and has Mark Type 4 on th base.

No.342. CHARRINGTON BEERS 135.00 75.00
TOBY MUG — measures 7^3/$_8$" h.
and has Mark Type 43A on the base.
These items were produced as displays
for advertising and not, as has often been
thought, lamps. The purpose of the hole in
the base is to prevent this item from being
used as a water jug as the inside did not
have the required glaze used for tableware.
Furthermore, had this been intended for
use as a lamp, the hole for the cord would
have been on the back rather than on the
bottom. This item was produced in the
early 1960's.

	U.S. $	British £

FIG.12. JUBELLEE STOUT   45.00   15.00
CIGARETTE LIGHTER — measures
3¹/₈" high and has Mark Type 42 on the base.
*(See also Nos.1234, 1235 and 1236 pg.105
of The W of W2)*

Fig. 12

No.343. WHITE WINE PLAQUE —   6.00   2.00
measures 3" long and has the impressed
reserve number S52/3 on the back.

No.344. "THE ENGLISH   130.00   60.00
GENTLEMAN'S CHOICE" WHISKY
DECANTER (early 1990's) — measures
10" high to top of stopper and has special
Mark Type S21 on the base.

No.345. THE "POTTERIES   300.00   150.00
DECANTER" (1994) —
measures 8" to top of stopper and is mold
marked: "Potteries" Decanter Wade along
with a paper label reading Potteries Decanter
by Wade 25 years old single malt Scotch
Whisky 50.3% alc/vol 70cl. Distilled
and matured at Glenngoyne Distillery,
Drumgoyne, Scotland. The molded design
of the decanter features scenes from the six
pottery towns of: Burslem, Stoke, Hanley,
Fenton, Longton and Tunstall. The price
quoted is for a full, sealed and boxed item.
According to records 500 decanters were
filled and distributed to clients and staff.
Empty decanters were made available to
collectors throught the Pottery Store.

No.346. THE "POTTERIES   250.00   125.00
DECANTER" (1995) — measures
8" to top of stopper and is mold marked:
"Potteries" Decanter Wade along with a
paper label reading Potteries Decanter by
Wade 25 years old single malt Scotch
Whisky 50.3% alc/vol 70cl. Distilled and
matured at Glenngoyne Distillery,
Drumgoyne, Scotland. The molded design
of the decanter features scenes from the six
pottery towns of: Burslem, Stoke, Hanley,
Fenton, Longto and Tunstall. The price
quoted is for a full, sealed and boxed item.
According to records 350 decanters were
filled and distributed to clients and staff.
Empty decanters were made available to
collectors through the Pottery Store.

No.347. "JOHN PAUL JONES"   85.00   50.00
DECANTER — measures
8¹/₂" high and is marked on the base:
Pussers Ltd. British Virgin Islands,
West Indies. Handcast & Hand Decorated,
Made in England. "The John Paul Jones"
U.S. Navy and Marine Corps. Ships
Decanter. This decanter is a companion
piece to the Nelson's Ship's Decanter.
(See No.838 pg.72 of The W of W2)

No.348. BLACK & WHITE SCOTCH   25.00   12.00
WHISKY WATER JUG —
measures 6¹/₈" high and has Mark
Type 46 on the base.

No.349. V - J DRY GIN WATER   25.00   12.00
JUG — measures 6¹/₂" high and
has Mark Type 43 on the base.

No.350. SPRINGBANK SCOTCH   30.00   15.00
WHISKY — measures
6" tall and has Mark Type 46 on the base.

No.351. ANCESTOR SCOTCH   30.00   15.00
WHISKY — measures
5⁷/₈" high and has Mark Type 46
on the base.

No.352. WHITE HORSE   30.00   10.00
SCOTCH WHISKY — measures
7" high and has Mark Type 45
on the base.

No.353. ROMANOFF VODKA —   30.00   10.00
water jug with ice check spout,
measures 8" high and has Mark Type 47
on the base.

	U.S. $	British £
No.354. MACKINLAY'S OLD SCOTCH WHISKY — measures 7" high and has Mark Type 46 on the base.	30.00	10.00
No.355. JAMES MARTIN'S V.V.O. — measures 7^1/$_8$" high and has Mark Type 46 on the base.	30.00	18.00
No.356. JOHN BEGG SCOTCH WHISKY — measures 5" high and has Mark Type 46 on the base.	30.00	18.00
No.357. "ASHBOURNE" NATURAL WATER — measures 3^1/$_2$" high at the front and 1^3/$_8$" high at the back by 5" dia. and has Mark Type 47 on the base.	45.00	20.00
No.358. SPEY ROYAL SCOTCH WHISKY — water jug with ice check spout, measures 5^1/$_2$" high and has Mark Type 47 on the base.	30.00	18.00
No.359. KING OF SCOTS FINEST SCOTCH WHISKY— measures 4^1/$_2$" high and has Mark Type 46 on the base.	30.00	18.00
No.360. DANDIE DINMONT SCOTCH WHISKY— water jug with ice check spout, measures 5^1/$_2$" high and has Mark Type 19 on the base.	50.00	30.00
No.361. LAUDER'S SCOTCH WHISKY — this water jug measures 5^1/$_8$" high and has Mark Type 47 on the base.	30.00	20.00
No.362. HOUSE OF PEERS SCOTCH WHISKY— measures 4^1/$_2$" high and has Mark Type 46 on the base.	30.00	18.00

FIG. 13.   A. J. WADE LTD. FIREPLACE DESIGNS (EARLY 1950S)

Wade fireplaces were produced at the Flaxman Tile Works from the late 19th century through to 1970. The fireplace designs illustrated are from an early 1950s catalogue. The technical aspects of the fireplace production are illustrated on pg. 15 of *The W of W2*.

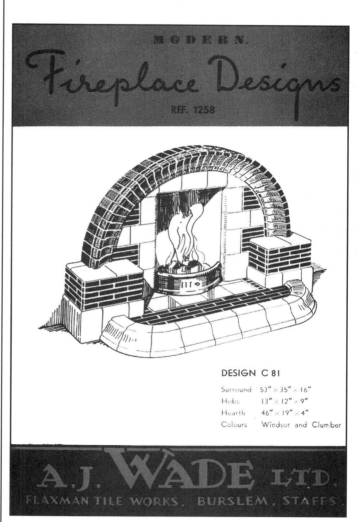

DESIGN C 43

Surround 54" · 36" · 16"
       6½" Return to Wa.
R Hearth 52" · 20" · 4½"
       1" Drop
Colours Sm. Norfolk and
       Sm. Wirral 3
       BM. 202 · M. 207

DESIGN C 149

Surround 48" · 36½" · 16"
       6" Return to Wa.
       2½" Recess
Easy Clean Hearth 44" · 18" · 3½"
       1" Drop
Colours Chester
       BM. 209 BM. 202

DESIGN C 138

Surround 42" · 36" · 16"
       6" Return to Wa.
       2½" Recess
Hearth 41" · 17" · 3"
       1" Drop
Colours Kendal and

DESIGN C 153

Surround 52" · 37" · 16"
       6" Return to Wa.
       2" Recess
Easy Clean Hearth 50" · 18" · 3"
       1" Drop
Colours Ludlow and Chepstow

DESIGN C 147

Surround 48" · 36" · 16"
       6" Return to Wa.
Easy Clean Hearth 4." · 17" · 3"
       1" Drop
Colours Ludlow and Chepstow

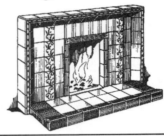

DESIGN C 154

Surround 53" · 37" · 16"
       6" Return to Wa.
       2½" Recess
Easy Clean Hearth 48" · 17" · 3½"
       1" Drop
Colours Maidstone

DESIGN C 156

Surround 54" · 38" · 16"
       6" Return to Wa.
       2½" Recess
Easy Clean Hearth 48" · 18" · 3½"
       1" Drop
Colours Chester and Chester

DESIGN C 168

Surround 54" · 36" · 16"
       6½" Return to Wa.
       2½" Recess
Hearth 50" · 18" · 3½"
       1" Drop
Colours BM. 202 and BM. 201

DESIGN C 158

Surround 54" · 37½" · 16"
       6" Return to Wall
       2" Recess
Easy Clean Hearth 48" · 18" · 3"
       1" Drop
Colours Arundel and Arundel

DESIGN C 171

Surround 52" · 48" · 16"
       6" Return to Wall
       2½" Recess
Hearth 48" · 18" · 3½"
       1" Drop
Colours BM. 202

DESIGN C 163

Surround 48" · 52" · 16"
       6½" Return to Wa.
       2½" Recess
Hearth 42" · 18" · 3"
       1" Drop
Colours Kendal and Windsor

DESIGN C 172

Surround 52" · 36" · 16"
       6½" Return to Wa.
       3" Recess
Hearth 48" · 18" · 3½"
       1" Drop
Colours Dudley and BM. 202
       or Dudley and BM. 213

DESIGN C 173

Surround 50" × 36" × 16"
6½" Return to Wall
3" Recess
Hearth 48" × 18" × 36"
1" Drop
Colours BM. 215 and BM. 202
or Ludlow and
Chepstow

DESIGN C 176

Surround 52" × 38½" × 16"
6½" Return to Wall
2½" Recess
Hearth 48" × 18" × 32"
1" Drop
Colours Dudley, Oban and
Maroon

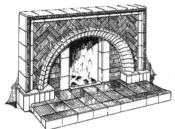

DESIGN C 174

Surround 59" × 47" × 16"
7" Return to Wall
4" Recess
Hearth 54" × 18" × 42"
1" Drop
Colours Dudley and Oban

DESIGN C 177

Surround 47" × 36" × 16"
6" Return to Wall
2½" Recess
Hearth 44" × 18" × 36"
1" Drop
Colours BM. 215 and BM. 202

DESIGN C 175

Surround 55" × 36" × 16"
7" Return to Wall
4" Recess
Hearth 48" × 18" × 36"
1" Drop
Colours Wigmore, Oba, Black
and Gold or Gunmetal,
Oban and Silver

DESIGN C 178

Surround 48" × 16½" × 16"
6½" Return to Wall
3" Recess
Hearth 44" × 18" × 32"
1" Drop
Colours BM. 215 and BM. 207

DESIGN C 179

Surround 54" × 36" × 16"
6" Return to Wall
3½" Recess
Hearth 48" × 18" × 36"
1" Drop
Colours BM. 215 and BM. 213

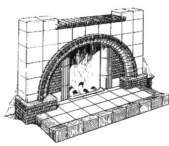

DESIGN C 180

Surround 58" × 36" × 16"
6" Return to Wall
4½" Recess
7" Gauge Depth
Hearth 50" × 20" × 42"
1" Drop
Colours BM. 215 and BM. 202

DESIGN C 181

Surround 48" × 36" × 16"
6" Return to Wall
3" Recess
Hearth 44" × 18" × 32"
1" Drop
Colours BM. 215 and BM. 207

COLOR PLATES
TO
WADE PRICE TRENDS

First Edition

©The Walt Disney Company

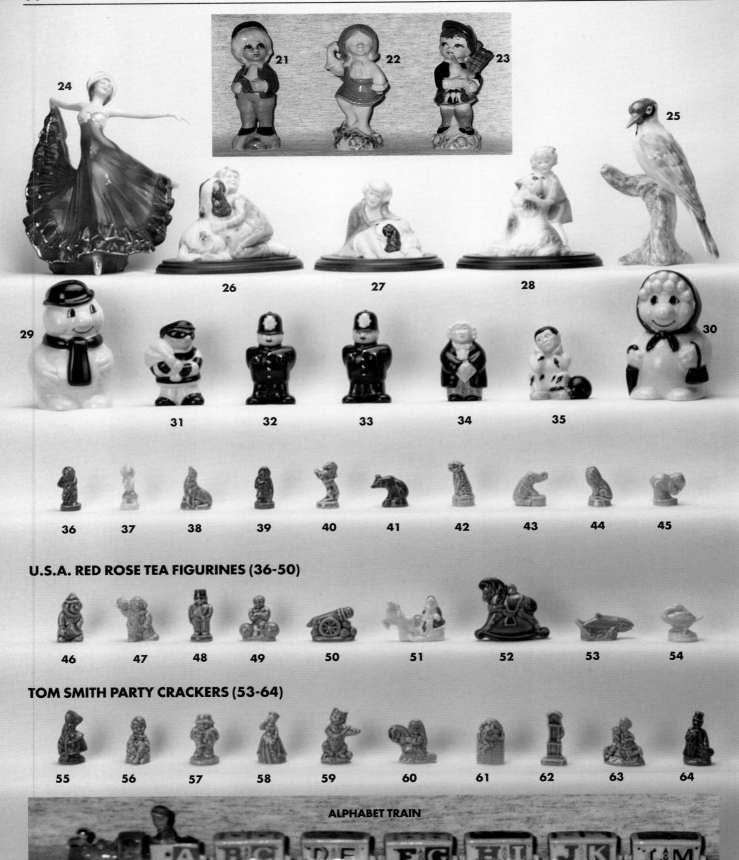

U.S.A. RED ROSE TEA FIGURINES (36-50)

TOM SMITH PARTY CRACKERS (53-64)

ALPHABET TRAIN

©The Walt Disney Company

66   67

68   69   70   71   72   73

74   75   76   77   78

79   80   81   82   83   84

85   86   87   88

BEAR AMBITIONS (89-94)

89   90   91   92   93   94   95   96   97

98   99   100   101   102

ELEPHANT TRAIN

103

104

105

108

106

107

109

110

111

112

113

114

115

116

117

118

119

120

121

122

123

124

125

126

127 128 129

130 131 132 133

134 135

136

137 138 139 140

141

142

143

144

145

©The Walt Disney Company

146 147

BREWMASTER
BREWED BY FLOWERS

151

154

152

153

157   158   159

155

156

160

162

163

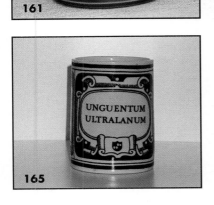

161

166

167

164

165

168

169

170 171
172 173

174

175

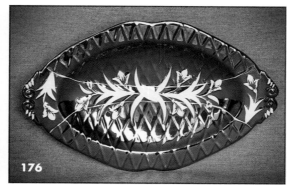

176

177

178

179
180

181

182

183 184

185

186 187

188

189

190

191

192

193

194

195

196

197

198

199

200

201

202

203

204

205

206

207

208

209

210

211

212

213

214

215

216

217

218

219

220

221

222

223

224   225

226   227

228

229   230

231

232   233   234

235

236   237   238

239

240   241

242

243

244

245

246

LONDON LIFE TEAPOTS (249-251)

247

248

249

250

251

252

254

255

253

256

257

258

259

264

265

266   267

268

BRITISH HOME STORES (264-273)

269

270

271   272   273

BOOTS THE CHEMIST (274-281, 287)

274

275

276

277

278

ENGLISH BREAKFAST TEA

279

HRH

280

Fish Face

281

HARRODS (282-286)

282

283

284

285

286

288

287

289

**RINGTONS LIMITED
TEA MERCHANTS
(290-313)**

290

291

292

293   294

295

296

297

298

299

300

301

301

302

303

304

305

306

307

308   309   310

311   312

313

J.W. THORNTON LTD.
(314)

314

315

316

INTERNATIONAL ASSOCIATION OF JIM BEAM BOTTLE AND SPECIALTIES CLUBS (315-333)

334

335

336

337

338

340

341

339

342

WADE (PDM) LTD. (334-362)

343

344

345

346

347

348

349

350

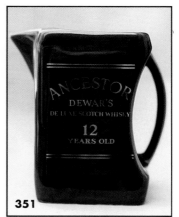

351

352

353

354

355

356

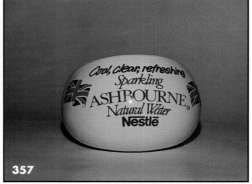

357

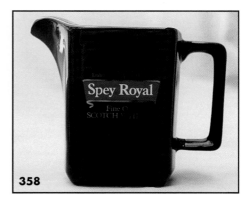

358

359

360

361

362

GEORGE WADE & SON LTD

BARBARA

ZENA

GRACE

CONCHITA

RHYTHM

MI-MI   CARMEN   ANTON AND GLORIA

LONDON SHOWROOMS TUESDAYS AND FRIDAYS...

MANCHESTER   POTTERY

BURSLEM · STOKE · ON · TRENT

LONDON SHOWROOMS
3 UNION BANK BUILDINGS, ELY PLACE, HOLBORN, LONDON. E.C.1

SPRING

The original models for these figures are made by artists at the top of their profession ; nothing is left undone to ensure Wade Figures being beautiful in form and delightful in colour.

Wade Figures are made like ordinary china until after the first firing, when they are decorated with Scintillite which gives a far fuller palette than is attainable with Ceramic Colour.

In texture and delicacy they have a charm of their own.

WADE Whimsies

they're great to collect

5. Spaniel

1. Fawn 2. Rabbit 3. Mongrel 4. Kitten

6. Duck 7. Corgi 8. Beaver 9. Bush Baby 10. Fox

WADE Whimsies

they're great to collect

12. Otter

11. Bear Cub 13. Setter 14. Owl 15. Trout

16. Lion 17. Elephant 18. Giraffe 19. Champ 20. Hippo

WADE Whimsies

they're great to collect

29. Horse

21. Squirrel 22. Hedgehog 23. Pine Marten 24. Field Mouse 25. Alsatian

26. Collie 27. Cow 28. Pig 30. Lamb

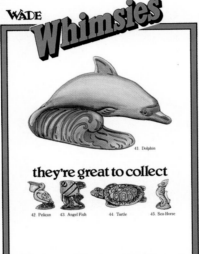

WADE Whimsies

they're great to collect

41. Dolphin

42. Pelican 43. Angel Fish 44. Turtle 45. Sea-Horse

WADE Whimsies

they're great to collect

38. Cat

31. Rhino 32. Leopard 33. Gorilla 34. Camel 35. Zebra

36. Donkey 37. Barn Owl 39. Mouse 40. Ram

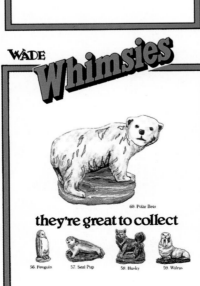

WADE Whimsies

they're great to collect

60. Polar Bear

56. Penguin 57. Seal Pup 58. Husky 59. Walrus

WADE Whimsies

they're great to collect

49. Koala Bear

46. Kangaroo 47. Orang-Utan 48. Tiger 50. Langur

51. Bison 52. Bluebird 53. Bullfrog 54. Wild Boar 55. Racoon

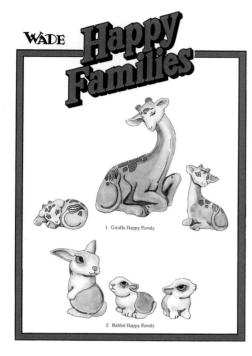

1. Giraffe Happy Family

2. Rabbit Happy Family

3. Hippo Happy Family

4. Mouse Happy Family

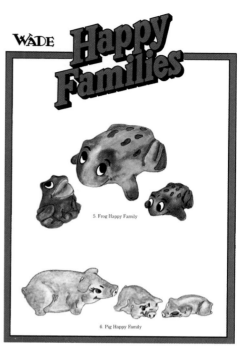

5. Frog Happy Family

6. Pig Happy Family

9. Chipmunk

...big brothers to the famous Whimsies

1. Polar Bear 2. Hippo 3. Brown Bear 4. Tiger 5. Elephant

6. Bison 7. Wolf 8. Bobcat 10. Racoon

7. Elephant Happy Family

8. Owl Happy Family

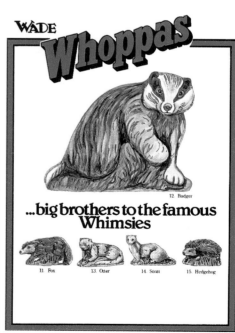

12. Badger

...big brothers to the famous Whimsies

11. Fox 13. Otter 14. Stoat 15. Hedgehog

WADE Nursery Favourites

nursery-rhyme characters brought to life by Wade

5. Humpty Dumpty

1. Jack   2. Jill   3. Little Miss Muffet   4. Little Jack Horner

6. Willie Winkie   7. Mary Lamb   8. Polly Kettle   9. King Cole   10. Tom Piper

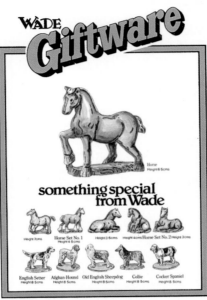

WADE Giftware

something special from Wade

Horse Height 6 cms

Height 7cms   Horse Set No. 1 Height 4.5cms   Height 3.5cms   Height 4cms Horse Set No. 2 Height 3cms

English Setter Height 8.5cms   Afghan Hound Height 8.5cms   Old English Sheepdog Height 8.5cms   Collie Height 8.5cms   Cocker Spaniel Height 8.5cms

WADE Nursery Favourites

nursery-rhyme characters brought to life by Wade

11. Boy Blue

12. Mary Mary   13. Cat & Fiddle   14. Queen of Hearts   15. Tommy Tucker

16. Three Bears   17. Bo-peep   18. Goosey Gander   19. Old Woman   20. Puss-in-Boots

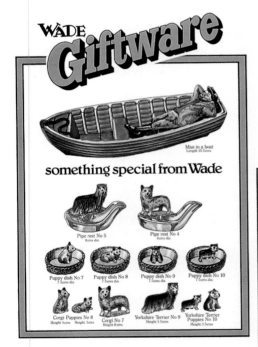

WADE Giftware

something special from Wade

Man in a boat Length 15.5cms

Pipe rest No 5 8cms dia   Pipe rest No 4 8cms dia

Puppy dish No 7 7.5cms dia   Puppy dish No 8 7.5cms dia   Puppy dish No 9 7.5cms dia   Puppy dish No 10 7.5cms dia

Corgi Puppies No 8 Height 4cms Height 3cms   Corgi No 7 Height 6cms   Yorkshire Terrier No 9 Height 5.5cms   Yorkshire Terrier Puppies No 10 Height 3.5cms

WADE Giftware

Puppy Dish 7.5cms dia

something special from Wade

Puppy Dishes 7.5cms dia

Pipe Rests 8cms dia   Cat Dish 7.5cms dia

WADE Giftware

Tom & Jerry Height 9cms Height 5cms

something special from Wade

Cairn Height 6cms   Red Setter Height 6cms   Alsatian Height 6cms

Cairn Puppies Height 4cms   Setter Puppies Height 3cms   Alsatian Puppies Height 4cms

Suggested Price Guide
to

THE WORLD OF WADE

First Edition

FIGURINES *by George Wade & Son Ltd. Circa 1927-1937*

PAGE 10
FIG.1. FIGURINES CIRCA 1927 - LATE 1930'S
(cellulose finish)

		U.S. $	British £
A.	Helga, 10" high	285.00	150.00
B.	Cherry, 10" high	330.00	175.00
C.	Grace, 9¼" high	330.00	175.00
D.	Ginger, 9½" high	485.00	275.00
E.	Carole, 8½" high	350.00	185.00
F.	Dawn, 8¼" high	400.00	225.00
G.	Conchita, 8¾" high	360.00	190.00
H.	Zena, 8⅞" high	285.00	155.00
I.	Rhythm, 9¾" high	330.00	175.00
J.	Carmen, 9¼"high	375.00	200.00
	(See also No. 23 pg. 50 of The W of W2)		
K.	Daisette, 10" high	500.00	250.00
L.	Argentina, 9½" high	400.00	210.00
M.	Joy, 9¼" high	410.00	215.00
N.	Blossoms, 7¾" high	475.00	250.00
O.	Springtime, 9" high	310.00	165.00
P.	Madonna and Child, 13½" high	750.00	400.00
Q.	Hille Bobbe, 10" high	475.00	250.00
R.	Christina, 11" high	410.00	215.00
	(See also No. 5 pg. 49 of The W of W2)		
S.	Colorado, 10" high	495.00	250.00
	(See also No. 3 pg. 49 of The W of W2)		
T.	Alsatian, 10¼" h. x 18" l.	350.00	185.00
U.	Sadie, 13½" high	375.00	200.00

PAGE 11
FIG.2. FIGURINES CIRCA 1927 - LATE 1930'S
(cellulose finish)

A.	Queenie, 4" high	170.00	90.00
B.	Cynthia, 5" high	160.00	85.00
C.	Tony, 4½" high	170.00	90.00
D.	Jose, 4½" high	160.00	80.00
E.	Betty, 5" high	160.00	85.00
F.	Strawberry Girl, 5¼" high	185.00	100.00
	(See also No. 7 pg. 49 of The W of W2)		

		U.S. $	British £
G.	Elf, 4" high	310.00	165.00
	(See also No. 10 pg. 49 of The W of W2)		
H.	Zena, 4" high	230.00	120.00
	(See also No. 4 pg. 49 of The W of W2)		
I.	Pavlova, 4½" high	185.00	100.00
J.	Tessa, 5" high	185.00	100.00
	(See also No. 9 pg. 49 of The W of W2)		
K.	Alice, 5½" high	485.00	275.00
L.	Sunshine, 6½" high	125.00	75.00
M.	Humoresque, 8¼" high	315.00	165.00
N.	Anton, 5¾" high	290.00	160.00
O.	Gloria, 5¾" high	300.00	160.00
	(See also No. 8 pg. 21 of WPT)		
P.	Alsatian, 4¾" h. x 8¾" l.	190.00	100.00
Q.	Jean, 6¾" high	330.00	175.00
R.	Barbara, 8½" high	350.00	190.00
S.	Pompadour, 6" high	175.00	120.00
T.	Curtsy, 5" high	160.00	85.00
U.	Harriet, 8" high	125.00	150.00
V.	Spaniel, 2½" h. x 5½" l.	230.00	155.00
W.	Joyce, 7¼" high	255.00	135.00
	(See also No. 1 pg. 49 of The W of W2)		
X.	Peggy, 6¾" high	255.00	135.00
	(See also No. 2 pg. 49 of The W of W2)		

PAGE 12
FIG.3.FIGURINES CIRCA 1927 - LATE 1930'S
(cellulose finish)

A.	Lotus, 9¾" high	285.00	150.00
B.	Sylvia, 7½" high	285.00	150.00
C.	Pavlova, 9¼" high	340.00	180.00
D.	H.R.H. Princess Elizabeth, 5¾" high	285.00	150.00
E.	June, 7" high	285.00	150.00
F.	Romance, 6" high	130.00	70.00
G.	Frolic, (Wall Mask)	780.00	450.00
	(See also No. 4 pg. 21 of WPT)		
H.	Dyllis, (Wall Mask)	1025.00	550.00
	(See also No. 3 pg. 21 of WPT)		

		U.S. $	British £
I.	Sonia, (Wall Mask) *(See also No. 5 pg. 21 of WPT)*	780.00	450.00
J.	Pan, (Wall Mask) *(See also Nos. 1 and 2 of WPT)*	1025.00	550.00
K.	Cynthia, 5" high	160.00	85.00
L.	Bride, 7^1/$_2$" high	285.00	150.00
M.	Tony, 4^1/$_2$" high	170.00	90.00
N.	Mimi, 7^3/$_4$" high	285.00	150.00
O.	Greta, 8" high	285.00	180.00
P.	Jeanette, 6^1/$_2$" high *(See also No. 2 pg. 33 of The W of W)*	285.00	150.00
R.	Springtime, 9" high *(See also No. 24 pg. 50 of The W of W2)*	340.00	180.00
S.	Anita, 6^3/$_4$" high	285.00	150.00

PAGE 13
FIG. 4. DOG MODELS CIRCA EARLY 1930'S
(cellulose finish)

	U.S. $	British £
Min. Alsatian, 4^3/$_4$" h. x 8^3/$_4$" l.	190.00	200.00
Setter, 6" h. x 9^3/$_4$" l.	380.00	200.00
Airedale, 7" h. x 8" l.	380.00	200.00
Spaniel, 5^1/$_2$" h. x 5" l.	380.00	200.00
Scottie, 4^3/$_4$" h. x 6^1/$_4$" l.	380.00	200.00
Spaniel, (Playful Puppy) 2^1/$_2$" h. x 5^1/$_2$" l.	230.00	155.00
Borzoi, 12" h. x 12^1/$_2$" l.	380.00	200.00
Alsatian, 10^1/$_4$" h. x 18" l.	350.00	185.00
Dalmatian, 8^3/$_4$" h. x 11^1/$_2$" l.	290.00	200.00
Terrier, 7" h. x 8" l.	290.00	200.00

PAGE 14
FIG. 5. MINIATURE ANIMAL FIGURES CIRCA EARLY 1930'S - 1939 (underglaze finish)

		U.S. $	British £
1.	Double Bunnies A, ^{7}/$_8$" h. x 1" l. *(See also No. 154 pg. 54 of The W of W2)*	90.00	55.00
	Double Bunnies B, 1^1/$_4$" h. x 1^3/$_4$" l. *(See also No. 153 pg. 54 of The W of W2)*	95.00	60.00
	Double Bunnies C, 1^5/$_8$" h. x 2^3/$_4$" l.	100.00	65.00

		U.S. $	British £
2.	Flying Ducks 3, 1^5/$_8$" h. x 1^3/$_4$" l. *(See also No. 161 pg. 54 of The W of W2)*	150.00	100.00
	Flying Ducks 1, 1^1/$_2$" h. x 1^1/$_4$" l.	150.00	100.00
	Flying Ducks 2, 1^1/$_2$" h. x 1^3/$_4$" l.	150.00	100.00
3.	Min. Monkey, 1^1/$_8$" h. x ^{3}/$_4$" l.	150.00	100.00
4.	Min. Bunny, ^{7}/$_8$" h. x 1^1/$_8$" l. *(See also No. 155 pg. 54 of The W of W2)*	50.00	30.00
5.	Large Lamb A, 2^1/$_8$" h. x 2" l. *(See also No. 139 pg. 54 of The W of W2)*	155.00	105.00
6.	Playful Lambs C, 2" h. x 2^3/$_8$" l.	155.00	105.00
	Playful Lambs B, 2" h. x 2^3/$_8$" l.	155.00	105.00
7.	Min. Lamb, 1^1/$_2$" h. x 1^1/$_4$" l. *(See also No. 138 pg. 54 of The W of W2)*	150.00	100.00
8.	Min. Deer, 1^1/$_8$" h. x 1^1/$_4$" l. *(See also No. 132 pg. 54 of The W of W2)*	150.00	100.00
9.	Min. Donkey, 1^7/$_8$" h. x 1^1/$_2$" l.	170.00	115.00
10.	Min. Foal, 1^1/$_2$" h. x 1^1/$_4$" l. *(See also No. 140 pg. 54 of The W of W2)*	155.00	105.00
11.	Cats A, 1^1/$_2$" h. x 2^1/$_8$" l. *(See also No. 148 pg. 54 of The W of W2)*	95.00	60.00
	Cats B, 1^1/$_8$" h. x 2^7/$_8$" l. *(See also No. 147 pg. 54 of The W of W2)*	95.00	60.00
	Cats C, 1^1/$_4$" h. x 1^3/$_4$" l. *(See also No. 146 pg. 54 of The W of W2)*	95.00	60.00
	Cats D, 1^1/$_2$" h. x 2^1/$_8$" l.	95.00	60.00
	Cats E, 1" h. x 2^3/$_4$" l.	95.00	60.00
	Cats F, 1" h. x 2^3/$_4$" l.	95.00	60.00
12.	Elephant, 2" h. x 2^1/$_4$" l. *(See also No. 142 pg. 54 of The W of W2)*	185.00	125.00
13.	Small Squirrel, 1^5/$_8$" h. x 2^1/$_8$" l. *(See also No. 149 pg. 54 of The W of W2)*	95.00	60.00
14.	Large Deer, 2^1/$_2$" h. x 1^3/$_4$" l.	155.00	105.00

		U.S. $	British £
15.	Chick, $1^3/_4$" h. x $2^1/_8$" l.	175.00	115.00
	(See also Nos.144 and 145 pg.54 of The W of W2)		
16.	Foals A, $2^1/_2$" h. x $2^1/_2$" l.	170.00	110.00
	Foals B, 2" h. x $2^1/_4$" l.	170.00	110.00
17.	Squirrel, $2^1/_2$" h. x $2^1/_2$" l.	160.00	110.00
18.	Bear, $1^5/_8$" h. x $2^1/_2$" l.	210.00	140.00
19.	Baby Panda, $1^1/_2$" h. x $2^1/_4$" l.	170.00	115.00
20.	Calf, $2^3/_8$" h. x $1^1/_4$" l.	170.00	115.00
	(See also No.137 pg.54 of The W of W2)		
21.	Ibex, $2^1/_4$" h. x $2^1/_4$" l.	170.00	115.00
22.	Dog, $3^1/_8$" h. x $1^3/_4$" l.	170.00	115.00
	(See also No.135 pg.54 of The W of W2)		
23.	Double Rabbits, $2^1/_2$" h. x $2^3/_4$" l.	95.00	60.00
24.	Single Rabbit, $2^5/_8$" h. x $1^3/_8$" l.	65.00	40.00
	(See also No.131 pg.54 of The W of W2)		
25.	Monkey, $2^1/_2$" h. x 2" l.	180.00	130.00
	(See also No.124 pg.28 of WPT)		
26.	Penguin, $2^3/_4$" h. x $2^1/_4$" l.	180.00	120.00
27.	Dachshund, $3^1/_8$" h. x $1^1/_2$" l.	155.00	100.00
28.	Min. Setter, $3^1/_2$" h. x $2^1/_4$" l.	160.00	110.00
	(See also No.143 pg.54 of The W of W2)		
29.	Ducks A, $2^3/_4$" h. x $2^1/_8$" l.	165.00	110.00
	(See also No.156 pg.54 of The W of W2)		
	Ducks B, $1^3/_4$" h. x $3^1/_8$" l.	165.00	110.00
	(See also No.159 pg.54 of The W of W2)		
	Ducks C, 3" h. x $3^1/_8$" l.	165.00	110.00
	(See also No.160 pg.54 of The W of W2)		
	Ducks D, 3" h. x $2^1/_8$" l.	165.00	110.00
30.	Mallard, $3^5/_8$" h. x $3^1/_2$" l.	165.00	110.00
31.	Drake and Daddy, $3^1/_8$" h. x 2" l.	210.00	140.00
	(See also No.157 pg.54 of The W of W2)		
32.	Long necked Duck—Head up, 2" h. x $^7/_8$" l.	120.00	80.00
33.	Long necked Duck—Head down, 2" h. x $^3/_4$" l.	120.00	80.00
34.	Large Long necked Duck, $3^3/_4$" h. x $1^3/_8$" l.	165.00	110.00

PAGE 15

FIG.7. LARGE ANIMAL FIGURES AND FIGURINES CIRCA 1935 - 1939

(underglaze finish)

		U.S. $	British £
1.	Chamois Kid, $5^1/_4$" h. x $3^1/_4$" l.	575.00	300.00
	(See also No.225 pg.57 of The W of W2)		
2.	Camel, $7^3/_4$" h. x $6^3/_4$" l.	660.00	400.00
3.	Ermine, $9^1/_2$" h. x 3" l.	575.00	300.00
	(See also No.224 pg.57 of The W of W2)		
4.	Panther, 8" h. x 5" l.	980.00	525.00
	(See also No.226 pg.57 of The W of W2)		
5.	Horse, $7^3/_4$" h. x $6^3/_4$" l.	660.00	400.00
6.	Large Dartmoor Pony, $4^7/_8$" h. x $4^1/_4$" l.	330.00	175.00
7.	Giraffe, 3" h. x 4" l.	330.00	175.00
8.	Medium Dartmoor Pony, 4" h. x 4" l.	330.00	175.00
9.	Lion Cub Paw up, $5^1/_4$" h. x $7^1/_4$" l.	600.00	325.00
10.	Lion Cub Paw down, $5^1/_4$" h. x $7^1/_4$" l.	600.00	325.00
11.	Otter, 4" h. x $10^3/_4$" l.	625.00	350.00
12.	Cynthia, 5" high	330.00	175.00
13.	Jose, $4^1/_2$" high	330.00	175.00
14.	Betty, 5" high	465.00	245.00
	(See also No. 3 pg. 33 of The W of W)		
15.	Queenie, $3^5/_8$" high	430.00	225.00
16.	Min. Zena, 4" high	400.00	215.00
17.	Min. Pavlova, $4^1/_2$" high	400.00	215.00

PAGE 16

FIG.8. LARGE ANIMAL FIGURES AND FIGURINES CIRCA 1935 - 1939

(underglaze finish)

A.	Ermine, $9^1/_2$" h. x 3" l.	575.00	300.00
	(See also No.224 pg.57 of The W of W2)		
B.	Choir Boy, $7^3/_8$" high	660.00	400.00
C.	Joy, $9^1/_4$" high	800.00	500.00
D.	Juliette, $9^1/_4$" high	660.00	400.00
	(See also No. 21 pg. 50 of The W of W2)		
E.	Panther, $8^1/_2$" high	980.00	525.00
	(See also No. 226 pg.57 of The W of W2)		
F.	Horse, $7^3/_4$" h. x $6^1/_4$" l.	660.00	400.00
G.	Camel, $7^3/_4$" h. x $6^3/_4$" l.	660.00	400.00

		U.S. $	British £
H.	Chamois Kid, 5¼" h. x 3¼" l.	575.00	300.00
	(See also No.225 pg.57 of The W of W2)		
I.	Lion Cub Paws up, 5¼" h. x 7¼" l.	600.00	325.00
J.	Otter, 4" h. x 10¾" l.	625.00	350.00
K.	Lion Cub Paws down, 5¼" h. x 7¼" l.	600.00	325.00
L.	Cockatoo, 5¾" high	825.00	450.00
M.	Double Budgerigar, 7¾" high	825.00	450.00
N.	Stag, 8¾" high	800.00	500.00
O.	Capuchin, 10" high	650.00	400.00
P.	Old Nanny, 9" high	620.00	350.00
Q.	Grebe, 9¼" high	950.00	550.00
	(See also No.121 pg.27 of WPT 1997)		
R.	Single Budgerigar, 6¾" high *(See also No.203 pg.56 of The W of W2)*	375.00	200.00
S.	Parrot, 10¼" high	1350.00	900.00
T.	Brown Bear, 9½" high	980.00	525.00
	(See also No.227 pg.57 of The W of W2)		

		U.S. $	British £
U.	Madonna and Child, 13½" high	650.00	450.00
V.	Aqua Vase and Base, 10¼" high	225.00	120.00
W.	Polar Bear, 7¼" high	850.00	475.00

PAGE 17
FIG.9. BIRDS LATE 1930'S - MID 1950'S
(underglaze finish)

		U.S. $	British £
1.	Goldfinch (wings open), 4" high	620.00	350.00
2.	Goldfinch (wings closed), 4" high	620.00	350.00
3.	Pelican (nut dish or ashtray), 5" high *(See also No.206 pg.56 of The W of W2)*	950.00	550.00
4.	Woodpecker, 6" high	620.00	350.00
5.	Budgerigar, 8" high *(See also No.203 pg.56 of The W of W2)*	375.00	200.00
6.	Cockatoo, 6" high	950.00	550.00
7.	Heron, 7" high *(See also No.214 pg.56 of The W of W2)*	620.00	350.00

WADE FLOWERS *by George Wade & Son Ltd. Circa 1930-1939*

The suggested prices for Wade Flowers are for items in very good condition i.e. with very few minor nicks. It is rare that these items will be found without some type of damage. Usually, damage is confined to the outer edges of the flower. Collectors should pay prices for Wade Flowers relative to the amount of damage.

PAGE 18
FIG.10. EARTHENWARE FLOWERS

		U.S. $	British £
1.	Posy Pot, G. Wild Rose	20.00	10.00
2.	Posy Pot, G. Tulips	20.00	10.00
3.	Large Rock Gardens	75.00	35.00
4.	Wicker Basket. Wild Rose	40.00	20.00
5.	Wicker Basket. Pansy	40.00	20.00
6.	Wicker Basket. Tulip	40.00	20.00
7.	Small Rock Garden	65.00	30.00
8.	Posy Pot, E. Tulips	20.00	10.00
9.	Posy Pot, G. Assorted	20.00	10.00
10.	Posy Pot, E. Assorted	20.00	10.00

		U.S. $	British £
11.	Small Rose Menu Holder	30.00	18.00
12.	Large Rose Menu Holder	30.00	18.00
13.	Black Bowl for Medium and Small size Centers	20.00	8.00
14.	Black Bowl for Large size Centre	20.00	10.00
15.	Large Lily Menu Holder	40.00	20.00
16.	Small Lily Menu Holder	30.00	18.00
17.	Posy Pot, E. Wild Rose	20.00	10.00
18.	Posy Pot, D. Assorted	20.00	10.00
19.	Posy Pot, D. Wild Rose	20.00	10.00
20.	Posy Pot, SB. Wild Rose	30.00	15.00
21.	Small Center Tulip	40.00	20.00
22.	Small Center Wild Rose	40.00	20.00
23.	Medium Center Pansy	40.00	22.50
24.	Medium Center Wild Rose	40.00	22.50
25.	Medium Center Tulip	55.00	30.00

		U.S. $	British £
26.	Posy Pot, SB. Assorted	25.00	12.50
27.	Posy Pot, SB. Tulip	25.00	12.50
28.	Posy Pot, D. Tulip	25.00	12.50
29.	Center, Six Flowers, Pansy	45.00	25.00
30.	Center, Six Flowers, Tulips	45.00	25.00
31.	Short-necked Jugs, Tulips	30.00	15.00
32.	Vulcan, Pansy	45.00	20.00
33.	Vulcan, Tulip	45.00	20.00
34.	Vulcan, Poppy	45.00	22.50
35.	Long-necked Jugs, Wild Rose	45.00	22.50
36.	Center, Six Flowers, Wild Rose	50.00	25.00
37.	Medium Witch Bowl, Ctr. Poppy	35.00	20.00

PAGE 19
FIG. 11. EARTHENWARE FLOWERS

38.	Min. Loose Center Anemones and Bowl	55.00	28.00
39.	Ajax Bowl, Anemone	45.00	22.50
40.	Ajax Bowl, Tulips	45.00	22.50
41.	Ajax Bowl, Pansy	45.00	22.50
42.	Min. Loose Center, Anemones, Roses and Bowl	55.00	28.00
43.	Center, 6" x 5" Wild Rose and Bowl	60.00	32.50
44.	Large Center Pansy and Bowl	60.00	32.50
45.	Large Center Poppy	60.00	30.00
46.	Large Center Tulip	60.00	30.00
47.	Large Center Delphinium	75.00	38.00
48.	Large Center Anemones	60.00	30.00
49.	No Name Available	60.00	32.50
50.	Loose Center Anemones and Bowl	65.00	35.00
51.	Streamline Jug, Assorted Flowers	130.00	62.00
52.	Brick, Assorted Flowers	115.00	55.00
53.	Globe Bowl, Assorted Flowers	115.00	55.00

PAGE 20
FIG. 12. EARTHENWARE FLOWERS

		U.S. $	British £
54.	Posy Basket	35.00	20.00
55.	Octagonal Bowl	30.00	15.00
56.	Medium Arch	75.00	35.00
57.	Small Arch	50.00	25.00
58.	Temple	50.00	20.00
59.	Posy Pansy Ring	50.00	20.00
60.	Small Saturn	60.00	28.00
61.	Medium Saturn	70.00	35.00
62.	Large Saturn	85.00	45.00
63.	Roman Jug	85.00	45.00
64.	Binnie	50.00	25.00
65.	Square (Table Decoration)	75.00	40.00

PAGE 21
FIG. 13. CHINA FLOWERS

80.	J. 5 Bowl Narcissus	55.00	25.00
81.	H. 1. Center Primula	55.00	25.00
82.	H. 2. Center Poppy,	55.00	25.00
83.	Small Vase, C.T. Carnation, Tulip	65.00	30.00
84.	Small Vase, D.V.T. Daisy, Violet, Tulip	65.00	30.00
85.	Small Vase, Oleander	65.00	30.00
86.	J. 18 Bowl Carnation	55.00	25.00
87.	E. Bowl Anemone	45.00	20.00
88.	S. B. Basket Roses	45.00	20.00
89.	J. V. F. Bowl, Violet, Forget-me-not	65.00	30.00
90.	J. 4 Bowl, Primrose	65.00	30.00
91.	J. P. F. Bowl, Primula, Forget-me-not	65.00	30.00
92.	S. B. Basket, Assorted	65.00	30.00
93.	J. 1 Bowl, Primula	65.00	30.00
94.	J. 6 Bowl, Forget-me-not	65.00	30.00
95.	J. 3 Bowl, Tulip	55.00	25.00
96.	H. 4. Center Primrose	70.00	30.00
97.	H. 3. Center Tulip	70.00	30.00
98.	H. 8. Center Daffodil	80.00	35.00
99.	K. 4 Bowl, Primrose	80.00	35.00

		U.S. $	British £
100.	Small Vase, Hibiscus	90.00	40.00
101.	H. 5. Center, Narcissus	90.00	40.00
102.	Center, Shamrock	90.00	40.00
103.	K. 5 Bowl, Narcissus	100.00	45.00
104.	K. P. F. Bowl, Primula, Forget-me-not	100.00	45.00
105.	K. 1 Bowl, Primula, Forget-me-not	100.00	45.00

		U.S. $	British £
106.	Small Cluster Anemones with Bowl	80.00	35.00
107.	K. V. F. Bowl, Violet, Forget-me-not	100.00	45.00
108.	K. Bowl, Buttercup	100.00	45.00
109.	K. 16 Bowl, Violets	100.00	45.00

ANIMAL FIGURES *by Wade Heath & Co Ltd. Circa 1937-late 1950's*

PAGE 22
FIG. 14. ANIMAL FIGURES CIRCA 1937 - 1939
(underglaze finish)

		U.S. $	British £
1.	Squirrel	160.00	85.00
2.	Laughing Rabbit (small)	135.00	70.00
3.	Laughing Rabbit (medium)	145.00	75.00
4.	Laughing Rabbit (large)	160.00	85.00
5.	Cheeky Duckling	190.00	100.00
6.	Rabbit (miniature)	85.00	45.00
7.	Rabbit (small)	105.00	55.00
8.	Rabbit (medium)	130.00	70.00
9.	Rabbit (large)	160.00	85.00
10.	Terrier	160.00	85.00
11.	Pongo (large)	120.00	65.00
12.	Pongo (medium)	95.00	50.00
13.	Pongo (small)	65.00	35.00
14.	Walking Scottie	160.00	85.00
15.	Jumbo	190.00	100.00
16.	Sitting Scottie	95.00	50.00
17.	Crouching Rabbit	160.00	85.00
18.	Old Buck	190.00	100.00

PAGE 23
FIG. 15. ANIMAL FIGURES AND FIGURINES CIRCA LATE 1940'S - LATE 1950'S
(underglaze finish)

		U.S. $	British £
1.	Seagull, 1" high	230.00	150.00
2.	Cat (George Wade mold), 1¹/₂" high	95.00	60.00

		U.S. $	British £
3.	Cat (George Wade mold), 1¹/₂" high	95.00	60.00
4.	Cat (George Wade mold), 1¹/₂" high	95.00	60.00
5.	Cat (George Wade mold), 1¹/₂" high	95.00	60.00
6.	Cat (George Wade mold), 1¹/₂" high	95.00	60.00
7.	Squirrel (George Wade mold), 1¹/₂" high	95.00	60.00
8.	Mrs. Duck, 2¹/₂" high *(See also No. 165 pg. 54 of The W of W2)*	160.00	120.00
9.	Dilly, 1¹/₂" high *(See also No. 163 pg. 54 of The W of W2)*	160.00	120.00
10.	Mr. Duck, 2¹/₂" high *(See also No. 162 pg. 54 of The W of W2)*	160.00	120.00
11.	Dack, 1¹/₂" high *(See also No. 164 pg. 54 of The W of W2)*	160.00	120.00
12.	Elephant, 2" high	185.00	125.00
13.	Single Rabbit, 2¹/₂" high	65.00	40.00
14.	Mrs. Penguin, 3" high	125.00	90.00
15.	Penny, 2" high	160.00	120.00
16.	Benny, 2" high	160.00	120.00
17.	Mr. Penguin, 3¹/₂" high	125.00	90.00
18.	Cheerful Charlie, 3¹/₂" high	115.00	150.00
19.	Doleful Dan, 3¹/₂" high	115.00	150.00
20.	Drake and Daddy, (George Wade mold), 3¹/₈" high	210.00	140.00
21.	Setter (George Wade mold), 3¹/₂" high	160.00	110.00

		U.S. $	British £
22.	Calf (George Wade mold), 2³/₈" high	170.00	115.00
23.	Long-necked Duck (George Wade mold), 2" high	120.00	80.00
24.	Long-necked Duck (George Wade mold), 2" high	120.00	80.00
25.	Mrs. Rabbit, 3¹/₂" high	160.00	120.00
26.	Fluff, 2" high	160.00	120.00
27.	Puff, 2" high	160.00	120.00
28.	Mr. Rabbit, 3¹/₂" high	160.00	120.00
29.	Lamb (George Wade mold), 2" high	155.00	105.00
30.	Lamb (George Wade mold), 2" high	155.00	105.00
31.	Double Rabbits, 2¹/₂" high *(See also No.151 pg.54 of The W of W2)*	95.00	60.00
32.	Double Bunnies, small size (George Wade mold), ⁷/₈" high	90.00	55.00
33.	Min. Bunny (George Wade mold),⁷/₈" high	50.00	30.00
34.	Double Bunnies, large size (George Wade mold), 1⁵/₈" high	100.00	65.00

		U.S. $	British £
35.	I've a Bear Behind, 2¹/₂" high *(See also No.32 pg.50 of The W of W2)*	200.00	140.00
36.	Blynken, 2" high *(See also No.30 pg.50 of The W of W2)*	195.00	130.00
37.	Nod, 2¹/₂" high *(See also No.31 pg.50 of The W of W2)*	195.00	140.00
38.	Wynken, 2¹/₂" high *(See also No.29 pg.50 of The W of W2)*	195.00	130.00

PAGE 24

FIG. 16. ANIMAL MINIATURES
(underglaze finish)

	U.S. $	British £
Dartmoor Pony (George Wade mold), 4" high	350.00	175.00
Begging Puppy	235.00	125.00
Miniature Deer (George Wade mold), 1¹/₈" high	185.00	100.00
Large Deer, 2¹/₂" high	285.00	150.00
Single Rabbit (George Wade mold), 2⁵/₈" high	150.00	90.00

NURSERY RHYME FIGURINES *by Wade Heath & Co. Ltd. circa 1949-1958*

PAGE 25

FIGS. 17 & 18. NURSERY RHYME FIGURES
(underglaze finish)

		U.S. $	British £
A.	Little Miss Muffet, 2³/₄" high	285.00	300.00
B.	Little Jack Horner, 2¹/₂" high	260.00	300.00
C.	Father Bear, 3¹/₂" high *(See also No. 36 pg.50 of W of W2)*	210.00	250.00

		U.S. $	British £
D.	Goldilocks, 4" high	240.00	225.00
E.	Baby Bear, 1³/₄" high *(See also No. 35 pg.50 of W of W2)*	210.00	250.00
F.	Mother Bear, 3³/₄" high *(See also No. 34 pg.50 of W of W2)*	300.00	250.00
	Soldier, 3" high *(See also No. 37 pg.50 of W of W2)*	200.00	140.00

FIGURINES *by George Wade & Son Ltd. 1956-1987*

PAGE 26

FIG. 19. SNIPPETS 1956 - 1958

	U.S. $	British £
Gretel, 2¹/₂" h. x 1¹/₂" *(See also No. 40 pg.50 of W of W2)*	140.00	95.00

FIG. 20. MABEL LUCIE ATTWELL FIGURINES 1959

	U.S. $	British £
Sam, 3¹/₈" h. x 3" l. *(See also No. 17 pg. 33 W of W and No. 41 pg.50 of W of W2)*	215.00	135.00

	U.S. $	British £
Sarah, 3" h. x 4" l. *(See also No. 42 pg.50 of W of W2)*	215.00	135.00

FIG. 21. CHILD STUDIES 1962

	U.S. $	British £
Boy wearing English National Costume, 4³/₄" high	480.00	325.00
Girl wearing Irish National Costume (decorated), 4¹/₂" high	480.00	325.00

	U.S. $	British £
Girl wearing Irish National Costume (undecorated), 4¹/₂" high	380.00	275.00
Boy wearing Scottish National Costume (decorated), 4³/₄" high	480.00	325.00
Boy wearing Scottish National Costume (undecorated), 4³/₄" high	380.00	275.00
Girl wearing Welsh National Costume, 5¹/₄" high	480.00	325.00

<u>PAGE 27</u>

FIG.22. BRITISH CHARACTER SET 1959

	U.S. $	British £
Lawyer, 2⁷/₈" high	230.00	130.00
(See also No. 22 pg.33 of W of W)		
Fish Porter, 3¹/₈" high	220.00	125.00
(See also No. 21 pg.33 of W of W)		
Pearly Queen, 2⁷/₈" high	170.00	85.00
(See also No. 19 pg.33 of W of W)		
Pearly King, 2³/₄" high	175.00	110.00
(See also No. 20 pg.33 of W of W)		

FIGS.23 & 24. AQUARIUM SET CIRCA 1975 - 1980

	U.S. $	British £
Lighthouse, 3" h. x 1³/₄" dia.	40.00	25.00
(See also No. 76 pg.51 of W of W 2)		
Bridge, 1³/₄" h. x 3¹/₄" w.	125.00	55.00
(See also No. 79 pg.51 of W of W 2)		

<u>PAGE 28</u>

FIG.25. NOVELTY ANIMAL FIGURES

		U.S. $	British £
A.	Bernie and Poo, 2" high	200.00	70.00
	(See also No. 184 pg.55 of W of W 2)		
B.	Kitten on the Keys, 1¹/₈" high	250.00	120.00
C.	Jonah and the Whale, 1¹/₂" high	200.00	70.00
D.	Dustbin Cat, 1³/₄" high	200.00	70.00
E.	Jumbo Jim, 1³/₄" high	215.00	110.00
	(See also No. 183 pg.55 of W of W 2)		

<u>PAGE 29</u>

FIG.26. DRUMBOX SERIES 1956 - 1959

	U.S. $	British £
Jem, 2" high	85.00	35.00
(See also No. 48 pg.34 of W of W)		
Clara, 2" high	90.00	50.00
(See also No. 47 pg.34 of W of W)		

	U.S. $	British £
Dora, 2¹/₈" high	125.00	70.00
Trunky, 2¹/₈" high	95.00	45.00
(See also No. 182 pg.55 of W of W2)		
Harpy, 2" high	85.00	40.00
(See also No. 181 pg.55 of W of W2)		

FIG.27. NODDY SET 1958

See also the advertisement on page 41 of The W of W2.

	U.S. $	British £
Noddy, 2³/₄" high	180.00	100.00
Big Ears, 2³/₄" high	180.00	100.00
(See also No. 38 pg.50 of W of W2)		
Mr. Plod, 2¹/₂" high	160.00	80.00
(See also No. 39 pg.50 of W of W2)		
Miss Fluffy Cat, 2¹/₂" high	80.00	50.00
(See also No. 49 pg.34 of W of W)		

<u>PAGE 30</u>

FIGS.28 & 29. MINIKINS 1956 - 1959

SERIES A

	U.S. $	British £
Shape 1. Rabbit with ears erect, 1¹/₈" high	25.00	12.00
Shape 2. Sitting Rabbit, 1¹/₈" high	25.00	12.00
(See also Nos. 185 and 186 pg.55 of W of W 2)		
Shape 3. Stalking Cat, ³/₄" high	25.00	12.00
(See also No. 187 pg.505 of W of W 2)		
Shape 4. Standing Cat with tail up, 1¹/₄" high *(See also No. 54 pg.35 of W of W)*	25.00	12.00

SERIES B

	U.S. $	British £
Shape 1. Kitten, 1" high	25.00	12.00
(See also No. 55 pg.35 of W of W)		
Shape 2. Bull, ⁷/₈" high	25.00	12.00
(See also No. 57 pg.35 of W of W)		
Shape 3. Cow, ⁷/₈" high	25.00	12.00
Shape 4. Rabbit, ⁷/₈" high	25.00	12.00

SERIES C

	U.S. $	British £
Shape 1. Donkey, 1¹/₄" high	25.00	12.00
Shape 2. Dog, 1¹/₈" high	25.00	12.00
Shape 3. Pelican, 1¹/₈" high	30.00	15.00
(See also No. 56 pg.35 of W of W)		
Shape 4. Donkey, 1¹/₄" high	25.00	12.00

<u>PAGE 31</u>

FIG.30. THE ELEPHANT CHAIN 1956

	U.S. $	British £
Set of five elephants (boxed)	900.00	400.00

THE WORLD OF WADE — COLOR PLATES

<u>PAGE 33</u>
FIGURINES

		U.S. $	British £
1.	Carnival, 7" high (cellulose finish)	285.00	150.00
2.	Jeanette, 6$^1/_2$" high (cellulose finish) *(See also No. P Fig.3 pg. 12 of The W of W)*	285.00	150.00
3.	Betty, 5" high (underglaze finish) *(See also No.14 Fig. 7 pg. 15 of The W of W)*	465.00	245.00
4.	Blynken, 2" high *(See also No. 30 pg. 50 of The W of W2)*	195.00	130.00
5.	Nod, 2$^1/_2$" high *(See also No.31 pg. 50 of The W of W2)*	195.00	140.00
6.	Goldilocks, 4" high *(See also Fig. 17 page 25 of The W of W)*	240.00	225.00
7.	Baby Bear, 1$^3/_4$" high *(See also Fig. 17 page 25 of The W of W)*	210.00	250.00
8.	Butcher, 3$^1/_4$" high *(See also Fig. 5 page 39 of The W of W2)*	350.00	210.00
9.	Little Jack Horner, 2$^1/_2$" high *(See also Fig. 17 page 25 of The W of W)*	260.00	300.00
10.	Tinker, 2$^1/_2$" high	200.00	125.00
11.	Tailor, 2$^1/_2$" high	200.00	125.00
	Soldier, 3" high *(See also Fig.18 pg. 25 of The W of W and No. 37 pg.50 of The W of W2)*	200.00	140.00
12.	Sailor, 3" high	200.00	140.00
13.	Rich Man, 3" high	200.00	125.00
14.	Poor Man, 3" high	200.00	125.00
15.	Beggar Man, 2$^1/_2$" high	200.00	125.00
16.	Thief, 3" high	200.00	135.00

MABEL LUCIE ATTWELL CHARACTERS

		U.S. $	British £
17.	Sam, 3$^1/_8$" high	215.00	135.00
	Sarah, 3" high *(See also Fig. 20 pg. 26 of The W of W and No. 41 pg. 50 of The W of W2)*	215.00	135.00

BISTO KIDS

		U.S. $	British £
18.	Bisto Kid, pepper shaker, 4" high	110.00	75.00
	Bisto Kid, salt shaker, 4$^3/_8$" high *(See also Nos. 43 and 44 pg. 50 of The W of W2)*	110.00	75.00

BRITISH CHARACTER SET

		U.S. $	British £
19.	Pearly Queen, 2$^7/_8$" high *(See also Fig.22 pg.327 of W of W)*	170.00	85.00
20.	Pearly King, 2$^3/_4$" high *(See also Fig.22 pg.327 of W of W)*	175.00	110.00
21.	Fish Porter, 3$^1/_8$" high *(See also Fig.22 pg.327 of W of W)*	220.00	125.00
22.	Lawyer, 2$^7/_8$" high *(See also Fig.22 pg.327 of W of W)*	230.00	130.00

AQUARIUM SET

For other items in this set, see Nos. 76-79 on pg. 51 of *The W of W2*.

		U.S. $	British £
23.	Mermaid, 2$^1/_2$" high	50.00	25.00
24.	Diver, 2$^3/_4$" high	28.00	12.50
	Lighthouse, 3" high *(See also No.76 pg. 51 of The W of W2)*	40.00	25.00
	Snail, 1$^1/_4$" high *(See also No. 77 pg. 51 of The W of W2)*	100.00	40.00
	Bridge, 1$^3/_4$" high *(See also No.79 pg. 51 of The W of W2)*	125.00	55.00
	Seahorse, 3" high *(See also Fig.11 pg. 44 of The W of W2)*	225.00	100.00

SNOW WHITE AND THE SEVEN DWARFS (1981-1986)

The cost of figurines when sold individually is higher than when sold as a complete set.

		U.S. $	British £
25.	Snow White, 2$^3/_4$" high	155.00	110.00
26.	Sleepy, 3" high	150.00	80.00
27.	Doc, 3" high	165.00	135.00
28.	Happy, 3$^1/_4$" high	155.00	100.00
29.	Bashful, 3$^1/_4$" high	155.00	90.00
30.	Grumpy, 3" high	155.00	80.00
31.	Sneezy, 3$^1/_4$" high	155.00	80.00
32.	Dopey, 3$^1/_4$" high	155.00	80.00
	Complete Set	1200.00	730.00

<u>PAGE 34</u>
ANIMAL FIGURES

		U.S. $	British £
33.	Playful Lamb, 2" high *(See also Fig. 5 pg.14 of The W of W)*	155.00	105.00

		U.S. $	British £
34.	Cat, 1^1/$_4$" high	95.00	60.00
	(See also Fig. 5 pg. 14 of The W of W)		
35.	Cat, 1" high	95.00	60.00
	(See also Fig. 5 pg. 14 of The W of W)		
36.	Panda, 1^1/$_2$" high	170.00	115.00
	(See also Fig. 5 pg. 14 of The W of W)		
37.	Single Rabbit, 2^5/$_8$" high	65.00	40.00
	(See also Fig. 5 pg. 14 of The W of W)		
38.	Dachshund, 3^1/$_8$" high	145.00	100.00
	(See also Fig. 5 pg. 14 of The W of W)		
39.	Doleful Dan, 3^1/$_2$" high	115.00	150.00
	(See also Fig. 15 pg. 23 of The W of W)		
40.	Squirrel, 1^5/$_8$" high	95.00	60.00
	(See also Fig. 5 pg. 14 of The W of W)		
41.	Duck Posy Bowl, 3^1/$_4$" high	130.00	85.00
42.	Mongrel Posy Bowl, 3^1/$_4$" high	130.00	85.00
43.	Rooster Posy Bowl, 3^3/$_4$" high	130.00	85.00
44.	Dachshund Posy Bowl, 3^1/$_2$" high	130.00	85.00
45.	Mallard Posy Bowl, 3^1/$_4$" high	130.00	85.00
46.	Kitten, 1^3/$_4$" high	250.00	130.00

DRUM BOX SERIES

		U.S. $	British £
47.	Clara, 2" high	90.00	50.00
48.	Jem, 2" high	85.00	35.00
	Harpy	85.00	40.00
	(See also No. 181 pg. 55 of The W of W2)		
	Trunky	95.00	45.00
	(See also No. 182 pg. 55 of The W of W2)		
	Dora (not illustrated)	125.00	70.00

NODDY SET

		U.S. $	British £
49.	Miss Fluffy Cat, 2^1/$_2$" high	80.00	50.00
	(See also Fig. 27 pg. 29 of The W of W)		
	Noddy (not illustrated)	180.00	100.00
	Big Ears, 2^3/$_4$" high	180.00	100.00
	(See also No. 38 pg. 50 of The W of W2)		
	Mr. Plod, 2^1/$_2$" high	160.00	80.00
	(See also No. 39 pg. 50 of The W of W2)		

WADE HEATH ANIMALS

		U.S. $	British £
50.	Rabbit, 6" high	130.00	70.00
51.	Laughing Rabbit, 7" high	145.00	75.00
	(See also Fig. 14 pg. 22 of The W of W)		

PAGE 35

TORTOISE ASHBOWLS

		U.S. $	British £
52.	Small Tortoise Ashbowl, 5^3/$_4$" dia.	30.00	20.00
53.	Large Tortoise Ashbowl, 7^1/$_4$" dia.	45.00	30.00

MINIKINS

		U.S. $	British £
54.	Cat—Minikin, 1^1/$_4$" high	25.00	12.00
	(See also Fig. 28 pg. 30 of The W of W)		
55.	Kitten— Minikin, 1" high	25.00	12.00
	(See also Fig. 28 pg. 30 of The W of W)		
56.	Pelican—Minikin, 1^1/$_8$" high	30.00	15.00
	(See also Fig. 29 pg. 30 of The W of W)		
57.	Bull—Minikin, ^{7}/$_8$" high	25.00	12.00
	(See also Fig. 28 pg. 30 of The W of W)		

THE TORTOISE FAMILY

		U.S. $	British £
58.	Baby Tortoise, 1^1/$_4$" h. x 3" l.	10.00	5.00
59.	Large Tortoise, 1^5/$_8$" h. x 4" l.	15.00	7.50
60.	Baby Tortoise, ^{7}/$_8$" h. x 2" l.	10.00	5.00
61.	"Slow Fe" Baby Tortoise, 1^1/$_4$" h. x 3" l.	60.00	45.00
62.	Jumbo Tortoise, 2^3/$_8$" h. x 6" l.	70.00	28.00

HANNA-BARBERA CARTOON CHARACTERS

		U.S. $	British £
63.	Huckleberry Hound, 2^3/$_8$" high	125.00	70.00
	(See also No. 179 pg. 55 of The W of W 2)		
64.	Yogi Bear, 2^1/$_2$" high	140.00	70.00
	(See also No. 178 pg. 55 of The W of W2)		
	Mr. Jinks, 2^3/$_8$" high	140.00	75.00
	(See also No. 180 pg. 55 of The W of W2)		

TV PET SERIES

For color illustration of Chee Chee, Bengo, Simon and Mitzi see Nos. 171-174 pg. 55 of *The W of W2*.

		U.S. $	British £
65.	Droopy Jnr., 2^1/$_4$" high	90.00	55.00
66.	Percy, 1^1/$_2$" high	90.00	55.00

	U.S. $	British £
67. Pepi, 2¹/₈" high	95.00	33.00
68. Fifi, 2⁵/₈" high	45.00	20.00
Chee-Chee, 2¹/₄" high	60.00	30.00
(See also No.171 pg. 55 of The W of W2)		
Bengo, 2³/₈" high	70.00	34.00
(See also No.172 pg. 55 of The W of W2)		
Simon, 2³/₈" high	65.00	25.00
(See also No.173 pg. 55 of The W of W2)		
Mitzi, 2" high	75.00	38.00
(See also No.174 pg. 55 of The W of W2)		
Bruno Jnr., 2¹/₂" high	110.00	50.00
(See Fig. 32 pg. 81 of The W of W)		
Whisky, 2" high	220.00	90.00
(See Fig. 32 pg. 81 of The W of W)		

TOM AND JERRY

	U.S. $	British £
69. Jerry, 1⁷/₈" high	75.00	35.00
70. Tom, 3⁵/₈" high	75.00	30.00

SPIRIT CONTAINERS

	U.S. $	British £
71. Baby Chick, 3³/₈" high	45.00	34.00
72. Cockatoo, 5" high	120.00	80.00
73. Penguin—middle size, 4¹/₄" high	40.00	40.00
Penguin—small size (not illustrated)	40.00	35.00
Penguin—large size (not illustrated)	50.00	45.00

PAGE 36
DISNEY MINIATURE FIGURINES

	U.S. $	British £
74. Big Mama, 1³/₄" high	37.00	25.00
75. Tod, 1³/₄" high	42.00	37.00
76. Copper, 1⁵/₈" high	28.00	17.00
77. Chief, 1⁷/₈" high	26.00	14.00
78. Rolly, 1⁵/₈" high	90.00	52.00
Lucky (not illustrated)	150.00	60.00
79. Sgt. Tibbs, 2" high	90.00	58.00
80. The Colonel, 2" high	90.00	38.00
81. Dumbo, 1³/₈" high	85.00	35.00
82. Merlin as a Hare, 2¹/₄" high	210.00	95.00
Merlin as a Turtle	350.00	155.00
(See also Fig.34 pg.82 of The W of W)		

	U.S. $	British £
Merlin as a Caterpillar	275.00	110.00
(See also Fig.34 pg.82 of The W of W)		
Girl Squirrel, 2" high	100.00	75.00
(See also No.177 pg. 55 of The W of W2)		
Archimedes, 2" high	150.00	80.00
(See also No.175 pg. 55 of The W of W2)		
Madam Mim	250.00	100.00
(See also Fig.34 pg.82 of The W of W)		
83. Jock, 1³/₄" high	30.00	12.00
Jock (no coat)	35.00	15.00
Jock (green coat)	35.00	15.00
Jock (blue coat)	40.00	18.00
84. Lady, 1¹/₂" high	25.00	10.00
85. Tramp (1956 - 1965), 2¹/₈" high	80.00	40.00
86. Tramp (1986 - 1987), 1⁷/₈" high	50.00	25.00
87. Am, 1⁷/₈" high	45.00	26.00
Si, 1³/₄" high	75.00	30.00
(See also No.176 pg.55 of The W of W2)		
88. Dachsie, 1³/₄" high	35.00	18.00
89. Thumper, 1⁷/₈" high	35.00	15.00
90. Bambi, 1¹/₂" high	24.00	12.00
91. Flower, 1¹/₂" high	65.00	25.00
92. Baby Pegasus, 1³/₄" high	75.00	30.00
93. Toughy, 2" high	50.00	40.00
94. Peg, 1¹/₂" high	25.00	10.00
95. Trusty, 2³/₈" high	35.00	12.00
96. Scamp, 1¹/₂" high	25.00	10.00
97. Boris, 2³/₈" high	65.00	30.00

DISNEY "BLOW-UPS"

For an advertisement of the "Blow-Up" figurines, see Figs. 38 and 39 on pg. 84 of *The W of W*. See also Nos. 166 -170 pg. 55 of *The W of W2*.

	U.S. $	British £
98. Scamp, 4¹/₈" high	235.00	90.00
99. Si, 5¹/₂" high	200.00	120.00
Am, 6" high	200.00	120.00
Dachie, 5" high	475.00	310.00
Jock, 4" high	475.00	310.00
Lady, 4¹/₄" high	235.00	150.00
(See also No.168 pg.55 of The W of W2)		
Tramp, 6" high	300.00	225.00
(See also No.169 pg.55 of The W of W2)		

	U.S. $	British £
Bambi, 4^1/$_2$" high	150.00	85.00

(See also No.167 pg.55 of The W of W2)

	U.S. $	British £
Thumper, 5^1/$_4$" high	300.00	165.00

(See also No.166 pg.55 of The W of W2)

	U.S. $	British £
Trusty, 5^7/$_8$" high	275.00	160.00

(See also No.170 pg.55 of The W of W2)

DOGS AND PUPPIES SERIES

		U.S. $	British £
100-1.	Alsatian (adult), 2^1/$_2$" high	25.00	9.00
100-2.	Alsatian (puppy), 1^1/$_4$" high	12.00	8.00
100-3.	Alsatian (puppy), 1^3/$_4$" high	12.00	8.00
101-1.	Corgi (adult), 2^1/$_4$" high	40.00	25.00
101-2.	Corgi (puppy), 1^5/$_8$" high	25.00	18.00
101-3.	Corgi (puppy), 1^1/$_8$" high	25.00	18.00
102-1.	Red Setter (adult), 2^1/$_4$" high	25.00	6.00
102-2.	Red Setter (puppy), 1^1/$_2$" high	12.00	6.00
102-3.	Red Setter (puppy), 1^1/$_2$" high	12.00	6.00
103-1.	Cairn (adult), 2^1/$_2$" high	20.00	8.00
103-2.	Cairn (puppy), 1^1/$_2$" high	12.00	7.00
103-3.	Cairn (puppy), 1^3/$_8$" high	12.00	6.00
104-1.	Yorkshire Terrier (adult), 2^1/$_8$" high	50.00	30.00
104-2.	Yorkshire Terrier (puppy), 1^3/$_8$" high	35.00	20.00
104-3.	Yorkshire Terrier (puppy), 1^1/$_2$" high	35.00	20.00

CAT AND PUPPY DISHES

		U.S. $	British £
105.	Cat Dish	35.00	12.00
106.	Alsatian Puppy Dish	20.00	7.00
107.	Alsatian Puppy Dish	20.00	7.00
108.	Red Setter Puppy Dish	20.00	8.00
109.	Red Setter Puppy Dish	20.00	8.00
110.	Cairn Puppy Dish	20.00	9.00
111.	Cairn Puppy Dish	20.00	9.00
112.	Yorkshire Terrier Puppy Dish	40.00	18.00

<u>PAGE 37</u>

NURSERY FAVORITES 1972 - 1981

		U.S. $	British £
113-1.	Jack, 2^7/$_8$" high	50.00	17.00
113-2.	Jill, 2^7/$_8$" high	40.00	16.00
113-3.	Miss Muffet, 2^5/$_8$" high	50.00	16.00
113-4.	Jack Horner, 1^7/$_8$" high	50.00	15.00
113-5.	Humpty Dumpty, 1^3/$_8$" high	25.00	15.00
114-6.	Willie Winky, 1^3/$_4$" high	25.00	15.00
114-7.	Mary Lamb, 2^7/$_8$" high	30.00	18.00
114-8.	Polly Kettle, 2^7/$_8$" high	48.00	18.00

(See also No. 46 pg. 50 of The W of W2)

		U.S. $	British £
114-9.	King Cole, 2^1/$_2$" high	50.00	15.00
114-10.	Tom Piper, 2^3/$_4$" high	52.00	20.00

(See also No. 47 pg. 50 of The W of W2)

		U.S. $	British £
115-11.	Boy Blue, 2^7/$_8$" high	48.00	28.00
115-12.	Mary Mary, 2^7/$_8$" high	56.00	28.00

(See also No. 45 pg. 50 of The W of W2)

		U.S. $	British £
115-13.	Cat 'n Fiddle, 2^7/$_8$" high	48.00	24.00
115-14.	Queen of Hearts, 2^7/$_8$" high	55.00	24.00
115-15.	Tommy Tucker, 3" high	42.00	20.00
116-16.	Puss in Boots, 2^7/$_8$" high	25.00	30.00
116-17.	Three Bears, 2^7/$_8$" high	60.00	40.00
116-18.	Goosey Gander, 2^5/$_8$" high	145.00	70.00

(See also No. 48 pg. 50 of The W of W2)

		U.S. $	British £
116-19.	Bo-Peep, 2^7/$_8$" high	65.00	45.00
116-20.	Old Woman, 2^1/$_2$" high	90.00	65.00

(See also No. 49 pg. 50 of The W of W2)

HAPPY FAMILIES

		U.S. $	British £
117-1.	Giraffe (baby), ^{5}/$_8$" high	8.00	4.50
117-2.	Giraffe (parent), 2^5/$_{16}$" high	14.00	7.50
117-3.	Giraffe (baby), 1^9/$_{16}$" high	10.00	8.50
118-1.	Rabbit (baby), 1^1/$_8$" high	12.00	4.50
118-2.	Rabbit (parent), 2" high	15.00	7.50
118-3.	Rabbit (baby), 1^1/$_4$" high	12.00	5.00
119-1.	Hippo (baby), ^{5}/$_8$" high	8.00	4.50
119-2.	Hippo (parent), 1^1/$_8$" high	9.00	7.50
119-3.	Hippo (baby), 1" high	9.00	8.50
120-1.	Mouse (baby), 1" high	10.00	4.50
120-2.	Mouse (parent), 2" high	15.00	6.50
120-3.	Mouse (baby), 1^1/$_{16}$" high	10.00	4.50
121-1.	Frog (baby), ^{5}/$_8$" high	10.00	4.50
121-2.	Frog (parent), ^{7}/$_8$" high	15.00	6.50
121-3.	Frog (baby), 1" high	10.00	10.00

		U.S. $	British £
122-1.	Pig (baby), 5/8" high	12.00	8.50
122-2.	Pig (parent), 1 1/8" high	15.00	8.50
122-3.	Pig (baby), 9/16" high	12.00	8.50
123-1.	Elephant (baby), 1 3/4" high	12.00	10.00
123-2.	Elephant (parent), 1 1/4" high	15.00	7.50
123-3.	Elephant (baby), 1" high	12.00	7.50
124-1.	Owl (baby), 1" high	12.00	6.00
124-2.	Owl (parent), 1 3/4" high	15.00	8.00
124-3.	Owl (baby), 7/8" high	12.00	10.00
125-1.	Cat (kitten), 1 1/4" high	12.00	7.50
125-2.	Cat (parent), 1 7/8" high	15.00	15.00
125-3.	Cat (kitten), 1 3/8" high	12.00	7.50
126-1.	Dog (puppy), 1 1/4" high	12.00	8.00
126-2.	Dog (parent), 2" high	15.00	10.00
126-3.	Dog (puppy), 1 1/4" high	12.00	8.00

PAGE 38
CHAMPIONSHIP DOGS

		U.S. $	British £
127.	English Setter, 2 3/4" high	100.00	50.00
128.	Afghan Hound, 3" high	100.00	40.00
129.	Old English Sheep Dog, 3 1/4" high	105.00	45.00
130.	Collie, 3 1/4" high	100.00	50.00
131.	Cocker Spaniel, 2 7/8" high	100.00	40.00

DOG PIPE RESTS

		U.S. $	British £
132.	Cairn Terrier	30.00	12.00
133.	Irish Setter	30.00	10.00
134.	Corgi	40.00	16.00
135.	German Shepherd (Alsatian)	30.00	10.00
	Yorkshire Terrier	45.00	25.00
	(See also No.344 pg.63 of The W of W2)		

WHOPPAS

		U.S. $	British £
136-1.	Polar Bear, 1 1/2" high	25.00	6.00
136-2.	Hippo, 1 3/8" high	25.00	6.00
136-3.	Brown Bear, 1 1/2" high	18.00	5.00
136-4.	Tiger, 1 1/8" high	20.00	5.00
136-5.	Elephant, 2 1/8" high	25.00	6.00
137-6.	Bison, 1 3/4" high	20.00	8.00

		U.S. $	British £
137-7.	Wolf, 2 1/4" high	30.00	12.00
137-8.	Bobcat, 1 1/2" high	30.00	15.00
137-9.	Chipmunk, 2 1/8" high	30.00	12.00
137-10.	Raccoon, 1 1/2" high	30.00	16.00
138-11.	Fox, 1 1/4" high	40.00	18.00
138-12.	Badger, 1 1/2" high	40.00	18.00
138-13.	Otter, 1 1/4" high	40.00	18.00
138-14.	Stoat, 1 1/2" high	40.00	18.00
138-15.	Hedgehog, 1 1/4" high	36.00	18.00

HORSE SETS

		U.S. $	British £
139-1.	Foal, 1 7/8" high	15.00	6.00
139-2.	Horse, 2 3/4" high	18.00	7.00
139-3.	Foal, 1 3/8" high	15.00	5.00
140-1.	Foal, 1 1/2" high	26.00	25.00
140-2.	Horse, 2 1/2" high	30.00	25.00
140-3.	Foal, 1 1/4" high	26.00	25.00

PAGE 39
WHIMSIES-LAND SERIES

		U.S. $	British £
141-1.	Retriever, 1 1/4" high	8.00	8.00
141-2.	Puppy, 1 3/8" high	8.00	5.00
141-3.	Rabbit, 2" high	20.00	10.00
141-4.	Kitten, 1" high	15.00	7.00
141-5.	Pony, 1 1/2" high	15.00	7.00
142-6.	Lion, 1 1/4" high	16.00	9.00
142-7.	Tiger, 3/4" high	8.00	8.00
142-8.	Elephant, 1 3/8" high	22.00	10.00
142-9.	Panda, 1 3/8" high	22.00	8.00
142-10.	Giraffe, 2" high	22.00	10.00
143-11.	Rooster, 2" high	24.00	10.00
143-12.	Duck, 1 5/8" high	24.00	10.00
143-13.	Cow, 1 1/4" high	28.00	12.00
143-14.	Pig, 1 1/8" high	15.00	10.00
143-15.	Goat, 1 1/4" high	20.00	10.00
144-16.	Squirrel, 1 1/2" high	10.00	6.00
144-17.	Fox, 1 3/8" high	30.00	15.00
144-18.	Hedgehog, 7/8" high	18.00	5.00
144-19.	Badger, 1" high	18.00	9.00
144-20.	Owl, 1 1/2" high	12.00	7.00

WHIMSIES 1953 - 1959

SET 1. 1953

	U.S. $	British £
145-1. Leaping Fawn, 1⁷/₈" high	45.00	20.00
145-2. Horse, 1¹/₂" high	38.00	18.00
145-3. Spaniel, 1" high	24.00	18.00
145-4. Poodle, 1¹/₂" high	42.00	24.00
145-5. Squirrel, 1¹/₄" high	25.00	15.00

SET 2. 1954

146-6. Bull, 1³/₄" high	64.00	48.00
146-7. Lamb, 1⁷/₈" high	44.00	24.00
146-8. Kitten, 1³/₈" high	95.00	40.00
146-9. Hare, 1¹/₈" high	35.00	16.00
146-10. Dachshund, 1¹/₈" high	70.00	45.00

SET 3. 1955

147-11. Badger, 1¹/₄" high	35.00	16.00
147-12. Fox Cub, 1³/₈" high	70.00	28.00
147-13. Stoat, 1¹/₈" high	48.00	26.00
147-14. Shetland Pony, 1³/₈" high	30.00	18.00
147-15. Retriever, 1¹/₄" high	28.00	20.00

SET 4. 1955

148-16. Lion, 1¹/₄" high	50.00	25.00
148-17. Crocodile, ³/₄" high	65.00	30.00
148-18. Monkey, 1⁷/₈" high	30.00	20.00
148-19. Rhinoceros, 1³/₄" high	35.00	16.00
148-20. Baby Elephant, 1¹/₄" high	50.00	26.00

SET 5. 1956

149-21. Mare, 1⁷/₈" high	40.00	20.00
149-22. Colt, 1⁷/₁₆" high	44.00	20.00
149-23. Beagle, ³/₄" high	65.00	25.00
149-24. Foal, 1¹/₄" high	45.00	22.00

SET 6. 1956

150-25. King Penguin, 1³/₁₆" high	40.00	16.00
150-26. Husky, 1¹/₄" high	40.00	14.00
150-27. Polar Bear, 1³/₄" high	35.00	16.00
150-28. Baby Seal, ⁷/₈" high	28.00	12.00
150-29. Baby Polar Bear, ⁷/₈" high	34.00	16.00

SET 7. 1957

	U.S. $	British £
151-30. Alsatian, 1³/₈" high	30.00	16.00
151-31. West Highland Terrier, 1" high	45.00	18.00
151-32. Corgi, 1" high	35.00	14.00
151-33. Boxer, 1³/₄" high	30.00	15.00
151-34. Saint Bernard, 1¹/₂" high	50.00	25.00

SET 8. 1958

152-35. Llama, 1³/₄" high	40.00	14.00
152-36. Lion Cub, 1" high	30.00	14.00
152-37. Giant Panda, 1¹/₂" high	35.00	18.00
(See also No. 209 pg. 56 of The W of W2)		
152-38. Bactrian Camel, 1¹/₂" high	35.00	20.00
152-39. Cockatoo, 1³/₈" high	50.00	20.00

SET 9. 1958

153-40. Snowy Owl, 1¹/₈" high	45.00	30.00
153-41. Raccoon, 1¹/₈" high	35.00	14.00
153-42. Grizzly Bear, 1⁷/₈" high	50.00	24.00
153-43. Bear Cub, 1¹/₈" high	30.00	12.00
153-44. Cougar, ³/₄" high	50.00	26.00

SET 10. 1959

154-45. Piglet, ⁷/₈" high	70.00	30.00
154-46. Italian Goat, 1³/₈" high	70.00	40.00
154-47. Foxhound, 1" high	70.00	40.00
154-48. Swan, ⁷/₈" high	190.00	85.00
Shire Horse, 2" high	230.00	105.00
(See also Fig. 41 pg. 91 of The W of W and Nos. 194 and 195 pg. 55 of The W of W2)		

PAGE 40
WHIMSIES 1971 - 1984

SET 1. 1971

155-1. Fawn, 1³/₈" high	5.00	1.50
155-2. Rabbit (ears apart), 1¹/₈" high	9.00	1.50
Rabbit (ears together)	12.00	3.00
(See also Fig. 42 pg. 91 of The W of W)		
155-3. Mongrel, 1³/₈" high	5.00	1.50
155-4. Kitten, 1³/₈" high	8.00	1.50
155-5. Spaniel, 1³/₈" high	5.50	1.50

	U.S. $	British £
SET 2. 1972		
156-6. Duck, 1¼" high	8.00	2.00
156-7. Corgie, 1½" high	8.00	2.00
156-8. Beaver, 1¼" high	5.00	1.00
(See also Fig. 43B pg. 92 of The W of W)		
156-9. Bushbaby, 1¼" high	4.50	1.50
156-10. Fox, 1³/₈" high	5.50	2.00
SET 3. 1972		
157-11. Bearcub, 1³/₈" high	5.00	1.50
(See also Fig. 43C pg. 92 of The W of W)		
157-12. Otter, 1¼" high	4.50	1.50
157-13. Setter, 1³/₈" high	5.00	1.50
157-14. Owl, 1½" high	6.00	2.00
(See also Fig. 43A pg. 92 of The W of W)		
157-15. Trout, 1⅛" high	6.00	2.00
SET 4. 1973		
158-16. Lion, 1³/₈" high	5.00	1.50
158-17. Elephant, 1³/₈" high	15.00	2.00
158-18. Giraffe, 1½" high	5.00	1.50
158-19. Chimp, 1½" high	5.00	1.50
158-20. Hippo, 1¹/₁₆" high	5.00	1.50
(See also Fig. 20 pg. 118 of The W of W2)		
SET 5. 1974		
159-21. Squirrel, 1³/₈" high	5.00	1.50
159-22. Hedgehog, ⅞" high	8.00	1.50
159-23. Pinemarten, 1³/₈" high	5.00	1.50
159-24. Field Mouse, 1½" high	8.00	1.50
159-25. Alsatian, 1¼" high	6.00	1.50
SET 6. 1975		
160-26. Collie, 1¼" high	6.00	1.50
160-27. Cow, 1¼" high	12.00	1.50
160-28. Pig, ¹⁵/₁₆" high	18.00	2.50
(See also Fig. 22 pg. 119 of The W of W2)		
160-29. Horse, 1⅝" high	17.00	2.00
160-30. Lamb, 1³/₈" high	10.00	1.50
SET 7. 1976		
161-31. Rhino, ⅞" high	5.00	1.50
161-32. Leopard, ⅞" high	5.00	2.00

	U.S. $	British £
161-33. Gorilla, 1½" high	5.00	2.00
161-34. Camel, 1³/₈" high	9.00	2.00
161-35. Zebra, 1⅝" high	9.00	2.00
SET 8. 1976		
162-36. Donkey, 1¼" high	14.00	4.00
162-37. Owl, 1½" high	16.00	4.00
162-38. Cat, 1½" high	16.00	4.00
162-39. Mouse, 1½" high	8.00	2.50
162-40. Ram, 1³/₁₆" high	10.00	2.00
SET 9. 1978		
163-41. Dolphin, 1¾" high	24.00	6.00
163-42. Pelican, 1¾" high	25.00	5.00
163-43. Angel Fish, 1³/₈" high	14.00	3.00
163-44. Turtle, ⁹/₁₆" high	10.00	3.00
163-45. Seahorse, 2" high	20.00	7.00
SET 10. 1979		
164-46. Kangaroo, 1⅝" high	14.00	2.00
164-47. Orangutan, 1¼" high	5.00	1.50
164-48. Tiger, 1½" high	14.00	2.00
164-49. Koala Bear, 1³/₈" high	20.00	4.00
164-50. Langur, 1³/₈" high	5.00	1.50
SET 11. 1979		
165-51. Bison, 1³/₈" high	5.00	2.00
(See also Fig. 21 pg. 119 of The W of W2)		
165-52. Bluebird, ⅝" high	10.00	1.50
165-53. Bullfrog, ⅞" high	18.00	5.00
165-54. Wild Boar, 1⅛" high	7.00	3.00
165-55. Raccoon, 1" high	14.00	2.00
SET 12. 1980		
166-56. Penguin, 1⅝" high	22.00	5.00
166-57. Seal Pup, 1" high	20.00	4.00
166-58. Husky, 1⁷/₁₆" high	22.00	4.00
166-59. Walrus, 1¼" high	10.00	1.50
166-60. Polar Bear, 1⅛" high	15.00	2.00

PAGE 40-41
THE WORLD OF SURVIVAL

		U.S. $	British £
167.	African Elephant	500.00	325.00
168.	Black Rhinoceros	400.00	300.00
169.	African Lion	400.00	250.00
170.	Polar Bear	400.00	250.00
171.	American Bison	500.00	250.00
172.	Hippopotamus	400.00	350.00
173.	American Brown Bear	500.00	325.00
174.	Tiger	425.00	275.00
175.	Gorilla	425.00	275.00
176.	American Cougar (Puma)	550.00	300.00
177.	African Buffalo (Cape Buffalo)	575.00	350.00
178.	Harp Seal & Pup	600.00	350.00

CONNOISSEUR'S COLLECTION

179.	Nuthatch	450.00	300.00
180.	Coaltit	450.00	300.00
181.	Kingfisher	325.00	250.00
182.	Yellow Wagtail	325.00	250.00
183.	Woodpecker	325.00	250.00
184.	Dipper	350.00	225.00
185.	Bullfinch	450.00	300.00
186.	Robin	325.00	250.00
187.	Wren	400.00	275.00
188.	Goldcrest	400.00	275.00

PAGE 42
MISCELLANEOUS PREMIUMS

189.	Black Zebra, 1⅝" high	70.00	15.00
190.	Brown Bear, 1⅝" high	75.00	20.00
191.	Rhino, 1" high	15.00	2.50
192.	Bronti, 1" high	15.00	3.50
193.	Tiger, 1½" high	20.00	5.00
194.	Dino, 1⅜" high	15.00	3.50

CANADA—RED ROSE TEA 1967 - 1973 (Non-retail)

195-26.	Frog, ⅞" high	8.00	2.50
196-27.	Butterfly, ½" high	8.00	3.50
197-28.	Poodle, 1⅝" high	10.00	4.00

		U.S. $	British £
198-29.	Seal, 1½" high	10.00	4.50
199-30.	Angel Fish, 1¼" high	8.00	2.50
200-31.	Terrapin, ⅜" high	10.00	2.50
201-32.	Alligator, ½" high	10.00	4.50

CANADA—RED ROSE TEA 1971 - 1979

202-1.	Old King Cole, 1½" high	8.00	7.00
203-2.	Little Jack Horner, 1⅜" high	8.00	5.00
204-3.	Humpty Dumpty, 1½" high	5.00	4.00
205-4.	Jack, 1¼" high	12.00	9.00
206-5.	Jill, 1⅛" high	12.00	9.00
207-6.	Tom the Piper's Son, 1⅝" high	15.00	8.00
208-7.	Little Boy Blue, 1⅝" high	16.00	7.50
209-8.	Little Miss Muffet, 1½" high	16.00	10.00
210-9.	The Pied Piper, 1¾" high	10.00	6.00
211-10.	Doctor Foster, 1¾" high	12.00	11.00
212-11.	Mother Goose, 1⅝" high	10.00	18.00
213-12.	Old Woman in Shoe, 1⅜" high	7.00	3.00
214-13.	Goosey Gander, 1⅜" high	6.00	5.00
215-14.	Wee Willy Winky, 1¾" high	12.00	4.00
216-15.	Little Bo-Peep, 1¾" high	5.00	3.00
217-16.	Three Bears, 1⅜" high	40.00	20.00
218-17.	Puss in Boots, 1¾" high	10.00	12.00
219-18.	House that Jack Built, 1¼" high	15.00	12.00
220-19.	Red Riding Hood, 1¾" high	6.00	4.00
221-20.	Queen of Hearts, 1¾" high (two large hearts)	15.00	20.00
	Queen of Hearts, 1¾" high (two small hearts)	15.00	20.00
	Queen of Hearts, 1¾" high (multi hearts) *(See also Fig.46 pg.99 of The W of W)*	40.00	30.00
222-21.	Baa Baa Black Sheep, ⅞" high	18.00	16.00
223-22.	Hickory Dickory Dock, 1¾" high	6.00	6.00
224-23.	Ginger Bread Man, 1⅝" high	40.00	28.00
225-24.	Cat 'n Fiddle, 1⅞" high	38.00	12.00

U.S.A.—RED ROSE TEA 1983 - 1985

	U.S. $	British £
226-1. Chimp, $1^1/_2$" high	5.00	6.50
227-2. Lion, $1^5/_{16}$" high	5.00	4.50
228-3. Bison, $1^3/_{16}$" high	5.00	2.00
229-4. Bush Baby, $1^1/_4$" high	5.00	6.00
230-5. Owl, $1^1/_2$" high	5.00	10.00
231-6. Bear Cub, $1^3/_8$" high	5.00	1.50
232-7. Rabbit (Hare), $1^1/_2$" high	6.00	8.00
233-8. Squirrel, $1^1/_2$" high	6.00	6.00
234-9. Bird, $^5/_8$" high	6.00	5.00
235-10. Otter, $1^1/_4$" high	6.00	2.00
236-11. Hippo, $^7/_8$" high	6.00	2.00
237-12. Seal, $1^1/_2$" high	8.00	3.00
238-13. Turtle, $^9/_{16}$" high	8.00	4.00
239-14. Wild Boar, $1^1/_8$" high	8.00	2.00
240-15. Elephant, $1^7/_8$" high	12.00	6.00

CANADA & U.S.A. RED ROSE TEA 1985

241-1. Koala Bear, $1^3/_8$" high	5.00	2.00
242-2. Giraffe, $1^1/_2$" high	4.00	2.00
243-3. Pine Marten, $1^3/_8$" high	3.00	2.00
244-4. Langur, $1^3/_8$" high	6.00	5.00
245-5. Gorilla, $1^1/_2$" high	3.00	5.00
246-6. Camel, $1^3/_8$" high	4.00	5.00
247-7. Kangaroo, $1^5/_8$" high	6.00	5.00
248-8. Tiger, $1^7/_{16}$" high	3.00	4.00
249-9. Zebra, $1^5/_8$" high	5.00	10.00
250-10. Polar Bear, $1^1/_8$" high	6.00	5.00
251-11. Orangutan, $1^1/_4$" high	5.00	3.00
252-12. Raccoon, 1" high	4.00	5.00
253-13. Rhino, $^7/_8$" high	5.00	3.00
254-14. Beaver, $1^1/_4$" high	6.00	5.00
255-15. Leopard, $^{13}/_{16}$" high	3.00	2.00

K. P. "FRIARS" 1983

256. Father Abbot, $1^3/_4$" high	8.00	6.00
257. Brother Peter, $1^5/_8$" high	11.00	6.50
258. Brother Benjamin, $1^5/_8$" high	10.00	6.00
259. Brother Crispin, $1^5/_8$" high	40.00	16.00

	U.S. $	British £
260. Brother Angelo, $1^7/_8$" high	40.00	16.00
261. Brother Francis, $1^5/_8$" high	40.00	16.00

ST. BRUNO TOBACCO 1986

262. St. Bernard Dog, $1^1/_4$" high (complete with chain)	20.00	12.00
St. Bernard Dog, $1^1/_4$" high (without chain)	10.00	6.00

PAGE 43
TOM SMITH PARTY CRACKERS

SAFARI SET 1976-1977

263-1. Lion, $1^1/_8$" high	12.00	4.00
263-2. Tiger, $1^3/_8$" high	8.00	2.00
263-3. Lemur, $1^3/_8$" high	6.00	3.00
263-4. Walrus, $1^1/_4$" high	8.00	2.00
263-5. Koala Bear, $1^1/_4$" high	12.00	3.00
263-6. Raccoon, 1" high	8.00	2.00
263-7. Polar Bear, $1^1/_8$" high	14.00	2.50
263-8. Musk Ox, 1" high	12.00	3.00
263-9. Kangaroo, $1^5/_8$" high	11.00	2.50
263-10. Orangutan, $1^1/_4$" high	5.00	2.00

CIRCUS ANIMAL SET 1978 - 1979

264-1. Male Monkey (Macaque), $1^5/_8$" high	12.00	3.00
264-2. Poodle, $1^3/_4$" high	10.00	4.00
264-3. Seal, $1^5/_8$" high	12.00	3.50
264-4. Female Monkey (Macaque), $1^1/_2$" high	12.00	3.00
264-5. Horse, $1^3/_4$" high	10.00	3.00
264-6. Bear, $1^3/_{16}$" high	10.00	4.00
264-7. Tiger, $1^5/_8$" high	10.00	3.00
264-8. Elephant, $1^1/_4$" high	14.00	3.50
264-9. Lion, $1^9/_{16}$" high	10.00	3.50
264-10. Elephant, $1^3/_{16}$" high	14.00	3.50

WILD LIFE SET 1980 - 1981

265-1. Field mouse, $1^1/_{16}$" high	10.00	2.50
265-2. Partridge, $1^1/_8$" high	10.00	3.00
265-3. Weasel, $1^3/_8$" high	10.00	2.00

	U.S. $	British £		U.S. $	British £
265-4. Mole, 7/8" high	10.00	2.50	**269-12.** Post Office	15.00	8.00
265-5. Hare, 1³/₄" high	10.00	2.00	**269-13.** Whimsey School	35.00	10.00
265-6. Squirrel, 1¹/₂" high	10.00	2.50	**269-14.** Water Mill	20.00	10.00
265-7. Badger, 1¹/₁₆" high	10.00	2.50	**269-15.** The Stag Hotel	18.00	9.50
265-8. Fox, 1³/₈" high	10.00	3.00	**269-16.** Windmill	70.00	38.00

FARMYARD SET 1982 - 1983

SET 3-1982

	U.S. $	British £		U.S. $	British £
266-1. Pig, 7/8" high	16.00	3.00	**270-17.** Tinker's Nook	12.00	7.00
266-2. Goose, 1³/₈" high	8.00	3.00	**270-18.** Whimsey Station	28.00	12.00
266-3. Duck, ¹⁵/₁₆" high	20.00	5.00	**270-19.** Merryweather Farm	34.00	18.00
266-4. Goat, 1¹/₂" high	12.00	3.00	**270-20.** The Vicarage	50.00	15.00
266-5. Horse, 1¹/₂" high	12.00	3.00	**270-21.** Broomyshaw Cottage	15.00	10.00
266-6. Cow, 1¹/₈" high	12.00	3.00	**270-22.** The Sweet Shop	15.00	10.00
266-7. Dog, 1" high	12.00	3.00	**270-23.** Briar Row	30.00	14.00
266-8. Bull, 1¹/₈" high	12.00	3.00	**270-24.** The Manor	25.00	10.00

SURVIVAL SET 1984 - 1985

SET 4-1984

	U.S. $	British £		U.S. $	British £
267-1. North American Bison, 1³/₁₆" high	8.00	2.50	**271-25.** District Bank	18.00	8.00
267-2. Gorilla, 1¹/₂" high	12.00	3.00	**271-26.** Old Smithy	15.00	10.00
267-3. Blue Whale, 7/8" high	18.00	5.50	**271-27.** Picture Palace	24.00	14.00

SET 4-1985

	U.S. $	British £		U.S. $	British £
267-4. Green Turtle, 1¹/₄" high	15.00	3.00	**271-28.** Butcher Shop	25.00	24.00
267-5. Armadillo, 1" high	15.00	3.00	**271-29.** The Barber Shop	25.00	24.00
267-6. Polar Bear, 1" high	16.00	2.00	**271-30.** Miss Prune's House	15.00	15.00
267-7. Golden Eagle, 1³/₄" high	16.00	4.00	**271-31.** Fire Station	15.00	15.00
267-8. Harp Seal, 1¹/₂" high	8.00	3.00	**271-32.** Market Hall	15.00	18.00

WHIMSEY-ON-WHY 1980 - 1987

SAN FRANCISCO MINI MANSIONS 1984 - 1986

SET 1. 1980

	U.S. $	British £		U.S. $	British £
268-1. Pump Cottage	14.00	5.00	**272-1.** Pink Lady	75.00	80.00
268-2. Morgan's the Chemist	20.00	7.00	**272-2.** White Lady	65.00	40.00
268-3. Doctor Healer's House	20.00	7.00	**272-3.** Brown Lady	65.00	45.00
268-4. Tobacconist's Shop	14.00	5.00	**272-4.** Yellow Lady	60.00	40.00
268-5. Why Knott Inn	14.00	6.00	**272-5.** Blue Lady	60.00	40.00
268-6. Bloodshott Hall	20.00	8.00	**272-6.** Cable Car	110.00	70.00
268-7. St. Sebastien's Church	28.00	14.00			
268-8. The Barley Mow	30.00	12.00			

PAGE 44

MISCELLANEOUS ITEMS

SET 2-1981

	U.S. $	British £		U.S. $	British £
269-9. Green Grocer's Shop	15.00	7.00	**273.** Bridge Posy Holder	16.00	6.00
269-10. Antique Shop	18.00	7.00	**274.** Straight Posy Log with Squirrel	20.00	6.00
269-11. Whimsey Service Station	18.00	8.00	**275.** "C" Shaped Posy Log	10.00	4.50
			276. "S" Shaped Posy Log	10.00	3.50

		U.S. $	British £
277.	"S" Shaped Posy Log with Rabbit	24.00	6.50
278.	Rabbit Butter Dish	25.00	10.00
279.	Large Traditional Posy Bowl	15.00	4.00
280.	Small Traditional Posy Bowl	10.00	2.50
281.	Chevaline Posy Bowl	40.00	14.00
282.	Small Mermaid Posy Bowl	35.00	14.00
283.	Large Mermaid Posy Bowl	45.00	18.00
284.	Scalloped Dishes each	15.00	6.00
285.	Dog Dish	35.00	22.00
286.	Souvenir Dish	25.00	10.00
287.	Souvenir Dish	25.00	10.00
288.	Barge Posy Bowl	30.00	20.00
289.	Leaf Dish (Horse Chestnut)	8.00	2.50
290.	Leaf Dish (Oak Leaf)	15.00	3.50
291.	Leaf Dish (Ash Leaf)	25.00	10.00
292.	Cherub Bowl	80.00	75.00
293.	Zamba Ware Ashtray	20.00	8.00
294.	Zamba Ware Bud Vase	25.00	12.00
295.	Zamba Ware Ashtray	20.00	8.00
296.	Blue Bird Tree Trunk Posy Vase	35.00	8.50
297.	Koala Bear Tree Trunk Posy Vase	30.00	12.00
298.	Aqua Dishes (Set 1) per set	12.00	8.00
299.	Blue Bird Dish	25.00	9.00
300.	Aqua Dishes (Set 2) per set	20.00	7.00
301.	Pet Face Dishes (Set 1) per set	30.00	12.00
302.	Pet Face Dishes (Set 2) per set	30.00	14.00
303.	Chimpanzee Posy Vase	35.00	12.00
304.	Starfish Tray	15.00	8.00
305.	Covered Shore Crab Dish	40.00	15.00
306.	Viking Ship Posy Bowl	25.00	8.00
307.	Covered Hedgehog Dish	60.00	30.00
308.	Treasure Chest Covered Dish	35.00	14.00
309.	Pet Dish—Cairn Terrier (unboxed)	30.00	15.00

		U.S. $	British £
310.	Pet Dish—Fawn (unboxed)	25.00	14.00
311.	Fawn Dish (unboxed)	40.00	15.00

PAGE 45
VILLAGE STORES 1982 - 1986

		U.S. $	British £
312-1.	Ye Olde Tea Room	60.00	35.00
313-2.	The Coffee House	60.00	35.00
314-3.	B. Loaf, Baker & Cakes	60.00	40.00
315-4.	Mrs. Smith, Ice Cream & Sweets	60.00	40.00
316-5.	The Chalk and Cheese	60.00	40.00
317-6.	The Village Store Post Office	55.00	45.00
318-7.	Post Office Salt Shaker, $2^1/_8$" high	25.00	10.00
319-8.	Post Office Royal Mail Pepper Shaker, $2^1/_8$" high	25.00	10.00
320-9.	A. Salt, Green Grocer Salt Shaker, $2^3/_4$" high	28.00	12.50
321-10.	B. Pepper, Family Butcher Pepper Shaker, $2^3/_4$" high	28.00	12.50

WHIMTRAYS 1958 - 1965

		U.S. $	British £
322.	Lion Cub	30.00	12.50
323.	Llama	30.00	12.50
324.	Polar Bear Cub	30.00	12.50
325.	Camel	30.00	12.50
326.	Penguin	30.00	12.50
327.	Husky	30.00	12.50
328.	Panda	30.00	12.50

WHIMTRAYS 1971 - 1987

		U.S. $	British £
329.	Fawn	20.00	6.50
330.	Duck	20.00	6.50
331.	Trout	20.00	6.50

BOULDRAY & PEERAGE TRAYS

		U.S. $	British £
332.	Blue Bird Bouldray Tray	26.00	8.00
333.	Elf Bouldray Tray	26.00	8.00
334.	Pekingese Peerage Tray	26.00	8.00

PAGE 46
ADDIS SHAVING MUGS

		U.S. $	British £
335.	"Steam Coach" by Gurney 1827	20.00	5.00
336.	"La Mancelle" by Bollee 1878	20.00	5.00
337.	"Steam Roller" by Abeling 1893	20.00	5.00
338.	1920's convertible	20.00	5.00
339.	Single engined Bi-plane	15.00	5.00

(See also No. 495 pg. 68 of The W of W2)

WESTMINSTER PIGGY BANK FAMILY

340-1.	Woody, 5" high	27.00	12.00
341-2.	Annabel, 6³/₈" high	34.00	20.00
342-3.	Maxwell, 6³/₄" high	68.00	48.00
343-4.	Lady Hillary, 7" high	42.00	25.00
344-5.	Sir Nathaniel, 7¹/₄" high	42.50	45.00

ROMANCE RANGE 1983 - 1985

345.	Rectangular Picture Frame	30.00	8.25
346.	Rectangular Trinket Box	15.00	12.50

(See also Fig. 73 pg. 116 and Figs. 74 and 75 pg. 117 of The W of W)

MAN IN BOAT 1978 - 1984

347.	Man in Boat, 6" long	105.00	50.00

PRICES CANDLE HOLDERS 1965 - 1982

348.	Mayfair Holder S2/15, 1¹/₄" high	12.00	3.00
349.	Venetian Holder S2/12, 2¹/₂" dia.	12.00	3.00
350.	Mini-Holder S2/11, 1³/₄" dia.	8.00	2.00
351.	Flowerlight Round Holder, 4" dia.	14.00	2.00

(See also Figs. 77 and 78 pg. 113 of The W of W and Nos. 383-389 pg. 64 of The W of W2)

LESNEY TRAYS CIRCA 1968 - 1975

352.	"Bus" Lesney Tray, 6" long	40.00	20.00

(See also Nos. 434 and 435 pg. 66 and Figs. 62, 63 and 64 pg. 153 The W of W2)

THOMAS THE TANK ENGINE AND FRIENDS 1985 - 1987

		U.S. $	British £
353.	"Percy" Money Bank, 7" long	145.00	125.00
354.	"Percy" miniature, 1¹/₂" long	95.00	50.00
355.	"Thomas" Money Bank, 6¹/₂" long	150.00	120.00
356.	"Thomas" miniature, 1⁵/₈" long	105.00	50.00

WAGON TRAIN DISHES 1960

357.	Wagon Train—Seth Adams	90.00	30.00
358.	Wagon Train—Flint McCullough	100.00	35.00

PAGE 47
WADE HEATH FLOWER JUGS CIRCA 1934 - 1955

359.	Flower Jug, 7³/₄" high	50.00	45.00
360.	Flower Jug, 8¹/₂" high	50.00	45.00
361.	Flower Jug, 9" high	50.00	55.00
	(See also No.589 pg.75 of The W of W2)		
362.	Flower Jug, 9" high	50.00	55.00
	(See also No.589 pg.75 of The W of W2)		
363.	Flower Jug, 8¹/₄" high	50.00	35.00
364.	Flower Jug, 5¹/₄" high	30.00	25.00
365.	Flower Jug, 5¹/₂" high	30.00	28.00
366.	Flower Jug, 5¹/₂" high	30.00	22.00
367.	Flower Jug, 7" high	125.00	70.00
368.	Flower Jug, 5¹/₂" high	30.00	28.00
369.	Flower Jug, 5¹/₄" high	25.00	25.00
370.	Flower Jug, 8¹/₄" high	75.00	55.00
371.	Vase, 5" high	50.00	45.00
372.	Flower Jug, 5¹/₂" high	35.00	28.00

PAGE 48

373.	Flower Jug, 10" high	50.00	35.00
374.	Flower Jug, 9" high	50.00	35.00
375.	Flower Jug, 8¹/₂" high	65.00	30.00
	(See also Fig.81A No.9 pg.126 of The W of W)		
376.	Flower Jug, 9" high	70.00	38.00
	(See also Fig.81 No.8 pg.123 of The W of W)		
377.	Flower Jug, 7¹/₂" high	75.00	44.00
378.	Flower Jug, 3" high	65.00	22.50
	(See also Nos.630 and 631 pg.76 of The W of W2)		

		U.S. $	British £
379.	Flower Jug, 7^1/$_2$" high	50.00	27.50
380.	Flower Jug, 8^3/$_4$" high	110.00	60.00
381.	Flower Jug, 4" high	65.00	32.50
382.	Flower Jug, 5^3/$_4$" high	35.00	20.00
383.	Flower Jug, 7^3/$_4$" high	65.00	30.00
384.	Flower Jug, 5^1/$_2$" high	35.00	20.00
385.	Flower Jug, 7^1/$_2$" high	55.00	35.00

PAGE 49

		U.S. $	British £
386.	Flower Jug, 7^3/$_4$" high	120.00	65.00
387.	Flower Jug, 9" high	50.00	35.00
	(See also Fig.81 No.12 pg.123		
	of The W of W and No.579 pg.74 of The W of W2)		
388.	Flower Jug, 8^1/$_4$" high	125.00	38.00
389.	Flower Jug, 9" high	80.00	35.00
	(See also Fig.81 No.1 pg.123 of The W of W)		
390.	Flower Jug, 7^1/$_2$" high	125.00	40.00
391.	Flower Jug, 6^1/$_4$" high	65.00	30.00
392.	Flower Jug, 6^1/$_4$" high	65.00	30.00
393.	Flower Jug, 6^1/$_4$" high	70.00	32.00
394.	Flower Jug, 5^1/$_2$" high	35.00	25.00
395.	Flower Jug, 5^1/$_4$" high	35.00	25.00
396.	The McCallum, 4^1/$_2$" high	80.00	50.00
	(See also Nos. 447-449 pg. 67		
	and No. 790 pg. 85 of The W of W2)		
397.	Golf Bag Creamer, 3^1/$_2$" high	35.00	28.00
	(See also Nos. 437 and 438 pg. 66 of The W of W2)		

PAGE 50-51
TABLEWARE CIRCA LATE 1930'S - 1960

398.	Peony Fruit Bowl	120.00	45.00
399.	Peony Plaque	85.00	58.00
400.	Bowl, 9" dia.	35.00	30.00
401.	Basket—Gothic, 7" high	150.00	60.00
402.	Vase—Gothic, 6^1/$_2$" high	60.00	40.00
403.	Cottage style Butter Dish, 4^1/$_2$" high	65.00	55.00
404.	Sweet Tray, 4^1/$_2$" dia.	45.00	20.00
405.	Cereal Bowl, 6" square	50.00	20.00
406.	Cup & Saucer	75.00	45.00
407.	Rose Wall Pocket, 8^1/$_2$" high	60.00	55.00

		U.S. $	British £
408.	Beehive Honey Pot, 4" high	45.00	25.00
409.	Flower Honey Pot, 4" high	45.00	25.00
410.	Butterfly Honey Pot, 4" high	45.00	25.00
411.	Flower Holder, 5" high	32.00	35.00

PAGE 51
CRANKY TANKARDS 1947 - EARLY 1950'S

412-1.	The Miasma, 5" high	75.00	38.00
413-2.	The Hangovah, 5" high	75.00	38.00
414-3.	The Drumble Tum, 5" high	75.00	38.00
415-4.	The Floppity, 5" high	75.00	38.00
416-5.	The Hyperfloogie, 5" high	75.00	38.00
417-6.	The Snoozle, 5" high	75.00	45.00
	(See also Fig. 73 pg. 156 of The W of W2)		

MISCELLANEOUS TABLEWARE 1939 - 1946

418.	Nut-Tray, 7" dia.	25.00	25.00
419.	Nut-Tray, 7" dia.	25.00	25.00
420.	Ashtray, 4" x 3"	10.00	10.00
421.	Basket, 5" high	35.00	20.00
	(See also Fig.81 No.14 pg.123 of The W of W)		
422.	Cup & Saucer	40.00	20.00
423.	Planter, 4^1/$_2$" high	60.00	40.00
424.	Ashtray, 4" x 3"	16.00	10.00
425.	Finger Bowl, 3" dia.	18.00	18.00
426.	Teapot Stand, 6^1/$_4$" dia.	22.00	28.00
427.	Finger Bowl, 4" dia.	18.00	15.00
428.	Cigarette Box, 1^3/$_4$" high	45.00	25.00

PAGE 52
BASKETWARE CIRCA 1946
AND GRAPE DECORATION CIRCA 1953

429.	Dish—Basket Ware, 9^1/$_4$" dia.	30.00	20.00
430.	Plate—Grape decoration, 7" dia.	75.00	50.00
431.	Cup & Saucer—Grape decoration	50.00	20.00
432.	Dish—Basket Ware, 9^1/$_4$" dia.	50.00	20.00
433.	Creamer—Regal Green, 3^1/$_2$" high	50.00	20.00

	U.S. $	British £
434. Teapot—Grape decoration, 6$^1/_2$" high	85.00	45.00
435. Sugar—Grape decoration, 3$^1/_2$" high	20.00	18.00
436. Creamer—Grape decoration, 3$^1/_2$" high	30.00	20.00
437. Salad Bowl—Rubytone, 11" long	80.00	45.00
438. Salad Servers—Rubytone, 8$^1/_2$" long, each	45.00	30.00
439. Honey Pot—Basket Ware, 5" high	40.00	25.00
440. Butter Dish—Basket Ware, 4$^1/_2$" dia.	40.00	15.00
441. Creamer—Basket Ware, 3$^1/_4$" high	18.00	15.00
442. Sugar—Basket Ware, 2" high	18.00	8.00
443. Covered Mustard—Basket Ware, 2$^3/_4$" high	25.00	10.00
444. Pepper Shaker—Basket Ware, 2$^3/_4$" high	15.00	10.00
445. Salt Shaker—Basket Ware, 2$^3/_4$" high *(See also Fig. 87 pg. 131 of The W of W)*	15.00	10.00
446. Sugar—Basket Ware, 2" high	18.00	8.00
447. Creamer, Basket Ware, 3$^1/_4$" high	18.00	15.00
448. Cheese Dish—Basket Ware, 4$^1/_4$" high	50.00	50.00

PAGE 53
MISCELLANEOUS TABLEWARE

	U.S. $	British £
449. Romance Wall Plate, 10$^1/_2$" dia.	75.00	40.00
450. Cretonne Wall Plate, 10$^1/_2$" dia.	30.00	18.00
451. Romance Wall Plate, 10$^1/_2$" dia. *(See also Nos. 940-943 pg. 92 of The W of W2)*	75.00	40.00
452. "Clara" Buddies Bud Vase, 4$^1/_2$" high	30.00	15.00
"Clarence" Buddies Bud Vase, 4$^1/_2$" high *(See also Fig. 90 pg. 133 of The W of W and Nos. 484 and 485 pg. 68 of The W of W2)*	30.00	15.00
453. Platter—Meadow, 11$^3/_4$" long	40.00	22.50

	U.S. $	British £
454. Plate—Meadow, 10" dia.	30.00	15.00
455. Everlasting Candles, 8$^1/_2$" high, pair *(See also Nos. 371 and 376 pg.64 of The W of W2)*	145.00	55.00
456. Covered Sugar "Rita," 3$^3/_4$" high	30.00	20.00
457. Cup & Saucer, "Rita"	25.00	22.50
458. Bread & Butter Plate "Capri," 6" dia.	20.00	18.50
459. Snack Set "Mode Ware"	30.00	20.00
460. "Ovenproof" dish, 7" square	30.00	20.00
461. Bowl "Shooting Star," 5$^1/_8$" long	15.00	6.00
462. Cigarette Box, 2" high	45.00	25.00
463. Butter Dish, Basket Ware "2", 4$^1/_2$" dia.	35.00	15.00
464. Honey Pot, Basket Ware "2", 4$^3/_4$" high	45.00	18.00

PAGE 54
BRAMBLE WARE

	U.S. $	British £
465. Bowl, 9" dia.	25.00	25.00
466. Bowl, 6" dia.	15.00	20.00
467. Bowl, 5" dia.	15.00	18.00
468. Bowl, 4" dia.	10.00	12.00
469. Bowl, 8" dia.	25.00	22.00
470. Salad Bowl, 6$^1/_2$" dia.	55.00	40.00
471. Salad Servers, 8$^1/_4$" long, ea.	50.00	25.00
472. Jug, 5$^3/_4$" high	30.00	28.00
473. Cream Jug, 3$^1/_2$" high	25.00	18.00
474. Jug, 4$^1/_2$" high	25.00	22.00
475. Honey Pot, 4$^1/_4$" high	30.00	22.00
476. Butter Dish, 3$^1/_2$" high	40.00	20.00
477. Sugar, 1$^3/_4$" high	15.00	10.00
478. Sugar, 2$^1/_4$" high	15.00	12.00
479. Cruet Set and Tray, complete	55.00	25.00
480. Oval Dish, 8" long	25.00	20.00
481. Cheese Dish, 7$^1/_4$" long	50.00	35.00
482. Triple Tray, 8" x 7$^3/_4$"	30.00	28.00
483. Sauce Boat and Tray	40.00	25.00

PAGE 55

		U.S. $	British £
484.	Oval Dish—"Emerald Gold," 8" long	25.00	18.00
485.	Teapot—"Emerald Gold," 5³/₄" high	75.00	40.00
486.	Star Dish—"Golden Turquoise," 9" dia.	30.00	25.00
487.	Teapot—"Golden Turquoise," 5³/₄" high	75.00	40.00
488.	Jug—"Golden Turquoise," 6¹/₄" high	25.00	20.00
489.	Covered Cheese—"Emerald Gold," 6¹/₄" long	50.00	25.00
490.	Jug—"Emerald Gold," 4¹/₂" high	45.00	25.00
491.	Salt and Pepper—"Black Velvet," 2¹/₄" high	40.00	22.00
492.	Teapot—"Black Velvet," 6³/₄" high	75.00	35.00
493.	Jug—"Black Velvet," 5¹/₄" high	30.00	25.00
494.	Sauce Boat and Tray, "Black Velvet"	45.00	25.00
495.	Cream Jug—Iridized, 3¹/₂" high	18.00	15.00
496.	Sugar—Iridized, 2¹/₄" high	12.00	10.00
497.	Oval Dish—"Autumn Tints," 8" long	20.00	20.00
498.	Sugar—"Autumn Tints," 1³/₄" high	12.00	10.00
499.	Cream Jug—"Autumn Tints," 2³/₄" high	18.00	12.00
500.	Honey Pot—"Autumn Tints," 4¹/₂" high	35.00	14.00
501.	Sugar—White Matte, 2¹/₄" high	12.00	18.00
502.	Cream Jug—White Matte, 3¹/₂" high	20.00	18.00
503.	Pinwheel Dish—"Gold Blush," 6" dia.	32.00	20.00
504.	Jug—"Gold Blush," 5¹/₄" high	25.00	20.00
505.	Oval Dish—"Gold Blush," 10" long	30.00	20.00

PAGE 56

COPPER LUSTRE

		U.S. $	British £
506.	Lattice Jug, 6" high	45.00	35.00
507.	Stag Jug, 5¹/₂" high	45.00	35.00
508.	Dandy Jug, 6" high	35.00	30.00
509.	Diamond Jug, 6" high	50.00	35.00
510.	Beer Mug, 5" high	35.00	20.00
511.	Diamond Jug, 5¹/₂" high	40.00	35.00
512.	Festival Jug, 5¹/₂" high	60.00	60.00
513.	Festival Jug, 5" high	45.00	55.00
514.	Polka Jug, 5" high	60.00	35.00
515.	Dandy Jug, 4¹/₂" high	40.00	35.00
516.	Stag Console Bowl, 11¹/₄" long	75.00	50.00
517.	Cigarette Box, 1³/₄" high	50.00	25.00
518.	Powder Bowl, 4¹/₄" dia.	35.00	22.00
519.	Candy Box, 7" long	65.00	40.00
520.	Oval Dish, 8" long	30.00	20.00
521.	Dandy Sugar, small size, 1³/₄" high	10.00	20.00
522.	Dandy Cream, small size, 3" high	15.00	20.00
523.	Dandy Sugar, small size, 1³/₄" high	8.00	15.00
524.	Dandy Cream, small size, 3" high	20.00	15.00
525.	Round Dish, 6" dia.	20.00	30.00
526.	Round Dish, 5" dia.	18.00	30.00

PAGE 57

		U.S. $	British £
527.	Dutch Jug, 42s (4" high)	60.00	35.00
528.	Dutch Jug, 42s (4" high)	65.00	45.00
529.	Dutch Jug, 42s (4" high)	60.00	35.00
530.	Dutch Jug, 30s (5" high)	50.00	25.00
531.	Dutch Jug, 30s (5" high)	50.00	25.00
532.	Dandy Jug, 5¹/₂" high	65.00	40.00
533.	Dandy Jug, 5¹/₂" high	65.00	40.00
534.	Dandy Jug, 5" high	65.00	40.00
535.	Dandy Jug, 5" high	65.00	40.00
536.	Dandy Jug, 5" high	65.00	40.00

		U.S. $	British £
537.	Dandy Cream, large size, 3¹/₂" high	20.00	15.00
538.	Dandy Jug, 4¹/₂" high	65.00	40.00
539.	Dandy Sugar, small size, 1³/₄" high	20.00	14.00
540.	Dandy Cream, small size, 3" high	25.00	20.00
541.	Dandy Cream, large size, 3¹/₂" high	25.00	20.00
542.	Dandy Sugar, small size, 1³/₄" high	20.00	15.00
543.	Dandy Sugar, small size, 1³/₄" high	20.00	15.00
544.	Dandy Cream, small size, 3" high	25.00	20.00
545.	Dandy Sugar, small size, 1³/₄" high	20.00	15.00
546.	Dandy Cream, large size, 3¹/₂" high	30.00	25.00
547.	Dandy Cream, small size, 3" high	20.00	15.00
548.	Dandy Sugar, large size, 2" high	15.00	10.00
549.	Dandy Cream, small size, 3" high	20.00	15.00
550.	Dandy Sugar, small size, 1³/₄" high	15.00	10.00
551.	Dandy Cream, small size, 3" high	20.00	15.00
552.	Dandy Cream, large size, 3¹/₂" high	30.00	25.00
553.	Dandy Sugar, large size, 2" high	20.00	15.00
554.	Sugar, 2" high	15.00	10.00
555.	Dandy Cream, small size 3" high	25.00	20.00
556.	Dandy Sugar, small size, 1³/₄" high	15.00	10.00
557.	Dandy Cream, small size, 3" high	25.00	20.00

PAGE 58
WADE HEATH TEAPOTS 1927 - 1987

		U.S. $	British £
558.	Poppy Teapot, 6¹/₂" high	25.00	15.00
559.	Paisley Design Teapot, 6³/₄" high	190.00	120.00

		U.S. $	British £
560.	Nelson Teapot, 24s, 5³/₄" high	70.00	60.00
561.	Nelson Teapot, 24s, 5³/₄" high	70.00	60.00
562.	Nelson Teapot, 36s, 5" high	70.00	60.00
563.	Nelson Teapot, 42s, 4¹/₂" high	70.00	60.00
564.	Nelson Teapot, 42s, 4¹/₂" high	70.00	60.00
565.	Eagle Teapot, 6" high	110.00	70.00
566.	Tea and Water Pot Stand, 8¹/₄" x 7"	25.00	20.00
567.	Hot Water Pot, 5¹/₂" high	110.00	70.00
568.	Teapot, 5¹/₂" high	110.00	70.00
569.	Caddy Teapot, 5¹/₄" high	135.00	100.00
570.	Caddy Teapot, 5³/₄" high	145.00	125.00

PAGE 59
VETERAN CAR TANKARDS

		U.S. $	British £
571.	Oldsmobile, 1 pt.	20.00	10.00
572.	Lanchester, 1 pt.	20.00	8.00
573.	Darracq, 1 pt.	20.00	6.00
574.	Wolsley, 1 pt.	20.00	15.00
575.	Hispano—Suiza, 1 pt.	20.00	12.00
576.	Sunbeam, 1 pt.	20.00	8.00
577.	Alfa Romeo, 1 pt.	20.00	8.00
	(See also advertisement pg.61 of The W of W)		
578.	1907 Fiat F2, 1 pt.	20.00	15.00
579.	Cadillac, 1 pt.	20.00	8.00
580.	Bugatti, 1 pt.	20.00	8.00
581.	Spyker, 1 pt.	20.00	6.00
582.	Itala, 1 pt.	20.00	8.00
583.	De Dion Bouton, 1 pt.	20.00	6.00
584.	1925 MG, ¹/₂ pt.	14.00	10.00
585.	Ford, ¹/₂ pt.	14.00	5.00
586.	Sunbeam, 1 pt.	18.00	6.00

PAGE 60
MISCELLANEOUS TANKARDS

		U.S. $	British £
587.	Trafalgar Square, 1 pt.	18.00	8.00
588.	Ryerson Polytechnical Institute, 1 pt.	18.00	10.00

		U.S. $	British £
589.	Plymouth Tankard, 1 pt.	18.00	10.00
590.	Yeoman Warder, 1 pt.	18.00	10.00
591.	The Gent's a Gourmet, 1 pt.	18.00	10.00
592.	Ryerson Polytechnical Institute, 1 pt.	18.00	10.00
593.	Golfers, 1 pt.	15.00	8.00
	(See also advertisement pg.61 of The W of W)		
594.	Dalhousie University, 1 pt.	18.00	10.00
595.	Plymouth Tankard, 1 pt.	18.00	12.00
596.	Traditional Tankard, ¹/₂ pt.	18.00	10.00
597.	Plymouth Tankard, ¹/₂ pt.	18.00	10.00
598.	Traditional Tankard, ¹/₂ pt.	18.00	10.00
599.	Traditional Tankard, ¹/₂ pt.	18.00	10.00
600.	Plymouth Tankard, ¹/₂ pt.	18.00	6.00
601.	Big Ben Tankard, ¹/₂ pt.	15.00	10.00
602.	Barrel Tankard, 1 pt.	15.00	5.00
	(See also advertisement pg.61 of The W of W)		
603.	Barrel Tankard, ¹/₂ pt.	15.00	5.00

PAGE 61
TANKARDS BY WADE ENGLAND

1.	Barrel Tankard, 1 pt.	15.00	5.00
	(See also No.602 pg.60 of The W of W)		
2.	Tavern Tankard, 1 pt.	15.00	15.00
3.	Plymouth Tankard, 1 pt.	15.00	6.00
4.	Veteran Car Tankard, 1 pt.	20.00	8.00
	(See also No.577 pg.59 of The W of W)		
5.	Rugby Football Tankard, 1 pt.	15.00	8.00
6.	Beer Drinkers Tankard, 1 pt.	15.00	8.00
7.	Golfers Tankard, 1 pt.	15.00	8.00
	(See also No.593 pg.60 of The W of W)		
8.	Countryman Tankard, 1 pt.	15.00	10.00
9.	Countryman Tankard, 1 pt.	15.00	10.00
10.	Countryman Tankard, 1 pt.	15.00	10.00
11.	Countryman Tankard, 1 pt.	15.00	10.00

SOUVENIRS

604.	Benz Oil Jug, 3¹/₂" high	25.00	8.00
605.	Big Ben Oil Jug, 3¹/₂" high	25.00	5.00

		U.S. $	British £
606.	Tower Bridge Oil Jug, 3¹/₂" high	25.00	5.00
607.	Trafalgar Square Oil Jug, 3¹/₂" high	25.00	5.00
608.	Bud Vase, 4¹/₂" high	15.00	5.00
609.	Bud Vase, 4¹/₂" high	15.00	5.00
610.	Bud Vase, 4¹/₂" high	15.00	6.00

MINIATURE TANKARDS

611.	Giraffe, 2" high	15.00	12.00
612.	Zebra, 2" high	15.00	12.00
613.	Rhinoceros, 2" high	15.00	12.00
614.	Gazelle, 2" high	15.00	12.00
615.	Elephant, 2" high	15.00	12.00
616.	Lion, 2" high	15.00	12.00
617.	Nova Scotia, 2" high	15.00	5.00
618.	Rolls-Royce, 2" high	15.00	5.00
619.	Sunbeam, 2" high	15.00	5.00
620.	Spyker, 2" high	15.00	5.00
621.	Darracq, 2" high	15.00	5.00

PAGE 62
SOUVENIR PLATES AND TRAYS 1954 - 1961

622.	British Columbia Wall Plate, 9¹/₂" dia.	15.00	20.00
623.	Province of Ontario Wall Plate, 9¹/₂" dia.	15.00	20.00
624.	Niagara Falls Wall Plate, 9¹/₂" dia.	15.00	20.00
625.	Baby Peugeot Tyre Dish, 5" dia.	15.00	10.00
626.	Ford Tyre Dish, 5" dia.	15.00	10.00
627.	Mayflower Tyre Dish, 5" dia.	20.00	8.00
628.	Trooper—Lifeguards Dish, 4¹/₂" dia.	10.00	8.00
629.	Deer and Rabbits tray, 4³/₈" wide	10.00	8.00
630.	Piper tray, 4³/₈" wide	10.00	8.00
631.	Mr. Pickwick tray, 4³/₈" wide	10.00	8.00
632.	Stage Coach tray, 4³/₈" wide	10.00	8.00
633.	Scottish Dancer tray, 4³/₈" wide	10.00	8.00

		U.S. $	British £
634.	The Westbury Hotel pin tray, 4¼" dia.	10.00	6.00
635.	Big Ben pin tray, 4¼" dia.	10.00	6.00
636.	Tower Bridge London pin tray, 4¼" dia.	10.00	6.00
637.	Tower Bridge pin tray, 4¼" dia.	10.00	6.00
638.	Eros—Piccadilly Circus pin tray 4¼" dia.	10.00	6.00
639.	Trafalgar Square pin tray, 4¼" dia.	10.00	6.00
640.	Bahamian Constable pin tray, 4¼" dia.	10.00	6.00
641.	New Brunswick Canada Wall Plate, 9½" dia.	15.00	20.00
642.	Historic Nova Scotia Wall Plate, 9½" dia.	15.00	20.00
643.	Prince Edward Island Wall Plate, 9½" dia.	15.00	20.00

POTTERY TRAYS

		U.S. $	British £
644.	Alexander Graham Bell, 4¼" sq.	10.00	10.00
645.	Nova Scotia, 5¼" sq.	10.00	15.00
646.	Great Britain, 4¼" sq.	10.00	10.00
647.	Tropical Fruit Gatherers, Sugar Cane, 4¼" sq.	10.00	6.00
648.	Tropical Fruit Gatherers, Coconuts, 4¼" sq.	10.00	6.00
649.	Fruits, 4¼" sq.	15.00	6.00
650.	Buckingham Palace, 4¼" sq.	15.00	6.00
651.	Trafalgar Square, 4¼" sq.	15.00	6.00
652.	St. Paul's Cathedral, 4¼" sq.	15.00	6.00
653.	Comic Golf Scene, 4¼" sq.	15.00	6.00
654.	New Brunswick Canada, 4¼" dia.	15.00	6.00
655.	The Lobster, 4¼" dia.	15.00	6.00
656.	Cape Breton Island, 4¼" dia.	15.00	6.00
657.	Nova Scotia, 4¼" dia.	15.00	6.00
658.	Flower Spray, 4¼" dia.	15.00	6.00
659.	King of Diamonds, 4¼" dia.	15.00	6.00
660.	Queen of Clubs, 4¼" dia.	15.00	6.00

(See also Nos. 454-457 pg. 67 of The W of W2)

PAGE 63

ROYAL COMMEMORATIVES 1937 - 1986

		U.S. $	British £
661.	Vase, 8¾" high	65.00	30.00
662.	Decanter—Prince William, 50 cl	70.00	30.00
663.	Decanter—Queen Elizabeth, 75 cl	75.00	35.00
664.	Decanter—Prince Andrew, 75 cl	75.00	35.00
665.	Coronation Pitcher, 5⅛" high	140.00	65.00
666.	Coronation Loving Cup, 5" high	260.00	120.00
667.	Coronation Pitcher, 5⅝" high	140.00	65.00
668.	Coronation Pitcher, 5½" high	140.00	65.00
669.	Coronation Jug, 4⅛" high	150.00	70.00
670.	Coronation Jug, 4" high	95.00	45.00
671.	Coronation Dish, 4¾" dia.	22.00	8.00
672.	Coronation Dish, 4¾" dia.	22.00	10.00
673.	Coronation Goblet, 4¾" high	22.00	10.00
674.	Silver Jubilee Dish, 4¾" dia.	18.00	8.00
675.	Silver Jubilee Dish, 4¾" dia.	18.00	8.00
676.	Silver Jubilee Dish, 4¾" dia.	18.00	8.00
677.	Miniature Loving Cup, 2" high	55.00	25.00
678.	Bell—Charles and Diana, 5¾" high	130.00	60.00
679.	Candlesticks— Charles and Diana, 5¾" high per pair	120.00	80.00

PAGE 64

IRISH PORCELAIN 1953 - 1986

		U.S. $	British £
680.	Tankard, 1 pt.	30.00	10.00
681.	Serpent Urn, 11½" high	75.00	25.00
682.	Serpent Urn, 5¾" high	50.00	25.00

(See also Nos. 1113-1114 pg. 100 of The W of W2)

		U.S. $	British £
683.	Irish Coffee Mug, 5" high	25.00	10.00
684.	Tankard, ½ pt.	20.00	15.00
685.	Tankard, 1 pt.	25.00	15.00
686.	Musical Tankard, 5½" high	65.00	20.00
687.	Candy Box, 5" long	60.00	25.00

		U.S. $	British £
688.	Irish Porcelain Advertising Sign, 5¹/₂" high	65.00	25.00
689.	Vase, 4" high	35.00	20.00
690.	Tankard, ¹/₂ pt.	25.00	8.00
691.	Goblet — Large, 4¹/₄" high	25.00	15.00
692.	Crinkled Ashtray — Large, 6" dia.	20.00	8.00
693.	Thistle Ashtray, 6" overall	20.00	10.00
694.	Ashtray — Large, 6" x 5"	20.00	8.00
695.	Butterdish, 5" dia.	15.00	8.00

COUNTRYWARE 1973 - 1984

696.	Storage Jar—Large, 5¹/₂" high	35.00	18.00
697.	Covered Mustard Pot, 2¹/₂" high	20.00	8.00
698.	Storage Jar—Small, 4¹/₄" high	25.00	15.00
699.	Soup Bowl, 5" dia.	25.00	15.00

PAGE 65

IRISH PORCELAIN CONTINUED

700.	Child's Tankard, 3" high	20.00	5.00
701.	Miniature Tankard, 2" high	10.00	5.00
702.	Miniature Tyrone Tankard, 3" high	15.00	5.00
703.	Miniature Sugar, 1¹/₂" high	12.00	3.00
704.	Miniature Creamer, 2" high	12.00	4.00
705.	Jardiniere, 8¹/₂" overall	40.00	6.00
706.	Jardiniere, 5³/₄" overall	40.00	6.00
707.	Donkey and Cart Vase, 6¹/₄" overall	45.00	20.00
708.	Cigarette Lighter, 4" high	45.00	15.00
709.	Egg Cup, 2¹/₂" high	12.00	8.00
710.	Irish Porcelain Advertising Sign, 4¹/₄" high	70.00	25.00
711.	Pipe Ashtray, 6" dia.	35.00	8.00
712.	Donnegal Cup & Saucer	45.00	25.00
713.	Raindrop Sugar, 2" high *(See also Nos. 1075 -1080 pg. 99 The W of W2)*	20.00	10.00
714.	Irish Cooking Pot, 2" high	15.00	5.00
715.	Footed Bon Bon Dish, 1¹/₂" high	8.00	4.00
716.	Preserve Jar, 4" high	30.00	15.00

		U.S. $	British £
717.	Pintray, 3" dia.	12.00	6.00
718.	Triangular Ashtray, 4" across	12.00	5.00
719.	Shamrock Ashtray, 3¹/₂" across	15.00	5.00
720.	Leprechaun Pintray, 3" dia.	25.00	5.00
721.	Leprechaun Pintray, 3" dia.	25.00	5.00

IRISH CHARACTER FIGURES EARLY 1970'S - 1986

722.	Danny Boy, 4" high	40.00	20.00
723.	Mother MacCree, 2¹/₂" high	40.00	15.00
724.	Molly Malone, 3¹/₄" high	40.00	25.00
725.	Kathleen, 2¹/₂" high	40.00	15.00
726.	Eileen Oge, 3³/₄" high	40.00	20.00
727.	Phil the Fluter, 3³/₄" high	60.00	40.00
728.	Paddy Reilly, 3³/₄" high	60.00	75.00
729.	Rose of Tralee, 4" high	40.00	20.00
730.	Paddy Maginty, 3¹/₄" high	40.00	20.00

LUCKY LEPRECHAUNS CIRCA 1956 - 1986

731.	Larry, 4" high	70.00	55.00
732.	Lester, 4" high	70.00	55.00
733.	Lucky Leprechaun, 2³/₄" high	25.00	20.00
734.	Leprechaun on a Pig, 1³/₄" high *(See also Fig. 125 pg. 165 of The W of W)*	55.00	20.00
735.	Leprechaun—Crock of Gold, 1¹/₂" high	20.00	8.00
736.	Leprechaun—Cobbler, 1¹/₂" high	20.00	8.00
737.	Leprechaun—Tailor, 1¹/₂" high	20.00	8.00
738.	Cottage, 2³/₄" long	50.00	22.50
739.	Leprechaun—Leaf Dish	25.00	8.50
740.	Shamrock Ashtray w/Pixie	25.00	12.00

BALLY-WHIM IRISH VILLAGE 1984 - 1987

741-1.	Undertaker's House, 2" high	25.00	10.00
742-2.	Moore's Post Office, 1¹/₂" high	25.00	10.00
743-3.	Barney Flynn's Cottage, 1¹/₈" high	25.00	10.00
744-4.	Kate's Cottage, 1¹/₈" high	15.00	12.00

	U.S. $	British £
745-5. The Dentist's House, 2" high	18.00	12.00
746-6. Mick Murphy's Bar, 1³/₄" high	25.00	12.00
747-7. W. Ryan's Hardware Store, 1¹/₂" high	25.00	12.00
748-8. Bally—Whim House, 2" high	25.00	12.00

<u>PAGE 66</u>

"MOURNE" RANGE CIRCA MID-1970'S

The text for the Mourne Range illustration No.749 is to be found on page 160 of *The W of W* where it was inadvertently misplaced.

		U.S. $	British £
749.	Vase, 4" high	35.00	25.00
	Vase, 3³/₄" high	35.00	25.00
	Vase, 7¹/₂" high	50.00	40.00
	Candy Box, 5" x 3³/₄"	75.00	35.00
	(See also No.1062 pg.98 of The W of W2)		
	Dish,	25.00	25.00
	Vase, 6⁵/₈" high	60.00	30.00
	(See also No.1056 pg.98 of The W of W2)		
	Tankard, ¹/₂ pt.	45.00	25.00
	(See also No.1059 pg.98 of The W of W2)		
	Tankard, 1 pt.	60.00	30.00
	(See also No.1060 pg.98 of The W of W2)		
	Preserve Jar and Lid, 3³/₄" high	75.00	35.00
	(See also No.1058 pg.98 of The W of W2)		
	Square Dish, 5¹/₂"	20.00	30.00
	Butter Box with Lid	60.00	35.00
	Cream Jug, 4¹/₄" high	60.00	30.00
	(See also No.1057 pg.98 of The W of W2)		
	Sugar Bowl	35.00	25.00
	Salt and Pepper per set	45.00	40.00
	Footed Dish, 7" x 5"	60.00	35.00
	(See also No.1061 pg.98 of The W of W2)		

<u>PAGE 67</u>

IRISH PORCELAIN SONG FIGURES 1962 - 1986

		U.S. $	British £
750.	1—Little Crooked Paddy	350.00	250.00
	2—Phil the Fluter	350.00	275.00
	3—Widda Cafferty	350.00	300.00
	4—The Bard of Armagh	350.00	300.00
	5—The Star of the County Down	350.00	300.00

	U.S. $	British £
6—The Irish Emigrant	350.00	300.00
7—Molly Malone	350.00	350.00
8—Micky Mulligan	350.00	350.00
9—Mother MacCree	450.00	250.00
10—Dan Murphy	350.00	250.00
11—Eileen Oge	350.00	275.00

<u>PAGE 68</u>

WADE (PDM) ADVERTISING ITEMS

		U.S. $	British £
751.	Water Jug—J&B Scotch Whisky, 6¹/₈" high	30.00	10.00
752.	Water Jug—Borzoi Vodka, 6¹/₄" high	30.00	10.00
753.	Water Jug—Carling Black Label, 6¹/₂" high	25.00	10.00
754.	Water Jug—Queen Ann Scotch Whisky, 5¹/₈" high	30.00	15.00
755.	Water Jug—Dewar's White Label Scotch Whisky, 6³/₄" high	30.00	15.00
756.	Water Jug—Teacher's Scotch Whisky, 5¹/₈" high	30.00	10.00
757.	Water Jug—Teacher's Scotch Whisky, 5" high	30.00	10.00
758.	Water Jug—White Horse Scotch Whisky, 5¹/₂" high	35.00	10.00
759.	Water Jug—White Horse Whisky, 5¹/₄" high	30.00	15.00
760.	Water Jug—Whyte-Mackays Scotch Whisky, 7¹/₄" high	30.00	8.00
761.	Water Jug—King George IV Old Scotch Whisky, 4¹/₂" high	35.00	15.00
762.	Water Jug—Star Beers, 4" high	40.00	25.00
763.	Water Jug—Old Parr Scotch Whisky, 5¹/₄" high	30.00	12.00
764.	Water Jug—Duncan MacGregor Scotch Whisky, 5¹/₄" high	30.00	12.00
765.	Water Jug—V-J Dry Gin, 4¹/₂" high	25.00	12.00
766.	Water Jug—Minster Ginger Ale 4⁵/₈" high	30.00	12.00
767.	Water Jug—Ambassador Delux Scotch Whisky, 5¹/₄" high	30.00	15.00
768.	Water Jug—King George IV Old Scotch Whisky, 4³/₄" high	35.00	15.00

		U.S. $	British £
769.	Water Jug—Tia Maria, 4^1/$_2$" high	35.00	12.00

PAGE 69

		U.S. $	British £
770.	Ashtray—Bombay London Dry Gin, 6" dia.	20.00	6.00
771.	Water Jug—Bombay London Dry Gin, 6" high	45.00	20.00
772.	Ice Bucket—Bombay London Dry Gin, 6^1/$_2$" high	45.00	30.00
773.	Water Jug—Beefeater Gin, 5^3/$_4$" high	40.00	15.00
774.	Decanter—Bell's Old Scotch Whisky, 750ml (empty)	25.00	8.00
	Decanter—Bell's Old Scotch Whisky, 750ml (full and boxed)	175.00	95.00
775.	Water Jug—Dewar's Scotch, 6^1/$_2$" high	30.00	20.00
776.	Ashtray—Dewar's Scotch Whisky, 6^1/$_2$" x 4^3/$_4$"	15.00	6.00
777.	Ashtray—Tanqueray English Gin, 7" long	15.00	4.00
778.	Water Jug—Mackinlay's Old Scotch Whisky, 6^1/$_4$" high	35.00	18.00
779.	Flagon—Pusser's Rum, 7" high, (full and boxed)	160.00	75.00
	Flagon—Pusser's Rum, 7" high, (empty)	50.00	28.00
780.	Decanter—Bell's Old Scotch Whisky, 373ml (empty)	20.00	5.00
	Decanter—Bell's Old Scotch Whisky, 373ml (full and sealed)	165.00	90.00
781.	Water Jug—King George IV Scotch Whisky, 4^3/$_8$" high	35.00	22.00
782.	Ashtray—King George IV Scotch Whisky, 4^1/$_8$" x 3^1/$_4$"	20.00	8.00
783.	Ashtray—Johnnie Walker, 6^1/$_2$ sq.	40.00	10.00
784.	Water Jug—Johnnie Walker, 5^1/$_4$" high	25.00	15.00
785.	Ashtray—Captain Morgan, 7^3/$_4$" long	70.00	25.00
786.	Decanter—Bell's Old Scotch Whisky, 6^3/$_8$" high (empty)	15.00	5.00
	Decanter—Bell's Old Scotch Whisky, 6^3/$_8$" high (full and sealed)	175.00	95.00

		U.S. $	British £
787.	Ashtray—White Horse, 5^1/$_2$" sq.	14.00	2.00
788.	Ashtray Mount Gay Barbados Rum, 5^1/$_8$" sq.	35.00	5.00
789.	Ashtray—Mackinlay's Scotch Whisky, 7^1/$_4$" long	30.00	10.00
790.	Ashtray—Cutty Sark Scotch Whisky, 5" dia.	10.00	5.00
791.	Decanter—Bell's Old Scotch Whisky, 4^1/$_4$" high (empty)	15.00	5.00
	Decanter—Bell's Old Scotch Whisky, 4^1/$_4$" high (full and sealed)	45.00	20.00

PAGE 70

ADVERTISING ASHTRAYS

		U.S. $	British £
792.	British Airways, 8^1/$_2$" dia.	25.00	10.00
793.	Johnnie Walker, 9" x 7"	25.00	10.00
794.	Johnnie Walker, 10" x 6"	25.00	15.00
795.	Vaux, 7" x 6^1/$_2$"	35.00	10.00
796.	J&B Scotch Whisky, 6" x 2^1/$_2$"	10.00	5.00
797.	Greenall Whitley, 8" dia.	15.00	5.00
798.	President Scotch Whisky, 7" x 4"	15.00	6.00
799.	Illini, 7" dia.	30.00	10.00
800.	Johnnie Walker Scotch Whisky, 5^1/$_8$" sq.	20.00	8.00
801.	Hudson's Bay Scotch Whisky, 6^1/$_4$" dia.	20.00	8.00
802.	Banks, 4^3/$_4$" dia.	20.00	6.00
803.	Menu Holder—Tetley Bitterman, 1^3/$_4$" high	20.00	8.00
804.	Teacher's Highland Cream Scotch Whisky, 6" dia.	15.00	4.00
805.	John Bull, 7" across	20.00	4.00
806.	Black & White Scotch Whisky, 5" dia.	10.00	5.00
807.	Parkinson's Doncaster, 5^3/$_8$" dia.	25.00	6.00
808.	Embassy Hotels, 4^3/$_4$" dia.	10.00	2.00
809.	Carlsberg, 5^1/$_2$" sq.	15.00	2.00
810.	Black & White Scotch Whisky, 5" sq.	10.00	5.00

PAGE 71
GILBEY'S WINE BARRELS CIRCA 1953

		U.S. $	British £
811.	Cognac Barrel Lamp, 5³/₄" high (without shade)	50.00	35.00
812.	Port Barrel, 5³/₄" high	25.00	15.00
813.	Irish Barrel, 5³/₄" high	25.00	25.00
814.	Scotch Barrel, 5³/₄" high	25.00	15.00

ROTHMAN'S TANKARD MID 1970'S

		U.S. $	British £
815.	Rothman's of Pall Mall, 4³/₄" high	20.00	10.00

BASS PROMOTIONAL ITEMS

		U.S. $	British £
816.	Ashtray—Bass Export Ale, 9" dia.	15.00	8.00
817.	Ashtray—Bass, 6¹/₄" sq.	15.00	8.00
818.	Ashtray—Stone's Best Bitter, 8¹/₄" x 5"	20.00	12.00
819.	Water Jug—Worthington E, 5¹/₂" high	30.00	15.00
820.	Water Jug—Bass, 6⁷/₈" high	45.00	15.00
821.	Ashtray—Great Stuff, Bass, 7" sq.	15.00	6.00

GILBEY'S WINE BARRELS CIRCA 1953

		U.S. $	British £
822.	Sherry Barrel, 4³/₄" high	20.00	8.00
823.	Gin Barrel, 4³/₄" high	20.00	8.00
824.	Scotch Barrel, 4³/₄" high	20.00	8.00
825.	Port Barrel, 4³/₄" high	20.00	8.00

BOTTLE POURERS

		U.S. $	British £
826.	McCallums Whisky, 1⁵/₈" dia.	10.00	5.00
827.	Martell Cognac, 1¹/₂" high	10.00	5.00
828.	Kiskadee, 2³/₈" high	10.00	5.00
829.	Smirnoff Vodka, 1¹/₂" dia.	10.00	5.00
830.	Croft Original Cream Sherry, 1¹/₂" high	10.00	5.00
831.	Vat 69, 1¹/₂" dia.	10.00	5.00
832.	Famous Grouse, 1¹/₂" high	10.00	5.00

GUINNESS PROMOTIONAL FIGURINES 1968

		U.S. $	British £
833.	Tony Weller, 3" high	200.00	95.00
834.	Tweedle Dum and Tweedle Dee, 2⁷/₈" high	200.00	115.00
835.	Mad Hatter, 3¹/₄" high	200.00	115.00
836.	Wellington Boot, 3¹/₂" high	200.00	95.00

LABATT'S TANKARD EARLY 1970'S

		U.S. $	British £
837.	Labatt's 50, 4³/₄" high	15.00	12.00

PAGE 72
NELSON SHIP DECANTER

This shape decanter was also used for the John Paul Jones Ships decanter. *(See the color section of the Wade Price Trends.)*

		U.S. $	British £
838.	Nelson's Ship Decanter, 1 litre (full and boxed)	175.00	85.00
	Nelson's Ship Decanter, 1 litre (empty)	60.00	40.00

FIGURINES *by George Wade & Son Ltd. 1956 - 1987*

PAGE 81
FIG. 31. SEA LION CORKSCREW 1960

	U.S. $	British £
Sea Lion Corkscrew, 5³/₄" high *(See also No. 316 pg. 62 of The W of W2)*	125.00	55.00

FIG. 32. TV PET SERIES 1959 - 1965

	U.S. $	British £
Bengo, 2³/₈" high *(See also No. 172 pg. 55 of The W of W2)*	70.00	34.00
Simon, 2³/₈" high *(See also No. 173 pg. 55 of The W of W2)*	65.00	25.00

	U.S. $	British £
Pepi, 2¹/₈" high *(See also No. 67 pg. 35 of The W of W)*	95.00	33.00
Fifi, 2⁵/₈" high *(See also No. 68 pg. 35 of The W of W)*	45.00	20.00
Mitzi, 2" high *(See also No. 174 pg. 55 of The W of W2)*	75.00	38.00
Chee-chee, 2¹/₄" high *(See also No. 171 pg. 55 of The W of W2)*	60.00	30.00
Bruno Jnr.	110.00	50.00

	U.S. $	British £
Droopy Jnr., 2¼" high	90.00	55.00
(See also No.65 pg.35 of The W of W)		
Percy, 1½" high	90.00	55.00
(See also No.66 pg.35 of The W of W)		
Whisky	220.00	90.00

PAGE 82
FIG. 34. THE SWORD IN THE STONE

	U.S. $	British £
Madam Mim (Hen)	250.00	100.00
Merlin as Turtle,	350.00	155.00
Archimedes (Owl), 2" high	150.00	80.00
(See also No.175 pg.55 of The W of W2)		
Merlin as Hare, 2¼" high	210.00	95.00
(See also No.82 pg.36 of The W of W)		
The Girl Squirrel, 2" high	100.00	75.00
(See also No.177 pg.55 of The W of W2)		
Merlin as Caterpillar	275.00	110.00

FIG. 36. DISNEY MONEY BOXES 1962

	U.S. $	British £
Money Box—Lady, 3¾" x 4"	250.00	130.00
Money Box—Scamp, 3¾" x 4"	250.00	130.00
Money Box—Jock, 3¾" x 4"	250.00	130.00
Money Box—Rolly, 3¾" x 4"	250.00	130.00
Money Box—Lucky, 3¾" x 4"	250.00	130.00

PAGE 84
FIG. 38. AND FIG. 39. DISNEY'S

	U.S. $	British £
Lady, 4¼" high	235.00	150.00
(See also No.168 pg.55 of The W of W2)		

	U.S. $	British £
Tramp, 6" high	300.00	225.00
(See also No.169 pg.55 of The W of W2)		
Bambi, 4½" high	150.00	85.00
(See also No.167 pg.55 of The W of W2)		
Scamp, 4⅛" high	235.00	90.00
(See also No.98 pg.36 of The W of W)		
Jock, 4" high	475.00	310.00
(See No.80 pg.51 of WPT)		
Si, 5½" high	200.00	120.00
(See also No.99 pg.36 of The W of W)		
Am, 6" high	200.00	120.00
(See No.79 pg.51 of WPT)		
Dachie, 5" high	475.00	310.00
(See No.81 pg.51 of WPT)		
Thumper, 5¼" high	300.00	165.00
(See also No.166 pg.55 of The W of W2)		
Trusty, 5⅞" high	275.00	160.00
(See also No.170 pg.55 of The W of W2)		

PAGE 88
FIG. 40. WHIMSIE-LAND BRITISH WILD LIFE 1987

For color illustrations of this set see Nos. 199-1 through 199-5 pg. 55 of *The W of W2*.

		U.S. $	British £
A.	Otter, 1½" high	20.00	15.00
B.	Field Mouse, 1¼" high	35.00	25.00
C.	Partridge, 1½" high	20.00	15.00
D.	Golden Eagle, 1⅜" high	40.00	20.00
E.	Pheasant, 1¼" high	40.00	25.00

WHIMSIES, THE WORLD OF SURVIVAL, AND THE CONNOISSEUR'S COLLECTION

PAGE 91
FIG. 41. SHIRE HORSE

For color illustration see Nos. 194 and 195 pg. 55 *The W of W2* and for Shire Horse reproductions information see pg. 242 *The W of W2*.

	U.S. $	British £
Shire Horse, 2" high	230.00	105.00

FIG. 42. WHIMSEY RABBIT

	U.S. $	British £
Rabbit (ears together)	12.00	3.00
Rabbit (ears apart)	9.00	1.50
(See also No.155-2 pg.40 of The W of W)		

PREMIUM AND PROMOTIONAL ITEMS *by George Wade & Son Ltd.*

PAGE 98
FIG. 45.NURSERIES 1979

	U.S. $	British £
Boxed set of five figurines	75.00	40.00

PAGE 99
FIG. 46.QUEEN OF HEARTS 1971 - 1979
Of the three variations of this figurine, A and B are fairly common but C is extremely rare.

		U.S. $	British £
A.	Queen of Hearts (two large hearts) *(See also No.221 pg.42 of The W of W)*	15.00	20.00
B.	Queen of Hearts (two small hearts)	15.00	20.00
C.	Queen of Hearts (multi hearts)	40.00	30.00

FIG. 47.LITTLE BO PEEP
This illustrates the difference between the Sharp's Easter Egg promotion figurine *(See also No. 215 pg. 56 The W of W2)* issued in 1971, and the Red Rose Tea figurine *(See also No. 216 pg. 42 of The W of W)* issued between 1971 - 1979.

	U.S. $	British £
Bo Peep—Sharp's Easter Egg promotion, 2⁵/₈" high	35.00	15.00
Bo Peep—Red Rose Tea promotion, 1³/₄" high	5.00	3.00

PAGE 101
FIG. 53.SALADA TEA PROMOTION 1984
For further information on this promotion see Fig. 52 and related text on pg. 101 of *The W of W.*

	U.S. $	British £
Tea Caddy, 7¹/₂" high	75.00	45.00

MISCELLANEOUS ITEMS *by George Wade & Son Ltd. and Wade Heath & Company Ltd.*

PAGE 107
FIG. 57.MISCELLANEOUS ITEMS

		U.S. $	British £
A.	Barbecue Tankard, 4¹/₂" high *(See also No. 319 pg. 62 of The W of W2)*	40.00	20.00
B.	Redskin Dish, 3¹/₂" dia.	130.00	70.00
C.	Egg Cup	40.00	6.00
D.	Santa Claus Egg Cup, 3¹/₂" high	250.00	100.00

FIG. 58.MISCELLANEOUS ITEMS

		U.S. $	British £
A.	Candy Dish, 4³/₄" dia.	30.00	10.00
B.	Honey Jar, 2³/₈" high	40.00	15.00

PAGE 109
FIG. 59.HARLEQUINS 1957 - 1958

	U.S. $	British £
Harlequin Tray, 3" sq. *(See also Nos. 467-470 pg. 67 of The W of W2)*	10.00	3.00

FIG. 60.PEGASUS POSY BOWL 1958 - 1959

	U.S. $	British £
Posy Bowl, 4³/₈" high *(See also No. 317 pg. 62 of The W of W2)*	125.00	70.00

PAGE 110
FIG. 63.BALLET DISHES LATE 1950'S

	U.S. $	British £
Bud Vase (shape No. 478), 12" high	35.00	35.00
Vase (shape No. 460), 7" high	35.00	30.00
Bud Vase (shape No. 483), 4¹/₂" high	25.00	10.00
Vase (shape No. 467), 4" high	25.00	10.00
Bud Vase (shape No. 484), 4¹/₂" high	25.00	8.00
Vase (shape No. 458), 7" high	30.00	25.00
Vase (shape No. 468), 9" high	35.00	40.00
Bud Vase (shape No. 477), 9" high	30.00	30.00
Individual Tray, 4¹/₄" sq. (boxed)	20.00	15.00
Individual Tray, 4¹/₄" sq. (unboxed) *(See also Nos. 512-513 pg. 68 of The W of W2)*	10.00	6.00
Boxed set of tray and two vases	60.00	25.00
Boxed set of four trays	45.00	30.00

<u>PAGE 112</u>
FIG. 66.T. T. TRAY 1959 - 1960

	U.S. $	British £
Ashtray, 2³/₄" high	160.00	100.00

(See also No. 330 pg. 62 of The W of W2)

FIG. 67.FAMOUS AIRCRAFT DISHES 1959

Set of three individually boxed dishes, each	20.00	15.00

FIG. 68.WADE "WILD FOWL" 1960

Shoveller Drake	550.00	375.00
Pintail	550.00	375.00
Mallard Drake	550.00	375.00
Shoveller	550.00	375.00

<u>PAGE 113</u>
FIG. 69.SILHOUETTE SERIES 1962

Viking Ship Tray, 4³/₄" long	35.00	15.00

(See also No. 328 pg. 62 of The W of W2)

Giraffe Vase, 4¹/₈" high	35.00	15.00

(See also No. 320 pg. 63 of The W of W2)

<u>PAGE 116 & 117</u>
FIG. 72.SHAVING MUG

Lord Admiral Horacio Nelson, 3¹/₄" high	15.00	5.00

(See also No. 492 pg. 68 of The W of W2)

FIG. 73, 74 & 75.ROMANCE RANGE 1983 - 1985

Heart Shaped Picture Frame, 5¹/₂" high	25.00	10.00
Pomander, 2³/₄" dia.	25.00	12.50
Egg Shaped Trinket Box, 2³/₄" long	25.00	12.50

(See also Nos. 345 and 346 pg. 46 of The W of W)

FIG. 76.SEAGULL BOAT 1961

Seagull Boat, 6" long	90.00	60.00

(See also No. 331 pg. 62 The W of W2)

<u>PAGE 121</u>
FIG. 79.FLOWER JUG

	U.S. $	British £
Flower Jug (shape No. 106), 7¹/₄" high	65.00	50.00

(See also No.812 pg. 87 of The W of W2)

FIG. 80.FLOWER JUG

Flower Jug (shape No. 14), 6³/₄" high	100.00	65.00

(See also No.538 pg. 71 of The W of W2)

<u>PAGE 123</u>
FIG. 81.FLAXMAN WARE

1.	Jug, 9" high	80.00	35.00

(See also No. 389 pg. 49 of The W of W)

2.	Vase, 9" high	30.00	20.00
3.	Vase, 9" high	30.00	20.00
4.	Vase 9" high	50.00	35.00
5.	Vase 9" high	30.00	20.00
6.	Vase, 9" high	30.00	20.00
7.	Jug, 9" high	50.00	35.00
8.	Jug, 9" high	70.00	38.00

(See also No. 376 pg. 48 of The W of W)

9.	Jug, 9" high	50.00	35.00
10.	Wall Pocket	60.00	55.00
11.	Jug, 9" high	60.00	45.00

(See also No. 597 pg. 75 of The W of W2)

12.	Jug, 9" high	50.00	35.00

(See also No. 387 pg. 49 of The W of W and No.579 pg.74 of The W of W2)

13.	Flower Holder, 5" high	60.00	45.00

(See also No. 637 pg. 76 of The W of W2)

14.	Basket, 2¹/₂" high	35.00	20.00

(See also No. 421 pg. 51 of The W of W)

15.	Basket, 2¹/₂" high	35.00	20.00

(See also Fig. 86 pg. 130 of The W of W)

16.	Basket, 2¹/₂" high	35.00	20.00
17.	Flower Holder, 5" high	32.00	35.00

(See also No. 411 pg. 51 of The W of W)

<u>PAGE 124</u>
FIG. 81A. FLAXMAN WARE

1.	Jug (shape No. 135), 9" high	40.00	25.00
2.	Vase (shape No. 214)	30.00	20.00

		U.S. $	British £
3.	Jug (shape No. 132), 9" high	40.00	30.00
4.	Jug (shape No. 134), 9" high	40.00	30.00
5.	Vase (shape No. 216), 5" high	65.00	50.00
	(See also No.600 pg.75 and No.615 pg.76 of The W of W2)		
6.	Jug (shape No. 133), 9" high	40.00	30.00

		U.S. $	British £
7.	Jug (shape No. 131), 8¹/₂" high	40.00	30.00
8.	Wall Pocket (shape No. 224), 8¹/₂" high	60.00	45.00
9.	Jug (shape No. 120), 8¹/₂" high	65.00	30.00
	(See also No.375 pg.48 of The W of W and No.564 pg.73 of The W of W2)		

TABLEWARE *by Wade Heath & Company Ltd.*

PAGE 127
FIG. 83.PEONY CIRCA 1947 - MID 1950'S

		U.S. $	British £
1.	Vase, 11" high	75.00	40.00
2.	Vase, 9" high	50.00	35.00
3.	Plaque, 12¹/₂" dia.	85.00	58.00
	(See also No. 399 pg. 50 of The W of W)		
4.	Vase, 9" high	50.00	35.00
5.	Jug, 11" high	75.00	50.00
6.	Vase, 9" high	60.00	40.00
7.	Vase, 9" high	50.00	35.00
8.	Vase, 9" high	50.00	35.00
9.	Vase, 9" high	60.00	40.00
10.	Basket, 2¹/₂" high	50.00	35.00
11.	Fruit Bowl, 14¹/₂" long	120.00	45.00
	(See also No. 398 pg. 50 of The W of W)		
12.	Vase, 8" high	60.00	40.00

PAGE 128
FIG. 84.GOTHIC LUSTRE WARE

		U.S. $	British £
1.	Vase, 6¹/₂" high	60.00	40.00
	(See also No. 402 pg. 50 of The W of W)		
2.	Wall Pocket, 6¹/₂" high	60.00	55.00
3.	Vase, 9" high	60.00	55.00
4.	Jug, 11¹/₂" high	100.00	65.00
5.	Jug, 9" high	55.00	40.00
	(See also No.617 pg.76 of The W of W2)		
6.	Vase, 9¹/₂" high	55.00	40.00

PAGE 129
FIG. 85.BUTTER DISH

	U.S. $	British £
Butter Dish—Dopey, 7" dia.	250.00	100.00
(See also No. 838 pg. 87 of The W of W2)		

PAGE 130
FIG. 86.FLAXMAN WARE BASKET

	U.S. $	British £
Basket (shape No. 246), 5¹/₄" high	35.00	20.00

PAGE 131
FIG. 87.BASKETWARE

	U.S. $	British £
Cruet set with tray	55.00	30.00
(See also Nos. 443-445 pg. 52 of The W of W and No. 820 pg. 87 of The W of W2)		

PAGE 133
FIG. 89.RUBYTONE CIRCA 1953
For color illustration of Rubytone tableware see Nos. 437 and 438 pg. 52 of *The W of W* and Nos. 852 - 861 pg. 88 of *The W of W2*.

	U.S. $	British £
Sauce Bowl and Stand, complete	40.00	25.00

FIG. 90.BUDDIES CIRCA 1960
For color illustration of Buddies bud vases see also No. 452 pg. 53 of *The W of W* and Nos.484 and 485 pg. 68 of *The W of W2*.

	U.S. $	British £
Clarence, 4¹/₂" high	30.00	15.00
Clara, 4¹/₂" high	30.00	15.00

PAGE 134
FIG. 91.ORB SHAPES EARLY 1950'S

Prices are given for complete sets of cup, saucer and plate.

		U.S. $	British £
1.	Decoration No. 4931	12.00	5.50
2.	Decoration No. 4942	12.00	5.50
3.	Decoration No. 4939	15.00	6.50
3A.	Decoration No. 4953 (not illustrated)	NPA	NPA
4.	Decoration No. 4950	15.00	6.50
5.	Decoration No. 4940	12.00	5.50
6.	Decoration No. 4953	12.00	5.50
6A.	Decoration No. 4939 (not illustrated)	NPA	NPA
7.	Decoration No. 4891	12.00	5.50
8.	Decoration No. 4868	12.00	5.50
9.	Decoration No. 4943	12.00	5.50
10.	Decoration No. 4932	12.00	5.50
11.	Decoration No. 4809	12.00	5.50
12.	Decoration No. 4806	12.00	5.50
13.	Decoration No. 4959	28.00	12.00
	(See also Nos. 1007-1012 pg. 95 of The W of W2)		
14.	Decoration No. 4808	12.00	5.50
15.	Decoration No. 4941	12.00	5.50
16.	Decoration No. 4964	12.00	5.50
17.	Decoration No. 4895	45.00	30.00
18.	Decoration No. 4937	45.00	30.00

PAGE 136
FIG. 93.QUACK QUACK NURSERY WARE

For color illustration of the Quack Quack Nursery Ware see Nos. 825-829 pg. 87 of *The W of W2* and for the Quack Quack Family figurines see Nos. 162-165 pg. 54 of *The W of W*.

1.	Heavy Baby Plate	55.00	40.00
2.	Oatmeal Bowl	50.00	37.50
3.	Jug, ½ pt.	55.00	40.00
4.	Cup and Saucer	55.00	50.00
5.	Mug	55.00	40.00
6.	Plate, 6¼" dia.	50.00	37.50
7.	Plate, 8" dia.	55.00	40.00

PAGE 137
FIG. 95 and 96.HARMONY TABLEWARE

Suggested prices are for the plain two-tone Harmony. For items decorated in either Shooting Star, Parasol, Carnival or Fern, prices are approximately 20 percent higher.

	U.S. $	British £
Bowl (shape No. 438)	20.00	15.00
Bowl (shape No. 439)	25.00	20.00
Bowl (shape No. 440)	35.00	25.00
Jug (shape No. 433)	20.00	15.00
Jug (shape No. 435)	30.00	25.00
Jug (shape No. 436)	20.00	15.00
Vase (shape No. 434)	20.00	15.00
Vase (shape No. 458)	20.00	15.00
Tray (shape No. 455)	20.00	15.00
Miniature Bowl (shape No. 449)	3.00	1.50
Miniature Bowl (shape No. 450)	3.00	1.50
Miniature Vase (shape No. 452)	3.00	1.50
Miniature Jug (shape No. 453)	4.00	2.00

PAGE 138
FIG. 97. LATTICE WARE DECORATION 6191

Salad Bowl	75.00	40.00
Salad Servers, each	45.00	30.00
Biscuit Barrel	55.00	30.00
Honey Pot	50.00	55.00
Tea Pot—large	60.00	35.00
Cream	35.00	20.00
Sugar	25.00	15.00
Covered Butter Dish	50.00	35.00
Oval Dish	30.00	20.00
Covered Cheese Dish	50.00	35.00
Dish, 5"	30.00	20.00
Cruet Set and Tray	55.00	30.00
Gravy Boat and Stand	40.00	25.00
Dish, 6"	30.00	20.00

PAGE 139

FIG. 98 and 100.FLAIR TABLEWARE

	U.S. $	British £
Teapot	35.00	15.00
Creamer	10.00	4.00
Open Sugar	8.00	3.50
Cup and Saucer	15.00	6.00
Bread and Butter Plate	8.00	3.00
Fruit set—Harlequin, complete 7 piece set	30.00	15.00

PAGE 140

FIG. 101. REGENCY COFFEE SET

For color illustration of the all-gold Regency Coffee Set see Nos. 862-867 pg. 88 *of The W of W2.* Suggested prices are given for items in all-gold decoration. For items in black/gold, maroon/gold, pink/gold and primrose/gold decoration add fifteen percent. For items in turquoise/gold decoration add twenty percent and for items in mother of pearl decoration add thirty percent.

	U.S. $	British £
Cup and Saucer	20.00	10.00

	U.S. $	British £
Open Sugar Bowl, 1³/₄" high	30.00	5.00
Cream Jug, 1⁷/₈" high	40.00	10.00
Coffee Pot, 6³/₄" high	50.00	30.00

FIG. 102.FANTASIA 1961

	U.S. $	British £
Tray (shape No. 5455), 7¹/₂" long	30.00	25.00
Vase (shape No. 5460), 7¹/₂" high	35.00	30.00
Bud Vase (shape No. 5477), 9" high	30.00	25.00
Vase (shape No. 5468), 9¹/₄" high	50.00	40.00

PAGE 143

FIG. 104. FESTIVAL 1954

	U.S. $	British £
Tankard, 4³/₄" high	55.00	50.00

(See also Nos. 512 and 513 pg. 56 of The W of W and Nos. 951-953 pg. 92 of The W of W2)

ROYAL COMMEMORATIVES *by George Wade & Son Ltd. and Wade Heath & Company Ltd.*

PAGE 154

FIG. 108. CORONATION FRUIT BOWL

	U.S. $	British £
Footed Fruit Bowl, 12" dia.	335.00	195.00

(See also Nos. 1031 and 1032 pg. 96 of The W of W2)

FIG. 109. COMMEMORATIVE TANKARD

	U.S. $	British £
Tankard, 3¹/₂" high	35.00	10.00

PAGE 155

FIG. 110. SILVER JUBILEE TANKARD

	U.S. $	British £
Tankard, 4" high	35.00	10.00

FIG. 111. TRINKET BOX

	U.S. $	British £
Trinket Box—1981 Royal Wedding, 1¹/₂" high	45.00	25.00

WADE (IRELAND) LTD.

PAGE 157

FIG. 112. IRISH TANKARD

	U.S. $	British £
Coronation Tankard, 4¹/₂" high	64.00	35.00

PAGE 158

FIG. 113. PRESERVE JAR

	U.S. $	British £
Covered Preserve Jar, 3¹/₂" high	30.00	15.00

FIG. 114. CELTIC PORCELAIN

	U.S. $	British £
Serpent Bowl (shape No. C.K. 6), 4³/₄" dia.	35.00	20.00

PAGE 160
FIG. 115. IRISH PORCELAIN

	U.S. $	British £
Cup and Saucer	45.00	25.00

FIG. 116. IRISH PORCELAIN

Items marked "discontinued" in Fig. 116 are neither listed nor priced below.

	U.S. $	British £
Half Pint Tankard (shape No. I.P. 1)	25.00	8.00
One Pint Tankard (shape No. I.P. 2)	30.00	10.00
Stein Tankard (shape No. I.P. 3)	30.00	12.00
Child's Tankard (shape No. I.P. 4)	20.00	5.00
Musical Tankard (shape No. I.P. 5)	65.00	20.00
Half Pint Knurled Tankard (shape No. I.P. 6)	20.00	15.00
Half Pint Tyrone Tankard (shape No. I.P. 8)	20.00	12.00
Min. Tyrone Tankard (shape No. I.P. 9)	15.00	5.00
One Pint Tyrone Tankard (shape No. I.P. 10)	35.00	20.00
Small Goblet (shape No. I.P. 10A)	20.00	10.00
Straight Sided Goblet (shape No. I.P. 12)	20.00	15.00
Preserve Jar (shape No. I.P. 23)	30.00	15.00
Violet Bowl (shape No. I.P. 34)	10.00	5.00
Killarny Urn (shape No. I.P. 41), 6" high	50.00	28.00
Killarny Urn (shape No. I.P. 42), 4¹/₂" high	30.00	12.00
Min. Killarny Urn (shape No. I.P. 43)	20.00	5.00
Irish Coffee Mug (shape No. I.P. 44)	25.00	10.00

	U.S. $	British £
Individual Cream & Sugar (shape No. I.P. 72/73)	24.00	8.00
Butter Dish (shape No. I.P. 75)	15.00	8.00
Nut Bowl (shape No. I.P. 76)	20.00	10.00
Candy Box (shape No. I.P. 92)	60.00	25.00
Barrel Vase (shape No. I.P. 93)	20.00	5.00
Bisquit Barrel (shape No. I.P. 94)	70.00	30.00
Footed Bon Bon Dish (shape No. I.P. 602)	15.00	5.00
Irish Cooking Pot (shape No. I.P. 603)	20.00	8.00
Salt and Pepper (shape No. I.P. 604-5)	12.00	8.00
Cruet and Stand (shape No. I.P. 606C)	55.00	25.00
Crinkled Edge Butter Dish (shape No. I.P. 607)	10.00	5.00
Shamrock Ashtray (shape No. I.P. 609)	15.00	5.00
Shamrock Ashtray and Pixie (shape No. I.P. 609P)	25.00	12.00
Square Ashtray (shape No. I.P. 611)	12.00	5.00
Triangle Ashtray (shape No. I.P. 612)	12.00	5.00
Min. Tankard (shape No. I.P. 614)	10.00	5.00
Butter Pat (shape No. I.P. 619)	8.00	4.00
Leprechaun Pintray (shape No. I.P. 619L)	25.00	5.00
Leprechaun (shape No. S11)	25.00	20.00
Large Crinkled Ashtray (shape No. I.P. 622)	20.00	8.00
Pipe Ashtray (shape No. I.P. 623)	35.00	8.00
Large Sq. Ashtray— Shamrock (shape No. I.P. 626)	20.00	8.00

	U.S. $	British £
Large dia. Ashtray—Rose (shape No. I.P. 627)	20.00	10.00
Large rd. Ashtray—Thistle (shape No. I.P. 628)	20.00	10.00
Single Egg Coddler (shape No. I.P. 631)	15.00	8.00
Double Egg Coddler (shape No. I.P. 632)	20.00	10.00
Jardiniere (shape No. C.302)	40.00	6.00
One Pint Raindrop Jug (shape No. C 305)	45.00	20.00
³/₄ pt. Raindrop Jug (shape No. C 306)	40.00	18.00
Half Pint Raindrop Jug (shape No. C 307)	35.00	12.00
One Pint Coffee Pot (shape No. C 308)	80.00	40.00
Tea Strainer (shape No. C 309)	30.00	15.00
Sugar and Cream (shape No. C 310-311), set	50.00	20.00
Teapot (shape No. C 312)	80.00	40.00
Donkey and Cart (shape No. C 338)	45.00	20.00
Lucky Leprechauns (shape No. S2)	20.00	8.00
Leprechaun on Pig's Back (shape No. S8)	55.00	20.00
Donegal Cup and Saucer (shape No. M. 336-7)	45.00	25.00
Donegal Plate 6" dia. (shape No. M. 334)	20.00	10.00

PAGE 162

FIG. 117. SHAMROCK RANGE TABLEWARE

		U.S. $	British £
1.	Teapot (shape No. SR 05)	60.00	35.00
2.	Coffee Pot (shape No. SR 04)	60.00	35.00
3.	Tea/Coffee Cup (shape No. SR 08)	50.00	25.00
4.	Sugar and Cream Set (shape No. SR 06)	40.00	20.00
5.	Salt and Pepper Set (shape No. SR 07)	20.00	12.00

FIG. 118. VASES

		U.S. $	British £
1.	Bud Vase (shape No. SR 09)	60.00	30.00
2.	Round Vase (shape No. SR 10)	50.00	25.00
3.	Oval Vase (shape No. SR 11)	50.00	25.00
4.	Shamrock Cooking Pot (shape No. SR 20)	20.00	8.00
5.	Shamrock Urn (shape No. SR 19)	30.00	12.00

PAGE 163

FIG. 119. MISCELLANEOUS ITEMS

1.	Half Pint Tankard (shape No. SR 01)	30.00	10.00
2.	One Pint Tankard (shape No. SR 02)	25.00	8.00
3.	Large Ashtray (shape No. SR 17)	20.00	8.00
4.	Small Ashtray (shape No. SR 18)	15.00	6.00
5.	Candlestick (shape No. SR 12), pair	60.00	20.00

FIG. 120. BELLS OF IRELAND

1.	Bunratty Castle (shape No. SR 03/3)	30.00	20.00
2.	Spinning Wheel (shape No. SR 03/4)	30.00	20.00
3.	Blarney Castle (shape No. SR 03/1)	30.00	20.00
4.	Ross Castle (shape No. SR 03/2)	30.00	20.00
5.	Christmas Bell (shape No. SR 03/7)	30.00	20.00
6.	Shamrocks (shape No. SR 03/5)	30.00	20.00
7.	Thatched Cottage (shape No. SR 03/8)	30.00	20.00

FIG. 121. IRISH GOBLETS

1.	Blarney Castle (shape No. SR 14/1)	30.00	20.00
2.	Spinning Wheel (shape No. SR 14/4)	30.00	20.00

		U.S. $	British £
3.	Thatched Cottage (shape No. SR 14/8)	30.00	20.00
4.	Ross Castle (shape No. SR 14/3)	30.00	20.00
5.	Bunratty Castle (shape No. SR 14/3)	30.00	20.00
6.	Shamrocks (shape No. SR 14/5)	30.00	20.00

FIG. 122. IRISH COFFEE MUGS

		U.S. $	British £
1.	Irish Coffee Mug (shape No. SR 16) each	30.00	20.00
2.	Decanter (shape No. SR 13)	50.00	30.00

PAGE 164

FIG. 123. FLYING BIRDS 1956 - 1959

	U.S. $	British £
Flying Birds—green, each	15.00	5.00
Flying Birds— yellow, each	15.00	10.00
Flying Birds— blue, each	15.00	5.00

(See also Nos. 1127-1129 pg. 100 of The W of W2)

WADE (PDM) LTD.

PAGE 170

FIG. 128. DEWAR'S SCOTCH WHISKY

	U.S. $	British £
Ashtray — Dewar's "White Label," 4³/₄" dia.	20.00	5.00

PAGE 172

FIG. 129. B.O.A.C.

	U.S. $	British £
Water Jug, 5¹/₄" high	30.00	20.00
Large Round Ashtray (not illustrated)	20.00	15.00
Pottery Dish (not illustrated)	10.00	8.00
One Pint Tankard (not illustrated)	18.00	10.00
Half Pint Tankard (not illustrated)	15.00	10.00

PAGE 173

FIG. 130. BULMERS WOODPECKER CIDER

	U.S. $	British £
Ashtray, 5¹/₂" x 6³/₄"	20.00	5.00

FIG. 124. GIFT FROM OLD IRELAND 1959

	U.S. $	British £
Cottage, 2" high	50.00	22.50
(See also No. 738 pg. 65 of The W of W)		
Wide Eyed Pig, 1³/₄" high	65.00	25.00
Pink Elephant, 1¹/₂" high	65.00	25.00
(See also Nos. 1124 and 1126 pg. 100 of The W of W2)		

PAGE 165

FIG. 125. LUCKY FAIRY FOLK

	U.S. $	British £
Leprechaun on Acorn, 1¹/₂" high	75.00	30.00
(See also No. 1086 pg. 99 of The W of W2)		
Leprechaun on Rabbit, 1¹/₂" high	75.00	35.00
(See also No. 1087 pg. 99 of The W of W2)		
Leprechaun on Pig, 1³/₄" high *(See also No. 734 pg. 65 of The W of W)*	55.00	20.00

FIG. 126. LEPRECHAUN AND COTTAGE 1960 -1970

	U.S. $	British £
Leprechaun and Cottage (shape No. S.9)	100.00	85.00
(See also No. 1107 pg. 100 of The W of W2)		

PAGE 174

FIG. 131. BEEFEATER GIN

	U.S. $	British £
Ashtray, 5¹/₂" sq.	15.00	5.00

PAGE 178

FIG. 135. WAITER TRAYS

		U.S. $	British £
A.	Gordon's Gin, 10¹/₂" dia.	10.00	6.00
B.	Extra Light by Bass, 12" dia.	10.00	6.00
C.	Toby Bitter, 10¹/₂" dia.	10.00	6.00
D.	Tetley Bittermen, 10¹/₂" dia.	10.00	6.00
E.	Worthington E, 10¹/₂" dia.	10.00	6.00
F.	Marston's, 10¹/₂" dia.	10.00	6.00
G.	Morland, 13¹/₂" sq.	15.00	8.00
H.	Stones Best Bitter, 12³/₄" sq.	15.00	8.00
J.	Springbank Scotch Whisky, 12³/₄" sq.	15.00	8.00

MISCELLANEOUS ITEMS *by the Wade Group of Potteries*

PAGES 181 - 182

	U.S. $	British £
FIG. 136		
Vase—Orcadia, 7" high	75.00	35.00
(See also No. 522 pg. 69 of The W of W2)		
FIG. 137		
Flower Jug—Orcadia, 6½" high	70.00	30.00
(See also No. 518 pg. 69 of The W of W2)		
FIG. 138		
Flower Jug, 9" high	110.00	65.00
(See also No. 528 pg. 70 of The W of W2)		
FIG. 139		
Flower Jug, 11¾" high	240.00	135.00
(See also No. 514 pg. 69 of The W of W2)		
FIG. 140		
Flower Jug, 6½" high	35.00	25.00
(See also No. 532 pg. 70 of The W of W2)		
FIG. 141		
Squirrel Butter Dish,	25.00	10.00
(See also No. 278 pg. 44 of The W of W)		
FIG. 142		
Tyre Dish, 5" dia.	15.00	10.00
(See also No. 426 pg. 66 of The W of W2)		
FIG. 143		
Plymouth Tankard with Spout, 3¾" high	35.00	20.00
(See also No. 489 pg. 68 of The W of W2)		
FIG. 144		
Sandeman Decanter, 8½" high	60.00	40.00
FIG. 145		
Tower Stout Hors d'oeuvre Dish, 10" h. x 8½" dia.	35.00	18.00
FIG. 146		
Ashtray—McCallum's, 4¾" dia.	60.00	40.00

PAGE 183
FIG. 147

	U.S. $	British £
Nutbowl, 6½" dia.	20.00	10.00
(See also I.P. 76 Fig. 116 pg. 161 of The W of W)		

PAGE 183
FIG. 148

	U.S. $	British £
Fruit Bowl, 5" dia.	15.00	8.00

	U.S. $	British £
FIG. 149		
Rose Dish, 5½" long	25.00	10.00
FIG. 150		
Covered Preserve Jar, 4½" high	50.00	25.00
(See also No. 1064 pg. 98 of The W of W2)		
FIG. 151		
Miniature Tyrone Tankard, 4" high	15.00	5.00
(See also I.P. 9 Fig. 116 pg. 160 of The W of W)		
FIG. 152		
Leprechaun on a Toad Stool, 4½" high	50.00	25.00

PAGE 184

	U.S. $	British £
FIG. 153		
Vase, 8¾" high	40.00	25.00
(See also No. 1017 pg. 96 of The W of W2)		
FIG. 154		
Toadstool Money Bank, 5½" high *(See also No. 390 pg. 64 of The W of W2)*	85.00	40.00
FIG. 155		
Kennel Money Bank, 4½" high *(See also No. 392 pg. 64 of The W of W2)*	45.00	25.00
FIG. 156		
Fawn Money Bank, 5¼" high	45.00	25.00
(See also No. 391 pg. 64 of The W of W2)		
FIG. 157		
Whimtray—1987, 4½" x 3½"	20.00	10.00
(See also No. 343 pg. 63 of The W of W2)		

FIG. 158 WHIMSEY-ON-WHY VILLAGE SETS
For color illustration of this set see Nos. 286-33 to 286-36 pg. 60 of *The W of W2*, and for the remainder of the series see Nos. 268-1 to 271-32 pg. 43 of *The W of W*.

		U.S. $	British £
A.	Schoolteacher's House (No. 33)	28.00	18.00
B.	Fishmonger's (No. 34)	30.00	18.00
C.	Police Station (No. 35)	35.00	18.00
D.	Library (No. 36)	25.00	18.00

SUGGESTED PRICE GUIDE
TO

THE WORLD OF WADE
BOOK 2

First Edition

DESIGNERS AND MODELLERS

PAGES 31, 32 & 33
FIG. 1. PROTOTYPE DESIGNS BY WILLIAM HARPER

		U.S. $	British £
A.	Pair of Cockatoos, 2⅞" high	NPA	NPA
B.	Pair of Owls (left), 2⅜" high	NPA	NPA
	Single Owl (right), 2" high	NPA	NPA
C.	Doleful Lion, 2" high	NPA	NPA
D.	The Butlin Beaver, 2½" high	NPA	NPA
E.	Longtailed Door Mouse, 4¼"high	NPA	NPA
F.	Cat, 2" high	NPA	NPA
G.	Babycham, 2⅞" high	NPA	NPA
H.	Mermaid Bowl, 6" h. x 11" across	NPA	NPA

		U.S. $	British £
I.	Caravan, 1⅝" h. x 2¼" l.	NPA	NPA
J.	Contemporary Bowl (left), 2" h. x 4" dia.	NPA	NPA
	Contemporary Bowl (right), 4" h. x 3¾" dia.	NPA	NPA
K.	Wall Plaque, 6" x 4"	NPA	NPA
L.	Bookend, 6" high.	NPA	NPA
M.	Austin Mini Ashtray, 1¾" high	NPA	NPA
N.	Scent Holder, 3¾" high	NPA	NPA
O.	Jack of Diamonds Ashtray (left), 4" x 4¾"	NPA	NPA
	Queen of Spades Ashtray (right), 4" x 4¼"	NPA	NPA

FIGURINES *by George Wade & Son Ltd., Wade Heath & Company Ltd. and Wade Ceramics Ltd. circa 1927 - 1993*

PAGE 38
FIG. 2 CURLS

	U.S. $	British £
Curls *(cellulose finish)*, 6" high	180.00	120.00

FIGS. 3 & 4 ASPREY & CO. DECANTER

	U.S. $	British £
Scotsman Decanter	400.00	215.00

PAGE 39
FIG. 5 NURSERY RHYME FIGURINES

		U.S. $	British £
A.	Butcher, 3¼" high	350.00	210.00
	(See also No. 8 pg. 33 of The W of W)		
B.	Baker, 3⅞" high	400.00	250.00
C.	Candlestickmaker, 4" high	400.00	250.00
	(See also No. 33 pg. 50 of The W of W2)		

PAGE 41
FIG. 6 THE ALPHABET TRAIN 1958-1959

	U.S. $	British £
Engine and six cars — decorated (complete set)	550.00	400.00

PAGE 41
FIG. 7 ALPAHBET TRAIN

	U.S. $	British £
Engine — undecorated	50.00	40.00
Car — undecorated, each	45.00	35.00

FIGS. 8 & 9 SOPHISTICATED LADIES 1991-1992

	U.S. $	British £
Emily — white glaze, 5¾" high	100.00	60.00
Susannah — white glaze, 6" high	100.00	60.00
Felicity — white glaze, 6" high	100.00	60.00
Roxanne-white glaze, 5¾" high	100.00	60.00

PAGE 43
FIG. 10 MY FAIR LADIES LIQUOR CONTAINERS 1992

	U.S. $	British £
Sarah, 3¾" high	35.00	20.00
Melissa, 4" high	60.00	50.00

THE WORLD OF WADE BOOK 2 — COLOR PLATES

		U.S. $	British £
22.	Pavlova, 9" high (cellulose finish) *(See also No.C Fig.3 pg.12 of The W of W)*	340.00	180.00
23.	Carmen, 9³/₄" high (cellulose finish) *(See also No.J Fig.1 pg.10 of The W of W)*	375.00	200.00
24.	Springtime, 9¹/₄" high (cellulose finish) *(See also No.R Fig.3 pg.12 of The W of W)*	340.00	180.00
25.	Romance, 6¹/₂" high	500.00	350.00
26.	Phyllis, 5¹/₄" high (cellulose finish)	250.00	150.00

NURSERY RHYME FIGURINES

27.	Wynken, 2³/₄" high (without flowers)	185.00	120.00
28.	Blynken, 2¹/₈" high (without flowers)	185.00	120.00
29.	Wynken, 2³/₄" high (with flowers)	195.00	130.00
30.	Blynken, 2¹/₈" high (with flowers)	195.00	130.00
31.	Nod, 2¹/₂" high (with flowers)	195.00	140.00
32.	I've a Bear Behind, 2¹/₂" high (with flowers)	200.00	140.00
33.	Candlestick Maker, 4" high *(See also Fig. 5 pg. 39 of The W of W2)*	400.00	250.00
34.	Mama Bear, 3³/₄" high	300.00	250.00
35.	Baby Bear, 1³/₄" high *(See also No.33 pg. 249 of The W of W)*	210.00	250.00
36.	Papa Bear, 3¹/₂" high *(See also Fig. 17 pg. 25 of The W of W)*	210.00	250.00
37.	Soldier, 3" high *(See also Nos. 10 - 16 pg. 33 of The W of W)*	200.00	140.00

NODDY SET 1958-1960

38.	Big Ears, 2³/₄" high	180.00	100.00
39.	Mr. Plod, 2¹/₂" high *(See Fig.27 pg.24 of The W of W and also the advertisement on page 41 of The W of W2)*	160.00	80.00

SNIPPETS 1956 - 1958

		U.S. $	British £
40.	Gretel, 2¹/₄" high *(See also Nos. 91 - 96 pg. 52 of The W of W2)*	140.00	95.00

MABEL LUCIE ATTWELL CHARACTERS 1959

41.	Sam, 3¹/₈" high *(See also No. 17 pg. 33 of The W of W)*	215.00	135.00
42.	Sarah, 3" high	215.00	135.00

BISTO KIDS CIRCA MID 1970'S

43.	Bisto-Kid — salt shaker, 4³/₈" high (girl)	110.00	75.00
44.	Bisto-Kid — pepper shaker, 4" high (boy) *(See also No. 18 pg. 33 of The W of W)*	110.00	75.00

NURSERY FAVOURITES 1990 - 1991

45.	Mary Mary, 2⁷/₈" high (1990 re-issue)	40.00	25.00
46.	Polly Kettle, 2⁷/₈" high (1990 re-issue)	35.00	15.00
47.	Tom Piper, 2³/₄" high (1990 re-issue)	40.00	15.00
48.	Goosey Gander, 2⁵/₈" high (1991 re-issue)	45.00	35.00
49.	Old Woman in the Shoe, 2¹/₂" high (1991 re-issue)	40.00	25.00

TETLEY TEA SALT AND PEPPER SHAKERS 1990 - 1992

50.	Brew Gaffer salt shaker, 3¹/₂" high	30.00	30.00
51.	Sidney pepper shaker, 3³/₄" high	30.00	30.00

<u>PAGE 51</u>

SOPHISTICATED LADIES 1991 - 1992

52.	Felicity, 6" high	135.00	105.00
53.	Susannah, 6" high	135.00	95.00
54.	Emily, 5³/₄" high	135.00	95.00
55.	Roxanne, 5³/₄" high	135.00	95.00

MY FAIR LADIES SET ONE 1990 - 1992

		U.S. $	British £
56.	Kate, 3⁷/₈" high	35.00	20.00
57.	Rachel, 3⁷/₈"	35.00	20.00
58.	Marie, 3³/₄" high	35.00	20.00
59.	Sarah, 3³/₄" high	35.00	20.00
60.	Lisa, 3³/₄" high	60.00	60.00
61.	Hannah, 3³/₄" high	55.00	25.00
62.	Caroline, 3⁷/₈" high	35.00	20.00
63.	Rebecca, 3⁷/₈" high	35.00	20.00

MY FAIR LADIES SET TWO 1991 - 1992

64.	Belinda, 3³/₄" high	35.00	25.00
65.	Anita, 3³/₄" high	35.00	25.00
66.	Emma, 4" high	35.00	25.00
67.	Natalie, 4" high	35.00	20.00
68.	Melissa, 4" high	60.00	50.00
69.	Amanda, 4" high	60.00	40.00
70.	Lucie, 4³/₄" high	35.00	30.00
71.	Diane, 3³/₄" high	35.00	25.00

ICI MAN CIRCA LATE 1960'S

72.	ICI Man, 3¹/₈" high	65.00	40.00

(See also No.96 pg. 51 of WPT)

SHERWOOD FOREST SERIES 1989 - PRESENT

73.	Robin Hood, (1989) 2³/₄" high	35.00	18.00
74.	Maid Marian, (1990) 2⁵/₈" high	35.00	20.00
75.	Friar Tuck, (1994) 1³/₄" high	35.00	18.00

AQUARIUM SET 1976 - 1980

The size of the bridge was incorrectly noted in *The W of W2*. The correct size is listed below. For color illustrations of other items in this set see Nos.23 and 24 pg.33 of *The W of W*.

76.	Lighhouse, 3" high	40.00	25.00
77.	Snail, 1¹/₄" high	100.00	40.00
78.	Seahorse, 1¹/₄" high (prototype) *(See also Fig. 11 pg. 44 of The W of W2)*	NPA	NPA
79.	Bridge, 1³/₄" h. x 3¹/₄" across	125.00	55.00
	Mermaid, 2¹/₂" high *(See also No.23 pg. 33 of The W of W)*	50.00	25.00
	Diver, 2³/₄" high *(See also No.24 pg. 33 of The W of W)*	28.00	12.50

HARROD'S DOORMAN 1991

Wade Ceramics Ltd. have made a number of items for Harrod's. These include teapots, and other items based on the doorman figure. For illlistrations see the color section of this book.

		U.S. $	British £
80.	Harrod's Doorman, 4" high (egg cup)	35.00	30.00

PAGE 52
MISCELLANEOUS FIGURINES EARLY 1930'S - 1993

81.	Daisette, 9³/₄" high (cellulose finish)	500.00	250.00
82.	"Welsh Lady" handle, 3¹/₂" high *(See also Fig. 12 pg. 44 of The W of W2)*	350.00	200.00
83.	King Henry VIII, 4¹/₂" high (cellulose finish) *(See also Fig. 13 pg. 45 of The W of W2 and advertisement in WPT)*	600.00	400.00
84.	Queen Elizabeth, 4³/₈" high (cellulose finish) *(See also Fig. 13 pg. 45 of The W of W2 and advertisement in WPT)*	600.00	400.00
85.	Blynken, 2¹/₈" high (cellulose finish-prototype)	350.00	200.00
86.	Winken, 2³/₄" high (cellulose finish-prototype)	350.00	200.00
87.	"Spanish Lady" handle, 3⁷/₈" high	350.00	200.00
88.	Fairy Candleholder, 3" high *(See also Figs. 172 and 173 pg. 224 of The W of W2)*	600.00	350.00
89.	"Fat Controller", 2" high (prototype)	400.00	250.00
90.	Burglar, 3¹/₄" high	50.00	45.00
91.	Gingi, 1³/₈" high	235.00	135.00
92.	Gretel, 2¹/₄" high *(See also No. 40 pg. 50 of The W of W2)*	140.00	95.00
93.	Hansel, 2¹/₂" high	140.00	95.00
94.	The Revenge, 1¹/₂" high	65.00	40.00
95.	The Santa Maria, 1³/₄" high	65.00	45.00
96.	The Mayflower, 2³/₈" high	65.00	50.00

THE KNIGHT TEMPLER 1991

97.	Knight Templar, 9⁵/₈" high	240.00	140.00

(See also Fig. 15 pg. 46 of The W of W2)

ROBERTSON'S GOLLIES EARLY TO MID 1960'S

For an illustration of the "Bandstand" see the inside back cover of this book.

		U.S. $	British £
98.	Saxophone Player, 2⁵/₈" high	200.00	120.00
99.	Trumpet Player, 2⁵/₈" high	200.00	120.00
100.	Accordion Player, 2⁵/₈" high	200.00	120.00
101.	Clarinet Player, 2⁵/₈" high	200.00	120.00
102.	Double Base Player, 2⁵/₈" high	200.00	120.00

WEE WILLIE WINKY WALL PLAQUE LATE 1950'S TO EARLY 1960'S

This set comprises four wall plaques, each with different illustrations of the nursery rhyme. Each plaque would be valued the same as item No. 103 below.

		U.S. $	British £
103.	"Tapping at the Windows" 4¹/₄" h. x 5³/₈" across	500.00	350.00

PAGE 53
MISCELLANEOUS PROTOTYPES

		U.S. $	British £
104.	Miss. Fluffy Cat, 2¹/₂" high	NPA	NPA
105.	Noddy, 2¹/₂" high	NPA	NPA
106.	Noddy, 2¹/₂" high	NPA	NPA
107.	Mr. Plod, 2³/₈" high	NPA	NPA
108.	Big Ears, 2³/₄" high	NPA	NPA
109.	Big Ears and Noddy Money Box, 4³/₄" high	NPA	NPA
110.	Girl on Motor Scooter, 3" high	NPA	NPA
111.	"I'm Hep" 1¹/₂" high	NPA	NPA
112.	Irish Leprechaun, 1¹/₂" high	NPA	NPA
113.	Big Ears and Noddy in a Motorcar, 3" high	NPA	NPA
114.	Airline Pilot, 2¹/₂" high	NPA	NPA
115.	Pogo, 2³/₄" high	NPA	NPA
116.	Cartoon Boy, 2³/₄" high	NPA	NPA
117.	Flook, 2" high	NPA	NPA
118.	Ship Bowl, 4" dia.	NPA	NPA
119.	Baby Zebra, 1¹/₄" high	NPA	NPA
120.	Baby Zebra, 1¹/₄" high	NPA	NPA
121.	Adult Zebra, 1¹/₂" high	NPA	NPA
122.	Yacht, 5¹/₄" high	NPA	NPA
123.	Canterbury Tales "The Reeve" 3¹/₂" high	NPA	NPA

		U.S. $	British £
124.	Canterbury Tales "The Squire" 3¹/₂" high	NPA	NPA
125.	Canterbury Tales "The Nun's Priest" 3¹/₂" high	NPA	NPA
126.	Canterbury Tales "The Prioress" 3¹/₂" high	NPA	NPA

PAGE 54
THE PENGUIN FAMILY LATE 1940'S MID 1950'S

		U.S. $	British £
127.	Mrs. Penguin, 3" high	125.00	90.00
128.	Benny, 2¹/₈" high	160.00	120.00
129.	Penny, 2" high	160.00	120.00
130.	Mr. Penguin, 3¹/₂" high	125.00	90.00

(See also Nos. 14,15,16,&17 pg. 23 of The W of W and Fig. 18 pg. 114 of The W of W2)

MISCELLANEOUS ANIMALS

		U.S. $	British £
131.	Standing Rabbit, 2³/₈" high	65.00	40.00

(See also Fig.5 No.24 pg.14 and Fig.15 No.13 pg.23 of The W of W)

| **132.** | Miniature Deer, 1¹/₈" high | 150.00 | 100.00 |

(See also Fig.5 No.8 pg.14 of The W of W)

| **133.** | Puff, 2" high (The Rabbit Family) | 160.00 | 120.00 |

(See also Fig.15 No.27 pg.23 of The W of W)

| **134.** | Mr. Rabbit, 3¹/₂" high (The Rabbit Family) | 160.00 | 120.00 |

(See also Fig. 15 No. 28 pg.23 of The W of W)

| **135.** | Dog, 3¹/₈" high | 170.00 | 115.00 |

(See also Fig.5 No.22 pg.14 of The W of W)

| **136.** | Dog, 3¹/₈" high | 170.00 | 115.00 |

(See also Fig.5 No.22 pg.14 of The W of W)

| **137.** | Calf, 1³/₄" high | 170.00 | 115.00 |

(See also Fig.5 No.20 pg.14 and Fig.15 No.22 pg.23 of The W of W)

| **138.** | Miniature Lamb, 1¹/₂" | 150.00 | 100.00 |

(See also Fig.5 No.7 pg.14 of The W of W)

| **139.** | Large Lamb, 2¹/₈" high | 155.00 | 105.00 |

(See also Fig.5 No.5 pg.14 of The W of W)

| **140.** | Miniature Foal, 1¹/₂" high | 155.00 | 105.00 |

(See also Fig.5 No.10 pg.14 of The W of W)

| **141.** | Mountain Goat, 2⁷/₈" high | 225.00 | 150.00 |
| **142.** | Elephant, 2" high | 185.00 | 125.00 |

(See also Fig.5 No.12 pg.14 and Fig.15 No.12 pg.23 of The W of W)

		U.S. $	British £
143.	English Setter, 2¼" high	160.00	110.00

(*See also Fig.5 No.28 pg.14 and Fig.15 No.21 pg.23 of The W of W*)

		U.S. $	British £
144.	Chick, 1¾" high	175.00	115.00

(*See also Fig.5 No.15 pg.14 of The W of W*)

| **145.** | Chick, 1¾" high | 175.00 | 115.00 |

(*See also Fig.5 No.15 pg.14 of The W of W*)

| **146.** | Kitten with Ball, 1¼" high | 95.00 | 60.00 |

(*See also Fig.5 No.11C pg.14 and Fig.15 No.5 pg.23 of The W of W*)

| **147.** | Kitten on Back, 1" high | 95.00 | 60.00 |

(*See also Fig.5 No.11B pg.14 and Fig.15 No.2 pg.23 of The W of W*)

| **148.** | Kitten with Ball and Bow, 1⅝" high | 95.00 | 60.00 |

(*See also Fig.5 No.11A pg.14 and Fig.15 No.2 pg.23 of The W of W*)

| **149.** | Squirrel, 1⅝" high | 95.00 | 60.00 |

(*See also Fig.5 No.13 pg.14 and Fig.15 No.7 pg.23 of The W of W*)

| **150.** | Squirrel, 1⅝" high | 95.00 | 60.00 |

(*See also Fig.5 No.13 pg.14 and Fig.15 No.7 pg.23 of The W of W*)

| **151.** | Kissing Rabbits, 2½" high | 95.00 | 60.00 |

(*See also Fig.15 No.31 pg.23 of The W of W*)

| **152.** | Kissing Rabbits, 2½" high | NPA | NPA |

(not made by Wade)

| **153.** | Large Double Bunnies, 1¼" high | 95.00 | 60.00 |

(*See also Fig.5 No.1B pg.14 and Fig.15 No.34 pg.23 of The W of W*)

| **154.** | Small Double Bunnies, ¾" high | 90.00 | 55.00 |

(*See also Fig.5 No.1A pg.14 and Fig.15 No.32 pg.23 of The W of W*)

| **155.** | Miniature Bunny, ⅞" high | 50.00 | 30.00 |

(*See also Fig.5 No.4 pg.14 and Fig.15 No.33 pg.23 of The W of W*)

| **156.** | Drake, 3" high | 165.00 | 110.00 |

(*See also Fig.5 No.29A pg.14 of The W of W*)

| **157.** | Drake and Daddy, 3" high | 210.00 | 140.00 |

(*See also Fig.5 No.31 pg.14 and Fig.15 No.20 pg.23 of The W of W*)

| **158.** | Drake, 3" high | 165.00 | 110.00 |

(*See also Fig.5 No.29A pg.14 of The W of W*)

| **159.** | Duck, 3" high | 165.00 | 110.00 |

(*See also Fig.5 No.29B pg.14 of The W of W*)

| **160.** | Duck, 2¾" high | 165.00 | 110.00 |

(*See also Fig.5 No.29C pg.14 of The W of W*)

		U.S. $	British £
161.	Drake, 1¾" high	150.00	100.00

(*See also Fig.5 No.(2)3 pg.14 of The W of W*)

THE QUACK QUACK FAMILY CIRCA 1952 - LATE 1950'S

162.	Mr. Duck, 2½" high	160.00	120.00

(*See also Fig.15 No.10 pg.23 of The W of W*)

| **163.** | Dilly, 1½" high | 160.00 | 120.00 |

(*See also Fig.15 No.9 pg.23 of The W of W*)

| **164.** | Dack, 1½" high | 160.00 | 120.00 |

(*See also Fig.15 No.11 pg.23 of The W of W*)

| **165.** | Mrs. Duck, 2½" high | 160.00 | 120.00 |

(*See also Fig.15 No.8 pg.23 of The W of W*)

PAGE 55

DISNEY'S 1961 - 1965

For color illustration of Scamp and Si see Nos.98 and 99 pg.36 of *The W of W.*

166.	Thumper, 5¼" high	300.00	165.00

(*See also Fig.39 pg.84 of The W of W*)

| **167.** | Bambi, 4½" high | 150.00 | 85.00 |

(*See also Fig.38 pg.84 of The W of W*)

| **168.** | Lady, 4¼" high | 235.00 | 150.00 |

(*See also Fig.38 pg.84 of The W of W*)

| **169.** | Tramp, 6" high | 300.00 | 225.00 |

(*See also Fig.38 pg.84 of The W of W*)

| **170.** | Trusty, 5⅞" high | 275.00 | 160.00 |

(*See also Fig.39 pg.84 of The W of W*)

TV PETS 1959 - 1965

For color illustration of Droopy, Percy, Pepi and Fifi see Nos.65 - 68 pg.35 of *The W of W.*

171.	Chee-Chee, 2¼" high	60.00	30.00

(*See also Fig.32 pg.81 of The W of W*)

| **172.** | Bengo, 2⅜" high | 70.00 | 34.00 |

(*See also Fig.32 pg.81 of The W of W*)

| **173.** | Simon, 2⅜" high | 65.00 | 25.00 |

(*See also Fig.32 pg.81 of The W of W*)

| **174.** | Mitzi, 2" high | 75.00 | 38.00 |

(*See also Fig.32 pg.81 of The W of W*)

DISNEY HAT BOX SERIES 1956 - 1965

175.	Archimedes, 2" high	150.00	80.00

(*See also Fig.34 pg.82 of The W of W*)

		U.S. $	British £
176.	Si, 1³/₄" high	75.00	30.00
177.	Girl Squirrel, 2" high	100.00	75.00
	(See also Fig.34 pg.82 of The W of W)		

HANNA BARBARA CARTOON CHARACTERS CIRCA 1962

178.	Yogi Bear, 2¹/₂" high	140.00	70.00
	(See also No.64 pg.35 of The W of W)		
179.	Huckleberry Hound, 2³/₈" high *(See also No.63 pg.35 of The W of W)*	125.00	70.00
180.	Mr. Jinks, 2³/₈" high	140.00	75.00

DRUM BOX SERIES 1956 - 1959

181.	Harpy, 2" high	85.00	40.00
	(See also Fig.26 pg.29 of The W of W)		
182.	Trunky, 2¹/₈" high	95.00	45.00
	(See also Fig.26 pg.29 of The W of W)		
	Jem, 2" high	85.00	35.00
	(See also Fig.26 pg.29 of The W of W)		
	Clara, 2" high	90.00	50.00
	(See also Fig.26 pg.29 of The W of W)		
	Dora, 2¹/₈" high	125.00	70.00
	(See also Fig.26 pg.29 of The W of W)		

NOVELTY ANIMAL FIGURINES 1955 - 1960

183.	Jumbo Jim, 1³/₄" high	215.00	110.00
	(See also No.E Fig.25 pg.28 of The W of W)		
184.	Bernie and Poo, 2" high	200.00	70.00
	(See also No.A Fig.25 pg.28 of The W of W)		
	Kitten on the Keys, 1¹/₈" high *(See also No.B Fig.25 pg.28 of The W of W)*	250.00	120.00
	Jonah and the Whale, 1¹/₂" high *(See also No.C Fig.25 pg.28 of The W of W)*	200.00	70.00
	Dustbin Cat, 1³/₄" high	200.00	70.00
	(See also No.D Fig.25 pg.28 of The W of W)		

MINIKINS 1956 - 1959

185.	Rabbit, 1" high	25.00	12.00
	(See also Fig.28 pg.30 of The W of W)		
186.	Rabbit, 1" high	18.00	12.00
	(See also Fig.28 pg.30 of The W of W)		
187.	Kitten, 1" high	25.00	12.00
	(See also Fig.28 pg.30 of The W of W)		

HAPPY FAMILIES 1962 - 1965

For additional figurines in this series see Nos. 117-1 to 126-3 pg. 37 of *The W of W*.

		U.S. $	British £
188.	Tiger (baby), 1¹/₂" high	70.00	30.00
189.	Tiger (baby), 1¹/₂" high	70.00	30.00
190.	Tiger (parent), 1³/₄" high	100.00	45.00

WHIMSIES 1971 - 1984

For the full set of Whimsies see Nos. 115-1 to 116-60 pg. 40 of *The W of W*.

191.	Lamb, 1³/₈" high	18.00	10.00
192.	Ram, 1³/₁₆" high	18.00	10.00
193.	Gorilla, 1¹/₂" high	20.00	12.00

WHIMSIES 1953 - 1959

For other figurines in this series, see Nos. 145-1 to 154-8 pg. 39 of *The W of W*.

194.	Shire Horse, 2" high (prototype)	300.00	190.00
195.	Shire Horse, 2" high	230.00	105.00
196.	Polar Bear, 1³/₄" high	35.00	16.00
	(See also No.150-27 pg.39 of The W of W)		
197.	Polar Bear "Blow-Up", 6" high	270.00	160.00
198.	Giant Panda, 1¹/₄" high	30.00	15.00

WHIMSIE - LAND SERIES 1984 - 1988

For additional figurines in this series, see Nos. 114-1 to 144-20 pg. 39 of *The W of W*.

199-1.	Pheasant, 1¹/₄" high	40.00	25.00
	(See also Fig.40 No.E pg.88 of The W of W)		
199-2.	Field Mouse, 1¹/₄" high	35.00	25.00
	(See also Fig.40 No.B pg.88 of The W of W)		
199-3.	Golden Eagle, 1¹/₈" high	40.00	20.00
	(See also Fig.40 No.D pg.88 of The W of W)		
199-4.	Otter, 1¹/₂" high	20.00	15.00
	(See also Fig.40 No.A pg.88 of The W of W)		
199-5.	Partridge, 1¹/₂" high	20.00	15.00
	(See also Fig.40 No.C pg.88 of The W of W)		

THE TORTOISE FAMILY 1958 - 1988

The text for Nos.200 and 202 was inadvertantly reveresed on pg.122 of *The W of W2*.

200.	Baby Tortoise, 1¹/₄" high	35.00	25.00

		U.S. $	British £
201.	Mini Tortoise, $^7/_8$" high	35.00	28.00
202.	Baby Tortoise-Devil's Hole Bermuda, $1^1/_4$" high	80.00	60.00

(See also "Slow-Fe" No.61 pg.35 of The W of W)

PAGE 56

ANIMAL AND BIRD FIGURINES

		U.S. $	British £
203.	Single Budgerigar, $7^1/_2$" high *(See also Fig.8 No.R pg.16 and Fig.9 No.5 pg.17 of The W of W)*	375.00	200.00
204.	Flicka, $4^1/_2$" high	300.00	175.00
205.	Bluebird, $3^1/_2$" high	450.00	350.00
206.	Pelican, $6^1/_4$" high *(See also Fig.9 No.3 pg.17 of The W of W)*	950.00	550.00
207.	Squirrel Posy Bowl, $2^3/_4$" high	145.00	85.00
208.	Standing Rabbit Posy Bowl, $2^3/_4$" high	120.00	70.00
209.	Panda, $1^1/_2$" high *(See also Fig.28 pg.123 of The W of W2)*	18.00	10.00
210.	Spiller's Dog, $1^1/_8$" high	25.00	15.00
211.	Laughing Rabbit, 7" high *(See also Fig.14 pg.22 and No.51 pg.34 of The W of W)*	145.00	75.00
212.	Duck Posy Bowl, $2^3/_4$" high	145.00	85.00
213.	Kissing Bunnies Posy Bowl, $2^3/_4$" high	145.00	85.00
	Kissing Bunnies Posy Bowl (single colors)	60.00	35.00
214.	Heron, $7^1/_2$" high *(See also Fig.9 No.7 pg.17 of The W of W)*	620.00	350.00

SHARP'S EASTER EGG PROMOTION 1970 - 1971

		U.S. $	British £
215.	Bo-Peep, $2^5/_8$" high	35.00	15.00
216.	Large Easter Bunny, $2^1/_2$" high	40.00	18.00
217.	Small Easter Bunny, 2" high (not made by Wade)	NPA	NPA

ANIMAL FIGURINES

		U.S. $	British £
218.	Alsatian, $5^1/_4$" h. x $7^1/_2$" l.	170.00	95.00
219.	Rabbit, 3" high *(See also Fig.14 pg.22 of The W of W)*	105.00	55.00

		U.S. $	British £
220.	Rabbit, $4^3/_4$" high *(See also Fig.14 pg.22 of The W of W)*	130.00	70.00
221.	Rabbit, $4^3/_4$" high *(See also Fig.14 pg.22 of The W of W)*	130.00	70.00
222.	Rabbit, $5^5/_8$" high *(See also Fig.14 pg.22 of The W of W)*	160.00	85.00
223.	Rabbit, 6" high *(See also Fig.14 pg.22 of The W of W)*	160.00	85.00

PAGE 57

		U.S. $	British £
224.	Ermine, $9^1/_4$" high *(See also Fig.7 No.3 pg.15 and Fig.8 No.A pg.16 of The W of W)*	575.00	300.00
225.	Chamois Kid, $5^3/_8$" high *(See also Fig.7 No.1 pg.15 and Fig.8 No.H pg.16 of The W of W)*	575.00	300.00
226.	Panther, $8^1/_2$" high *(See also Fig.7 No.4 pg.15 and Fig.8 No.E pg.16 of The W of W)*	980.00	525.00
227.	Brown Bear, $9^1/_2$" high *(See also Fig.8 No.T pg.16 of The W of W)*	980.00	525.00
228.	Hippopotamus, $1^3/_8$" h. x $4^1/_2$" l.	485.00	310.00
229.	Tortoise, $1^1/_4$" h. x 3" l.	485.00	310.00
230.	Pup in Basket, 6" high	175.00	100.00
231.	Cheeky Duckling, 7" high *(See also Fig.14 No.5 pg.22 of The W of W)*	190.00	100.00
232.	Dachshund, $3^1/_2$" h. x $6^1/_2$" l.	220.00	130.00
233.	"Salty" the Seal, $6^1/_2$" high	300.00	175.00
234.	Pluto, $4^1/_2$" high	425.00	250.00
235.	Pluto's Pup No.1, $2^1/_2$" high	380.00	225.00
236.	Pluto's Pup No.2, 4" high	380.00	225.00
237.	Open-Mouthed Bird, $6^3/_4$" high *(See also Fig.27 No.B pg.122 of The W of W2)*	170.00	90.00
238.	Pluto's Pup No.1, $2^1/_2$" high	380.00	225.00
239.	Terrier Pup, $6^3/_8$" high	150.00	110.00

PAGE 58

		U.S. $	British £
240.	Razor Back, 5" high	990.00	550.00
241.	"Survival"	7500.00	2500.00

TRAUFLER PROMOTIONAL ITEMS 1992

		U.S. $	British £
242.	Hen Pepper Shaker, $3^5/_8$" high	15.00	12.00

		U.S. $	British £
243.	Rooster Salt Shaker, 4⁵/₈" high	15.00	12.00
244.	White Sheep, 1⁵/₈" high (small)	15.00	12.00
245.	Black Sheep, 1⁵/₈" high (small)	15.00	12.00
246.	White Sheep, 2³/₄" high (large)	20.00	18.00

MISCELLANEOUS GIFTWARE

		U.S. $	British £
247.	Bengo Money Box, 6" high	280.00	155.00
248.	Pig Family Cruet Set:		
	Mr. Pig, 3³/₄" high	120.00	80.00
	Mrs. Pig, 3¹/₈" high	120.00	80.00
	Tray, 5¹/₄" long	45.00	20.00
249.	Exotic Fish Wall Plaque, 3³/₄" long	275.00	145.00
250.	Exotic Fish Wall Plaque, 3³/₄" long	275.00	145.00
251.	Exotic Fish Wall Plaque, 3³/₄" long	275.00	145.00
252.	Exotic Fish Wall Plaque, 3³/₄" long	275.00	145.00
253.	Frog, 1¹/₂" high	285.00	150.00
254.	Ruddy Duck, 1³/₈" high	325.00	200.00

DINOSAUR SET 1993

		U.S. $	British £
255.	Camarasaurus, 2" h. x 1³/₄" l.	6.00	4.00
256.	Protoceratops, 1¹/₈" h. x 2³/₈" l.	6.00	4.00
257.	Euoplocephalus, 1" h. x 2¹/₄" l.	6.00	4.00
258.	Tyrannosaurus Rex, 1³/₄" h. x 2³/₈" l.	6.00	4.00
259.	Spinosaurus, 1⁵/₈" h. x 2³/₈" l.	6.00	4.00

PAGE 59

WADE FLOWERS

For additional flower arrangements see Figs. 10, 11, 12 & 13 pgs. 18, 19, 20 & 21 of *The W of W.*

		U.S. $	British £
260.	Anemones, 6" high	60.00	32.50
261.	Pansy, 3⁵/₈" high	40.00	22.50
262.	Pansy, 3³/₄" high	40.00	22.50
263.	Pansies, 6" high	65.00	35.00

		U.S. $	British £
264.	Triangular Table Decoration, 5" across	75.00	40.00
265.	Small Arch, 5" high	50.00	25.00
266.	Small Saturn, 5" high	60.00	28.00
267.	Posy Basket, 3¹/₂" high	35.00	20.00
268.	Posy Pot, 3" high	45.00	20.00
269.	Posy Pot Assorted, 3" high	45.00	20.00
270.	Posy Pot, 2³/₄" high	40.00	20.00
271.	Jug Flower Arrangement, 3" high	30.00	15.00
272.	Basket Arrangement, 4¹/₂" long	100.00	50.00
273.	Primroses, 1⁵/₈" high	70.00	35.00
274.	Basket Arrangement, 2¹/₂" high	100.00	50.00
275.	Jug Flower Arrangement, 3" high	35.00	20.00
276.	Posy Pot, 2¹/₂" high	40.00	20.00
277.	Posy Pot Assorted, 1¹/₂" high	20.00	10.00
278.	Wild Rose, 1¹/₈" high	20.00	10.00
279.	Posy Pot, 1¹/₂" high	20.00	10.00
280.	Tulip Posy, 1¹/₄" high	20.00	10.00
281.	Wild Rose Posy Pot, 2" high	35.00	20.00

PAGE 60

CORONATION STREET 1988 - 1989

		U.S. $	British £
282-1.	The Rover's Return, 1⁷/₈" high	20.00	15.00
282-2.	No. 9 The Duckworths, 1⁵/₈" high	15.00	10.00
282-3.	The Corner Shop, 1⁵/₈" high	15.00	10.00

BRIGHTON PAVILION 1988

		U.S. $	British £
283.	Small two-domed building, 1⁷/₈" h. x 2" l.	10.00	4.00
284.	Large single-domed building, 2⁷/₈" h. x 2" in dia.	15.00	8.00
285.	Small two-domed building, 1⁷/₈" h. x 2" l.	10.00	4.00

WHIMSEY-ON-WHY VILLAGE SET 1987

For additional models in this series see Nos. 268-1 to 271-32 pg. 43 of *The W of W*.

		U.S. $	British £
286-33.	Schoolteacher's House, 1³/₄" high	28.00	18.00
	(See also Fig.158 No.A pg.184 of The W of W)		
286-34.	Fishmonger's Shop, 1⁵/₈" high	30.00	18.00
	(See also Fig.158 No.B pg.184 of The W of W)		
286-35.	Police Station, 1⁵/₈" high	35.00	18.00
	(See also Fig.158 No.C pg.184 of The W of W)		
286-36.	Library, 2" high	25.00	18.00
	(See also Fig.158 No.D pg.184 of The W of W)		

TOM SMITH PARTY CRACKERS 1986 - 1992
WILD LIFE SET 1986-1987

		U.S. $	British £
287-1.	Dolphin, 1¹/₈" high	12.00	4.00
287-2.	Penguin, 1⁵/₈" high	10.00	4.00
287-3.	Wild Boar, 1¹/₈" high	8.00	3.00
287-4.	Koala Bear, 1³/₈" high	6.00	2.00
287-5.	Orang-Utan, 1¹/₄" high	5.00	2.00
287-6.	Rhino, ⁷/₈" high	5.00	2.00
287-7.	Kangaroo, 1⁵/₈" high	10.00	4.00
287-8.	Leopard, ⁷/₈" high	5.00	2.00

MINIATURE HOUSES SET 1988

288-1.	Village Store, 1³/₈" high	28.00	10.00
288-2.	Rose Cottage, 1¹/₈" high	28.00	15.00
288-3.	The Coach House Garage, 1¹/₂" high	28.00	15.00
288-4.	Pink House, 1⁵/₈" high	28.00	12.00
288-5.	The Chapel, 1³/₄" high	28.00	15.00

FAMILY PETS SET 1988-1989

289-1.	Parrot, 1³/₈" high	6.00	2.00
289-2.	Kitten, 1" high	5.00	3.00
289-3.	Rabbit, 1¹/₈" high	6.00	3.00
289-4.	Puppy, 1" high	6.00	2.00
289-5.	Pony, 1" high	6.00	3.00
289-6.	Mouse, ¹/₂" high	12.00	3.00
289-7.	Fish, 1" high	10.00	3.00
289-8.	Guinea Pig, ³/₄" high	10.00	3.00

WORLD OF DOGS SET 1990-1991

		U.S. $	British £
290-1.	Poodle, 1¹/₂" high	10.00	2.00
290-2.	Alsatian, 1¹/₄" high	8.00	2.00
290-3.	Corgi, 1¹/₂" high	10.00	2.00
290-4.	West Highland Terrier, 1¹/₄" high	8.00	2.00
290-5.	Bulldog, 1" high	10.00	3.00
290-6.	Husky, 1³/₈" high	8.00	2.00
290-7.	Mongrel, 1¹/₄" high	8.00	2.00
290-8.	Spaniel, 1³/₈" high	8.00	2.00

POSY BOWLS 1950'S

291.	Barge Posy Bowl, 2¹/₂" h. x 8" l.	30.00	20.00
292.	Straight Log Posy Bowl, 1¹/₄" h. x 4³/₄" l.	8.00	3.00
293.	"S" Shaped Log Posy Bowl, 1¹/₂" h. x 6¹/₂" l.	15.00	4.00
294.	Straight Log Posy Bowl, 1¹/₄" h. x 4³/₄" l.	10.00	4.00
295.	"S" Shaped Log Posy Bowl, 1¹/₂" h. x 6¹/₂" l.	15.00	4.00
296.	"C" Shaped Log Posy Bowl, 6" across	24.00	8.00
297.	"C" Shaped Log Posy Bowl, 6" across	30.00	8.00

U.S.A. RED ROSE TEA FIGURINES 1990

For additional Red Rose Tea Figurines see pg. 42 of *The W of W*.

298-16.	Puppy, 1" high	6.00	2.00
298-17.	Cock-a-Teel, 1³/₈" high	6.00	2.00
298-18.	Kitten, 1" high	5.00	3.00
298-19.	Pony, 1" high	6.00	3.00
298-20.	Rabbit, 1¹/₈" high	6.00	3.00

PAGE 61

TOM SMITH PARTY CRACKERS 1992 - 1993
BIRD SET 1992-1993

299-1.	Rooster, 2" high	12.00	4.00
299-2.	Eagle, 1³/₄" high	10.00	3.00
299-3.	Goose, 1³/₈" high	6.00	3.00

		U.S. $	British £
299-4.	Wren, 1½" high	15.00	5.00
299-5.	Barn Owl, 1½" high	6.00	4.00
299-6.	Partridge, 1½" high	10.00	5.00
299-7.	Duck, 1⅝" high	12.00	5.00
299-8.	Pelican, 1¾" high	6.00	5.00

SNOW ANIMAL SET 1992-1993

		U.S. $	British £
300-1.	Hare, 1¾" high	6.00	3.00
300-2.	Fox, 1⅜" high	6.00	3.00
300-3.	Seal Pup, 1" high	6.00	3.00
300-4.	Reindeer, 1¼" high	6.00	4.00
300-5.	Polar Bear, 1⅛" high	6.00	3.00
300-6.	Walrus, 1¼" high	5.00	3.00
300-7.	Owl, 1½" high	6.00	5.00
300-8.	Penguin, 1⅝" high	6.00	4.00

MISCELLANEOUS PREMIUMS

		U.S. $	British £
301.	Polar Bear, 1⅛" high (From the Tom Smith Safari Set 1976-1977)	14.00	2.00
302.	Polar Bear, 1⅛" high (See also No.166-60 pg.43 of The W of W)	15.00	2.00
303.	Duck, ¹⁵/₁₆" high	15.00	6.00
304.	Blue Bird, ⅝" high	15.00	6.00
305.	Old Woman in the Shoe, 1⅜" high	7.00	3.00
306.	Poodle, 1⅝" high	10.00	4.00

WHIMSEY-IN-THE-VALE 1993

		U.S. $	British £
307-1.	St. Lawrence Church, 2⅛" high	12.00	10.00
307-2.	Town Garage, 1⅞" high	12.00	10.00
307-3.	Vale Farm, 1⅞" high	12.00	10.00
307-4.	Boar's Head Pub, 1½" high	12.00	10.00
307-5.	St. John's School, 1⅝" high	10.00	8.00
307-6.	Jubilee Terrace, 1⅜" high	12.00	10.00
307-7.	Antique Shop, 1⅜" high	10.00	8.00
307-8.	Whimsey Post Office, 1½" high	10.00	8.00
307-9.	Rose Cottage, 1½" high	10.00	8.00
307-10.	Florist Shop, 1½" high	10.00	8.00

MISCELLANEOUS ITEMS
EARLY 1950'S - MID 1960'S

		U.S. $	British £
308.	Dumbo, (prototype), 1⅜" high	NPA	NPA
309.	Dumbo, (production model), 1⅜" high (See also No.81 pg.36 of The W of W)	85.00	35.00
310.	Thumper Candle Holder, 2" long	110.00	45.00
	Bambi Candle Holder	100.00	40.00
	Rolly Candle Holder	165.00	80.00
	Lucky Candle Holder	165.00	80.00
311.	Seahorse, 3¾" high (prototype)	NPA	NPA
312.	Seahorse, (prototype), 4" high	NPA	NPA
313.	Seahorse, (prototype), 3" high	NPA	NPA
314.	Seahorse, (prototype), 2¾" high	NPA	NPA
315.	Seahorse, (prototype), 4¼" high	NPA	NPA

PAGE 62

MISCELLANEOUS GIFTWARE ITEMS

		U.S. $	British £
316.	Sea Lion Corkscrew, 5¾" high	125.00	55.00
317.	Pegasus Posy Bowl, 4⅜" high (See also Fig.60 pg.109 of The W of W)	125.00	70.00
318.	Palermo Posy Bowl, 3¼" high	25.00	10.00
319.	Barbecue Tankard, 4½" high (See also Fig.57 No.A pg.107 of The W of W)	40.00	20.00
320.	Silhouette Giraffe Vase, 4⅛" high (See also Fig.69 pg.113 of The W of W)	35.00	15.00
321.	Blue Bird Tree Trunk Posy Vase, 4" high (See also No.296 pg.44 of The W of W)	35.00	8.50
322.	Tree Trunk Salt, 2⅛" high	8.00	5.00
323.	Tree Trunk Pepper, 2⅛" high	8.00	5.00
324.	Tree Trunk Mustard, 1½" high	8.00	5.00
325.	Tree Trunk Salt, 2⅛" high	8.00	5.00
326.	Tree Trunk Pepper, 2⅛" high	8.00	5.00
327.	Blue Bird Tree Trunk Posy Vase, 4" high (See also No.296 pg.44 of The W of W)	35.00	8.50

		U.S. $	British £
328.	Silhouette Viking Ship Tray, 4³/₄" l. x 3³/₈" w.	35.00	15.00
329.	Silhouette Zebra Tray, 4¹/₂" l. x 3¹/₄" w.	40.00	18.00
330.	T.T. Tray, 2³/₄" high *(See also Fig.66 pg.112 of The W of W)*	160.00	100.00
331.	Sea-gull Boat, 2¹/₄" h. x 6¹/₄" l. *(See also Fig.76 pg.117 of The W of W)*	90.00	60.00
332.	Bridge Posy Bowl, 1³/₈" h. x 6" l. *(See also No.273 pg.44 of The W of W)*	16.00	6.00
333.	Swan Egg Cup, 2¹/₄" high	55.00	20.00
334.	Swan Egg Cup, 2¹/₄" high	55.00	20.00
335.	Arched Bridge Posy Bowl, 1³/₄" h. x 6" l.	16.00	12.00
336.	Viking Ship Posy Bowl, 2³/₄" h. x 7³/₈" l. *(See also No.306 pg.44 of The W of W)*	25.00	8.00
337.	Poppy Bowl, 1³/₄" high	45.00	30.00
338.	Large Traditional Posy Bowl, 3" high *(See also No.279 pg.44 of The W of W)*	15.00	4.00

PAGE 63

WHIMTRAYS 1987 - 1988

339.	Puppy, 4¹/₂" l. x 3¹/₂" w.	20.00	10.00
340.	Pony, 4¹/₂" l. x 3¹/₂" w.	20.00	10.00
341.	Squirrel, 4¹/₂" l. x 3¹/₂" w.	20.00	10.00
342.	Owl, 4¹/₂" l. x 3¹/₂" w.	20.00	10.00
343.	Duck, 4¹/₂" l. x 3¹/₂" w. *(See also Fig.157 pg.184 of The W of W)*	20.00	10.00

DOG PIPE RESTS 1973 - 1981

344.	Yorkshire Terrier, 2¹/₄" h. x 3¹/₄" dia. *(See also Nos.132 - 135 pg.38 of The W of W)*	45.00	25.00

ZOO LIGHTS 1959

345.	Camel, 1³/₄" w. x 1³/₄" deep	40.00	14.00
346.	Husky, 1³/₄" w. x 1³/₄" deep	40.00	14.00
347.	West Highland Terrier, 1³/₄" w. x 1³/₄" deep	40.00	14.00

		U.S. $	British £
348.	Baby Polar Bear, 1³/₄" w. x 1³/₄" deep	40.00	14.00
349.	Baby Polar Bear, 1³/₄" w. x 1³/₄" deep	40.00	14.00
350.	Corgi, 1³/₄" w. x 1³/₄" deep	40.00	14.00
351.	Hare, 1³/₄" w. x 1³/₄" deep	40.00	14.00
352.	Llama, 1³/₄" w. x 1³/₄" deep	40.00	14.00
353.	Boxer, 1³/₄" w. x 1³/₄" deep	40.00	14.00
354.	Snowy Owl, 1³/₄" w. x 1³/₄" deep	40.00	14.00

ANGEL TRAYS AND FIGURINES 1959 - EARLY 1960'S

355.	Angel Dish, 2" high	100.00	45.00
356.	Angel Figure, 1¹/₂" high (standing)	90.00	40.00
357.	Angel Figure, 1³/₈" high (kneeling)	90.00	40.00
358.	Angel Dish, 2" high	100.00	45.00

WHIMTRAYS, BOULDRAY AND PEERAGE TRAYS

359.	Alsatian Whimtray, 3" dia.	30.00	12.50
360.	Monkey Whimtray, 3" dia.	30.00	12.50
361.	Candle Holder, 2³/₄" high	26.00	8.00
362.	Lady "Bouldray" Tray, 3" dia.	26.00	8.00
363.	Boxer Whimtray, 3" dia.	30.00	12.50
364.	Camel Whimtray, 3" dia.	30.00	12.50
365.	Cockatoo Whimtray, 3" dia.	30.00	12.50

DOG DISH CIRCA 1957

366.	Spaniel Dog Dish, 1⁵/₈" h. x 4" l.	35.00	22.00

TEENAGE POTTERY EARLY 1960'S

367.	Frankie Vaughan Heart Shaped Casket, 1⁵/₈" h. x 3¹/₂" w.	130.00	85.00
368.	Marty Wilde Heart Shaped Casket, 1⁵/₈" h. x 3¹/₂" w.	130.00	85.00
369.	Marty Wilde, 2³/₄" h. x 1⁷/₈" w.	280.00	175.00

GARDNER MERCHANT TRINKET BOX 1986

		U.S. $	British £
370.	Gardner Merchant Trinket Box, 1⅝" h. x 3" w.	25.00	15.00

PAGE 64

MISCELLANEOUS GIFTWARE 1953 - 1992

371.	Everlasting Candle 8½" high (pair)	145.00	55.00
372.	Kawa Clock, 6¼" high	60.00	22.00
373.	Kawa Powder Jar, 2¾" high	25.00	12.00
374.	Jacobean Powder Jar, 2¾" high	25.00	12.00
375.	Jacobean Clock, 6¼" high	60.00	22.00
376.	Everlasting Candles, 8½" high (pair)	145.00	55.00
377.	Teddy Bear Bookend, 6⅜" high	20.00	20.00
378.	Teddy Bear Utility Jar, 5¼" high	20.00	17.50
379.	Teddy Bear Bookend, 6⅜" high	20.00	20.00
380.	T.V. Pen and Pencil Holder, 3¼" high	10.00	6.00
381.	Oak Leaf Candle Holder, 1⅞" h. x 4¼" l.	10.00	5.00
382.	Oak Leaf Candle Holder, 1⅞" h. x 4¼" l.	10.00	5.00

PRICE'S PATENT CANDLE COMPANY LIMITED 1963 - 1982

383.	Flower Light Leaf Holder, 1⅜" h. x 6¼" l.	10.00	2.00
384.	Plain Round Holder, 4" dia.	5.00	1.00
385.	Cube Holder, 2" high	12.00	3.00
386.	Tulip Holder, 1¾" high *(See also Fig.49 No.A pg.144 of The W of W2)*	12.00	3.00
387.	Tulip Holder, 1¾" high *(See also Fig.49 No.A pg.144 of The W of W2)*	12.00	3.00
388.	Venetian Scatter Holder, 1¾" high	10.00	2.00
389.	Plain Arch Holder, 1½" high	10.00	2.00

MONEY BANKS EARLY 1960'S TO 1983

		U.S. $	British £
390.	Toadstool Money Bank, 5½" h. x 6" w. *(See also Fig.154 pg.184 of The W of W)*	85.00	40.00
391.	Fawn Money Bank, 5¼" h. x 5" l. *(See also Fig.156 pg.184 of The W of W and Fig.50 No.A pg.146 of The W of W 2)*	45.00	25.00
392.	Kennel Money Bank, 4½" h. x 5¼" l. *(See also Fig.155 pg.184 of The W of W)*	45.00	25.00
393.	"Brew Gaffer" Money Bank, 5¼" h. x 3¾" across	60.00	50.00
394.	Natwest Panda Money Box, 4½" high	40.00	18.00
395.	Peter the Polar Bear Money Box, 6" high	40.00	15.00
396.	Lyon's Vintage Van Money Bank, 5¼" h. x 8" l.	65.00	55.00
397.	Monster Munch Money Bank, 6½" high	200.00	75.00
398.	Letter Box Money Bank, 7" h. x 4¾" dia.	45.00	20.00
399.	Tetley Vintage Van Money Bank, 5¼" h. x 8" l.	50.00	45.00

PAGE 65

MISCELLANEOUS PROTOTYPES MID 1950'S LATE 1950'S

400.	Bowl, 3" dia.	NPA	NPA
401.	Bowl, 4" dia.	NPA	NPA
402.	Treasure Chest Covered Dish, 1½" h. x 3⅝" l.	NPA	NPA
403.	Covered Shore Crab Dish, ¾" h. x 3¾" w.	NPA	NPA
404.	Covered Shore Crab Dish, ¾" h. x 3¾" w.	NPA	NPA
405.	Stacking Ashtrays, 3⅞" w.	NPA	NPA
406.	Treasure Chest Covered Dish, 1½" h. x 3⅝" l.	NPA	NPA
407.	Pineapple Bowl, 3" dia.	NPA	NPA
408.	Lizard Ashtray, 3½" high	NPA	NPA
409.	Tree Stump Lidded Box, 2" h. x 3" dia.	NPA	NPA

	U.S. $	British £
410. Rose Box, 3" h. x 4" across	NPA	NPA
411. Vase, 11¹/₂" high	NPA	NPA
412. Seated Lady, 7¹/₄" high	NPA	NPA
413. Wall Plaque, 13¹/₄" dia.	NPA	NPA
414. Vase, 11" high	NPA	NPA

PAGE 66

WALL PLATES, TANKARDS AND POTTERY TRAYS

	U.S. $	British £
415. Nova Scotia Wall Plate, 9¹/₂" dia.	15.00	20.00
416. London Map Wall Plate, 8" dia.	15.00	12.00
417. Wellyphant Plate, 7⁵/₈" dia.	25.00	15.00
418. Maritime Lobster — Trap Wall Plate, 9¹/₂" dia.	15.00	20.00
419. Barrel Tankard — Jumbo (4pint), 7¹/₂" high	40.00	45.00
420. Barrel Tankard (1 pint), 5" high	15.00	5.00
421. Barrel Tankard (1/2 pint), 3³/₄" high	15.00	5.00
422. Barrel Tankard (mini), 2" high	10.00	3.00
423. Drum Horse Traditional Tankard, 4³/₄" high	10.00	12.00
424. Lakehead University Tankard, 6" high	20.00	14.00
425. "Itala" Tyre Dish, 5" dia.	15.00	10.00
426. "Sunbeam" Tyre Dish, 5" dia. *(See also Fig.142 pg.182 of The W of W)*	15.00	10.00
427. "Nassau, Bahamas" Tyre Dish, 5" dia.	15.00	10.00
428. "Reversing Falls" Pottery Tray, 4¹/₂" dia.	10.00	6.00
429. "Covered Bridge" Pottery Tray, 4¹/₂" dia.	10.00	6.00
430. "Ann of Green Gables" Pottery Tray, 4¹/₂" dia.	10.00	6.00
431. "Ann of Green Gables" Pottery Tray, 4¹/₂" dia.	10.00	6.00
432. Plymouth Tankard Mini, 2" high	10.00	3.00
433. Traditional Tankard Mini, 2" high	15.00	12.00

	U.S. $	British £
434. "Horse Drawn Bus" Lesney Tray, 6" long	35.00	20.00
435. "Windsor Castle" Lesney Tray, 6" long	35.00	15.00
436. "Tower Bridge" Souvenir Dish, 4" long	25.00	10.00
437. "Golf Ball" Sugar Bowl, 2" high	35.00	28.00
438. "Golf Bag" Creamer, 3¹/₂" high *(See also No.397 pg.49 of The W of W)*	35.00	28.00
439. Pin Trays (boxed set of two), 4³/₈" dia.	35.00	25.00
440. Nut Dish, 1¹/₈" h. x 5" overall	25.00	10.00
441. Nut Dish (boxed set of two), 4¹/₈" dia.	35.00	25.00

PAGE 67

TANKARDS, JUGS AND POTTERY TRAYS

	U.S. $	British £
442. "British Columbia" Traditional Tankard, 4¹/₂" high	25.00	15.00
443. Tavern Tankard, 4⁷/₈" high	15.00	15.00
444. "Winston Churchill Roll out the Barrel" Tankard, 5³/₄" high	100.00	55.00
"Winston Churchill Roll out the Barrel" Tankard, 5³/₄" high, green	150.00	80.00
445. "Rothman's of Pall Mall" Traditional Tankard, 4¹/₂" high	15.00	12.00
446. "The Same Again Please" Traditional Tankard, 4¹/₂" high	15.00	8.00
447. McCallum Jug, 6³/₄" high	95.00	60.00
448. McCallum Jug, 4¹/₂" high *(See also No.396 pg.49 of The W of W)*	80.00	50.00
449. McCallum Jug, 2³/₄" high	75.00	45.00
450. "Ryerson Polytechnical Institute" Tankard, 6" high	25.00	12.00
451. "Ludwig Van Beethoven" Tankard, 6" high	25.00	12.00
452. "W.A.Mozart" Tankard, 7³/₈" high	35.00	15.00
453. McCullum Ashtray, 4³/₄" dia. *(See also Fig.146 pg.182 of The W of W)*	60.00	40.00
454. King of Spades Pottery Tray, 4¹/₄" dia.	15.00	6.00

	U.S. $	British £
455. Queen of Hearts Pottery Tray, 4¼" dia.	15.00	6.00
456. Queen of Clubs Pottery Tray, 4¼" dia. *(See also No.660 pg.62 of The W of W)*	15.00	6.00
457. King of Diamonds Pottery Tray, 4¼" dia. *(See also No.659 pg.62 of The W of W)*	15.00	6.00
458. Bagpipes Pottery Tray, 4¼" dia.	15.00	6.00
459. Stacking Ashtray, 4⅞" across rests *(See also No.405 pg.65 of The W of W2)*	10.00	18.00
460. Stacking Ashtray, 4⅞" across rests *(See also No.405 pg.65 of The W of W2)*	10.00	18.00
461. Stacking Ashtray, 4⅞" across rests *(See also No.405 pg.65 of The W of W2)*	10.00	6.50
462. Stacking Ashtray, 4⅞" across rests *(See also No.405 pg.65 of The W of W2)*	10.00	18.00
463. Stacking Ashtray, 4⅞" across rests *(See also No.405 pg.65 of The W of W2)*	10.00	18.00
464. "Trafalgar Square" Traditional Tankard, 2" high	15.00	5.00
465. "Piccadilly Circle" Traditional Tankard, 2" high	15.00	5.00
466. "Tower Bridge" Traditional Tankard, 2" high	15.00	5.00
467. "Harlequin" Tray, 3" square	10.00	3.00
468. "Harlequin" Tray, 3" square	10.00	3.00
469. "Harlequin" Tray, 3" square	10.00	3.00
470. "Harlequin" Tray, 3" square	10.00	3.00
471. "Humber College" Traditional Tankard, 4¾" high	18.00	10.00
472. "Professional Merchandiser" Traditional Tankard, 4¾" high	18.00	10.00
473. "New Brunswick" Jug, 4" high	25.00	20.00
474. "Nova Scotia" Jug, 4" high	25.00	20.00
475. "Piccadilly Circus" Traditional Tankard, 4¾" high	18.00	10.00

PAGE 68

MISCELLANEOUS GIFTWARE ITEMS

	U.S. $	British £
476. "Cheerio" Traditional Tankard, 4¾" high	15.00	18.00
477. "Royal Canadian Air Force" Traditional Tankard, 4½" high	30.00	10.00
478. "Buckingham Palace" Traditional Tankard, 4½" high	18.00	10.00
479. Funnel, 3½" high	85.00	50.00
480. "Sunbeam 1904" Half Pint Tankard, 3¾" high	14.00	5.00
481. "Benz 1899" One Pint Tankard, 4½" high	20.00	8.00
482. Bud Vase, 4¾" high	15.00	5.00
483. Barrel Tankard, 5" high	15.00	5.00
484. "Clara" Buddies Bud Vase, 4½" high *(See also No.452 pg.53 of The W of W)*	30.00	15.00
485. "Clarence" Buddies Bud Vase, 4½" high	30.00	15.00
486. Shaving Mug, 3⅛" high	20.00	5.00
487. "Nova Scotia" Souvenir Vase, 4½" high	15.00	5.00
488. "New Brunswick" Souvenir Vase, 4½" high	15.00	5.00
489. "New Brunswick" Souvenir Jug, 3¾" high *(See also Fig.143 pg.182 of The W of W)*	35.00	20.00
490. Bud Vase, 5½" high	20.00	10.00
491. Shaving Mug, 3⅜" high	15.00	5.00
492. "Admiral Lord Horatio Nelson" Shaving Mug, 3¼" high	15.00	5.00
493. "Nelson's Column" Shaving Mug, 3¼" high	15.00	5.00
494. "H.M.S. Victory" Shaving Mug, 3¼" high	15.00	5.00
495. "Veteran Car" Shaving Mug, 3½" high	15.00	5.00
496. "New Brunswick" Traditional Tankard, 3¾" high	18.00	10.00
497. "Nassau Bahamas" Traditional Tankard, 3¾" high	18.00	10.00
498. "New Brunswick" Pottery Tray, 5¼" square	10.00	15.00

	U.S. $	British £
499. Taunton Traditional Cider Mug, 3¹/₄" high	55.00	15.00
500. "Prince Edward Island" Traditional Tankard, 3³/₄" high	18.00	10.00
501. "Tower Bridge" Pottery Tray, 4¹/₄" square	15.00	6.00
502. "Houses of Parliament" Pottery Tray, 4¹/₄" square	15.00	6.00
503. Shell Dish, 3¹/₂" across	20.00	5.00
504. Shell Dish, 3¹/₂" across	20.00	5.00
505. Shell Dish, 3¹/₂" across	20.00	5.00
506. "Guernsey" Pottery Tray, 4¹/₄" square	15.00	6.00
507. "Piccadilly Circus" Pottery Tray, 4¹/₄" square	15.00	6.00
508. "Emett Dish" Pottery Tray, 4¹/₄" square	20.00	6.00
509. "Emett Dish" Pottery Tray, 4¹/₄" square	20.00	6.00
510. "Emett Dish" Pottery Tray, 4¹/₄" square	20.00	6.00
511. "Poodle" Pottery Tray, 4¹/₄" dia.	12.00	6.00
512. "Ballet Dish" Pottery Tray, 4¹/₄" square	10.00	6.00
513. "Ballet Dish" Pottery Tray, 4¹/₄" square	10.00	6.00

PAGE 69

FLOWER JUGS AND VASES LATE 1920'S - 1960

	U.S. $	British £
514. Flower Jug, 11³/₄" high *(See also Fig.139 pg.181 of The W of W)*	240.00	135.00
515. Orcadia Vase, 6¹/₄" high	50.00	35.00
516. Orcadia Vase, 6" high	50.00	35.00
517. Flower Jug, 11" high *(See also No.602 pg.75 of The W of W2)*	100.00	75.00
518. Orcadia Flower Jug, 6¹/₂" high *(See also Fig.137 pg.181 of The W of W)*	70.00	30.00
519. Orcadia Vase, 6¹/₄" high	50.00	35.00
520. Orcadia Vase and Flower Holder, 5¹/₂" high	90.00	65.00
521. Orcadia Vase, 7¹/₂" high	60.00	30.00
522. Orcadia Vase, 7" high *(See also Fig.136 pg.181 of The W of W)*	75.00	35.00

	U.S. $	British £
523. Orcadia Vase, 5³/₄" high	75.00	35.00
524. Vase (Phoenix shape), 5" high	45.00	35.00
525. Flower Jug, 9" high	65.00	40.00

PAGE 70

	U.S. $	British £
526. Flower Jug, 9" high	80.00	60.00
527. Flower Jug, 8" high	110.00	65.00
528. Flower Jug, 9" high *(See also Fig.138 pg.181 of The W of W)*	110.00	65.00
529. Flower Jug, 8³/₄" high	50.00	35.00
530. Flower Jug, 8" high	50.00	45.00
531. Flower Jug, 7¹/₂" high	75.00	50.00
532. Flower Jug, 7" high *(See also Fig.140 pg.181 of The W of W)*	35.00	25.00
533. Flower Jug, 5¹/₄" high	45.00	30.00
534. Flower Jug, 5⁵/₈" high	25.00	20.00
535. Jug, 3⁷/₈" high	25.00	20.00

PAGE 71

	U.S. $	British £
536. Flower Jug, 9" high	75.00	50.00
537. Flower Jug, 6³/₄" high	100.00	65.00
538. Flower Jug, 6³/₄" high *(See also Fig.80 pg.121 of The W of W)*	100.00	65.00
539. Flower Jug, 9" high	75.00	50.00
540. Vase, 7" high	60.00	30.00
541. Flower Jug, 7¹/₄" high	90.00	50.00
542. Flower Jug, 7" high	110.00	70.00
543. Flower Jug, 7¹/₂" high	120.00	75.00
544. Flower Jug, 5⁷/₈" high *(See also No.366 pg.47 of The W of W)*	30.00	22.00
545. Flower Jug, 5⁵/₈" high *(See also Nos.365 and 368 pg.47 of The W of W)*	30.00	28.00
546. Flower Jug, 5⁵/₈" high *(See also No.366 pg.47 of The W of W)*	30.00	22.00
547. Flower Jug, 5¹/₄" high	40.00	30.00

PAGE 72

	U.S. $	British £
548. Flower Jug, 9" high	50.00	35.00
549. Flower Jug, 9" high	50.00	35.00
550. Flower Jug, 9" high	75.00	55.00
551. Flower Jug, 9" high	75.00	55.00

		U.S. $	British £
552.	Flower Jug, 9" high	55.00	40.00
553.	Flower Jug, 7^3/$_4$" high	50.00	35.00
554.	Flower Jug, 7^1/$_2$" high	40.00	30.00
	(See also No.613 pg.76 of The W of W2)		
555.	Flower Jug, 7^1/$_4$" high	70.00	50.00
556.	Flower Jug, 5^1/$_2$" high	40.00	28.00
557.	Flower Jug, 5^1/$_2$" high	35.00	20.00
558.	Jug, 4" high	65.00	50.00
559.	Jug, 4" high	65.00	50.00
560.	Flower Jug, 5^5/$_8$" high	35.00	20.00
	(See also No.384 pg.48 of The W of W)		

PAGE 73

		U.S. $	British £
561.	Flower Jug, 8^3/$_4$" high	40.00	30.00
562.	Flower Jug, 8" high	280.00	100.00

PAGE 73

		U.S. $	British £
563.	Flower Jug, 9" high	40.00	30.00
564.	Flower Jug, 8^3/$_4$" high	65.00	30.00
	(See also No.375 pg.48 and Fig.81A No.9 pg.124 of The W of W)		
565.	Flower Jug, 7^1/$_2$" high	50.00	27.50
	(See also No.379 pg.48 of The W of W)		
566.	Flower Jug, 7^1/$_2$" high	65.00	30.00
	(See also No.383 pg.48 of The W of W)		
567.	Flower Jug, 8^3/$_4$" high	65.00	30.00
568.	Handled Flower Vase, 6^1/$_2$" high	75.00	50.00
569.	Jug, 5^1/$_2$" high	50.00	45.00
570.	Jug, 5^1/$_2$" high	50.00	30.00
571.	Jug, 5^1/$_2$" high	35.00	20.00

PAGE 74

		U.S. $	British £
572.	"Birdbath" Flower Jug, 10^1/$_4$" high	80.00	55.00
573.	"Birdbath" Flower Jug, 10^1/$_4$" high	70.00	50.00
574.	"Birdbath" Flower Jug, 10^1/$_4$" high	80.00	55.00
575.	"Birdbath" Flower Jug, 10^1/$_4$" high	80.00	55.00
576.	Flower Jug, 9" high	50.00	35.00

		U.S. $	British £
577.	Flower Jug, 8^1/$_4$" high	70.00	50.00
578.	Flower Jug, 9" high	90.00	65.00
579.	Flower Jug, 8^7/$_8$" high	50.00	35.00
	(See also No.387 pg.49 of The W of W)		
580.	Vase, 6^1/$_2$" high	35.00	30.00
	(See also No.618 pg.76 of The W of W2)		
581.	"Birdbath" Flower Jug, 6^1/$_4$" high (See also No.393 pg.49 of The W of W)	70.00	32.00
582.	Jug (Ross shape), 4^1/$_2$" high	50.00	30.00
583.	Flower Jug, 6^1/$_4$" high	50.00	35.00
	(See also No.592 pg.75 of The W of W2)		

PAGE 75

		U.S. $	British £
584.	Flower Jug, 8^3/$_4$" high	120.00	75.00
	(See also Fig.94 pg.172 of The W of W2)		
585.	Coffee Pot, 7^1/$_2$" high	110.00	70.00
586.	Flower Jug, 7^3/$_4$" high	60.00	40.00
587.	Flower Jug, 8^1/$_2$" high	80.00	55.00
588.	Flower Jug, 11^1/$_4$" high	115.00	80.00
589.	Flower Jug, 8^3/$_4$" high	50.00	55.00
	(See also Nos.361 and 362 pg.47 of The W of W)		
590.	Handled Flower Vase, 6^1/$_2$" high (See also No.568 pg.73 of The W of W2)	75.00	50.00
591.	Covered Jar, 5" high	45.00	20.00
592.	Flower Jug, 6^1/$_4$" high	50.00	35.00
	(See also No.583 pg.74 of The W of W2)		
593.	Vase, 7^1/$_8$" high	50.00	35.00
594.	Flower Jug, 8^3/$_4$" high	80.00	50.00
595.	Flower Jug, 8^1/$_2$" high	75.00	55.00
596.	Flower Jug, 8^3/$_4$" high	60.00	45.00
597.	Flower Jug, 8^1/$_2$" high	60.00	45.00
598.	Flower Jug, 6^1/$_4$" high	80.00	50.00
599.	Flower Jug, 5^5/$_8$" high	70.00	40.00
600.	Vase, 5" high	65.00	50.00
	(See also Fig.81A No.5 of The W of W and No.615 pg.76 of The W of W2)		
601.	Flower Jug, 7^1/$_2$" high	55.00	40.00
602.	Flower Jug, 11^3/$_4$" high	100.00	75.00
	(See also No.517 pg.69 of The W of W2)		
603.	Flower Jug, 9" high	50.00	55.00
	(See also Nos.361 and 362 pg.47 of The W of W and No.589 pg.75 of The W of W2)		

		U.S. $	British £
604.	Plate, 5" dia.	35.00	20.00
605.	Flower Holder, 5³/₄" high	60.00	45.00
	(See also Fig.81 No.13 pg.123		
	of The W of W and No.637 pg.76 of The W of W2)		
606.	Jug, 5" high	50.00	30.00
607.	Vase, 9" high	50.00	35.00
608.	Butter Dish, 3¹/₂" h. x 7" dia.	35.00	25.00
609.	Flower Jug, 5¹/₂" high	35.00	20.00
610.	Vase, 3¹/₂" high	15.00	10.00
611.	Vase, 3³/₄" high	55.00	30.00
612.	Vase, 5" high	45.00	35.00

PAGE 76

		U.S. $	British £
613.	Flower Jug, 7¹/₂" high	40.00	30.00
	(See also No.554 pg.72 of The W of W2)		
614.	Vase, 6¹/₄" high	50.00	35.00
615.	Vase, 5" high	65.00	50.00
616.	Flower Jug, 5¹/₈" high	65.00	50.00
617.	Flower Jug, 9" high	55.00	40.00
	(See also Fig.84 No.5 pg.128 of The W of W)		
618.	Vase, 6¹/₂" high	35.00	30.00
	(See also No.580 pg.74 of The W of W2)		
619.	Vase, 6¹/₂" high	60.00	40.00
620.	Vase, 11¹/₂" high	140.00	75.00
621.	Vase and Flower Frog, 6³/₄" high	200.00	80.00
622.	Vase, 8³/₄" high	75.00	50.00
623.	"Lambeth Walk" Mug, 4³/₄" high	70.00	50.00
624.	"Lambeth Walk" Pitcher, 10³/₈" high	375.00	200.00
	"Lambeth Walk" Musical Jug, 10³/₈" high	525.00	280.00
625.	"Lambeth Walk"" Mug, 4³/₄" high	70.00	50.00
626.	"Big Bad Wolf" Musical Jug, 9³/₄" high	1200.00	500.00
627.	Vase, 8³/₄" high	60.00	40.00
628.	Bowl, 3¹/₄" h. x 7³/₄" dia.	35.00	25.00
629.	Basket, 7¹/₂" h. x 10" overall	110.00	60.00
630.	Flower Jug, 3" high	65.00	22.50
	(See also No.378 pg.48 of The W of W)		

		U.S. $	British £
631.	Flower Jug, 3" high	65.00	22.50
	(See also No.378 pg.48 of The W of W)		
632.	Footed Cake Plate, 7³/₄" dia.	25.00	15.00
633.	Flower Jug, 8¹/₂" high	70.00	55.00
634.	Vase, 8³/₄" high	90.00	65.00
635.	Flower Jug, 8¹/₂" high	60.00	45.00
636.	Flower Jug, 8⁷/₈" high	65.00	55.00
637.	Vase, 5¹/₂" high	60.00	45.00
	(See also Fig.81 No.13 pg.123		
	of The W of W and No.605 pg.75 of The W of W2)		
638.	Butter Dish, 4" h. x 7" l.	65.00	50.00
639.	Jam Dish, 4" h. x 3" square	60.00	37.50
640.	Teapot (Queen shape), 5¹/₄" high	110.00	55.00

PAGE 77

TEAPOTS, TEA CADDIES AND CREAM & SUGARS LATE 1920'S - 1992

		U.S. $	British £
641.	Teapot (Peking shape), 7¹/₄" high	120.00	65.00
642.	Cookie Jar, 7¹/₄" high	130.00	70.00
643.	Hot Water Pot, 7¹/₄" high	130.00	70.00
	(See also No.660 pg.78 of The W of W2)		
644.	Cookie Jar, 7¹/₄" high	115.00	60.00
645.	"Bird's Nest" Teapot, 6" high	130.00	70.00
646.	Cookie Jar, 6" high	115.00	60.00
	(See also Fig.96. pg.178 of The W of W2)		
647.	Teapot, 6¹/₂" high	130.00	70.00
648.	Teapot (Windsor shape), 6" high	70.00	50.00
649.	"Donald Duck" Teapot, 6¹/₂" high	850.00	400.00
650.	Cookie Jar, 7¹/₄" high	450.00	200.00
651.	Coffee Pot, 7³/₄" high	475.00	225.00
652.	Circular Tray, 9" dia.	225.00	105.00
653.	Teapot, 6¹/₂" high	500.00	240.00
654.	Covered Sugar, 3³/₄" high	190.00	85.00
655.	Creamer, 4" high	190.00	85.00

PAGE 78

		U.S. $	British £
656.	Coffee Pot, 7³/₄" high	100.00	40.00
657.	Teapot, 5¹/₂" high	110.00	50.00

		U.S. $	British £
658.	Hot Water Pot, 5^1/$_2$" high	110.00	50.00
659.	Tray, 8^1/$_4$" l. x 7^1/$_4$" w.	55.00	25.00
660.	Hot Water Pot, 7^1/$_4$" high	130.00	70.00
	(See also No.643 pg.77 of The W of W2)		
661.	Teapot, 5^3/$_4$" high	50.00	35.00
662.	Duck Teapot, 5" high	300.00	120.00
663.	Teapot, 6^1/$_4$" high	110.00	50.00
664.	Teapot (Bramble), 6" high	90.00	50.00
665.	Creamer (Bramble), 2^3/$_4$" high	25.00	18.00
	(See also No.473 pg.54 of The W of W)		
666.	Sugar (Bramble), 1^3/$_4$" high	15.00	10.00
	(See also No.477 pg.54 of The W of W)		
667.	Teapot (Bramble), 5^3/$_4$" high	65.00	35.00
668.	Teapot (Bramble), 6" high	75.00	40.00
	(See also No.487 pg.55 of The W of W)		
669.	Teapot (Kew shape), 5^1/$_2$" high	90.00	50.00
670.	Teapot (Nelson shape), 5" high	70.00	60.00
	(See also No.562 pg.58 of The W of W)		
671.	Hot Water Pot, 5^1/$_2$" high	75.00	40.00
672.	Tray, 8^1/$_4$" l. x 7^1/$_4$" w.	30.00	20.00

PAGE 79

TEAPOTS, CREAM AND SUGARS

		U.S. $	British £
673.	Teapot (Eagle shape), 6" high	110.00	70.00
674.	Sugar, 2" high	25.00	15.00
675.	Creamer, 3^1/$_2$" high	25.00	15.00
676.	Milk Jug, 4^1/$_2$" high	45.00	25.00
677.	Creamer, 3^1/$_2$" high	25.00	15.00
678.	Sugar, 2" high	25.00	15.00
679.	Teapot (Nelson shape), 5^1/$_2$" high	70.00	40.00
680.	Plate (Chintz Floral & Butterfly), 8^3/$_4$" dia.	40.00	20.00
681.	Teapot (Chintz Floral & Butterfly), 5^1/$_2$" high	95.00	50.00
682.	Cup (Chintz Floral & Butterfly), 2^3/$_4$" high	30.00	20.00
683.	Saucer (Chintz Floral & Butterfly), 5^3/$_4$" dia.	15.00	10.00
684.	Teapot (Nelson shape), 5^1/$_4$" high	70.00	30.00

		U.S. $	British £
685.	Teapot (Floral Trellis), 6^1/$_2$" high	35.00	18.00
686.	Sugar (Floral Trellis), 2^3/$_4$" high	15.00	8.00
687.	Creamer (Floral Trellis), 3^3/$_4$" high	15.00	8.00
688.	Teapot (Old Coach House, York), 6^1/$_2$" high	30.00	20.00
689.	Teapot (Finn MacCoul), 6^1/$_2$" high	30.00	20.00

TEA CADDIES

		U.S. $	British £
690.	Tea Caddy (Chinese Rose), 3^1/$_2$" high	25.00	15.00
691.	Tea Caddy (Poinsettia), 3^1/$_2$" high	25.00	15.00
692.	Tea Caddy (Snow Man), 3^1/$_2$" high	25.00	15.00
693.	Tea Caddy (Ringtons Ltd. 1989), 5" high	65.00	30.00
694.	Tea Caddy (Ringtons Ltd. 1987), 3^1/$_2$" high	60.00	30.00
	(See also Figs.102 and 103 pg.181 of The W of W2)		

PAGE 80

TEAPOTS

		U.S. $	British £
695.	Teapot (Cat Burglar), 6^1/$_2$" high	35.00	20.00
696.	Teapot (Macy's 1989), 5^3/$_4$" high	40.00	25.00
697.	Teapot (Valor Gas 1990), 6" high	70.00	50.00
698.	Teapot (Cross Stitch), 6^1/$_2$" high	30.00	15.00
699.	Teapot (Cat-Fish), 5" high	35.00	20.00
700.	Teapot (Cat-Fish), 4^1/$_2$" high	30.00	15.00
701.	Creamer (Tutti-Fruitti), 3^1/$_2$" high	15.00	8.00
702.	Covered Sugar (Tutti-Fruitti), 4" high	15.00	8.00
703.	Teapot (Tutti-Fruitti), 5^1/$_2$" high	32.00	18.00
704.	Teapot (Cat-Litter), 6^1/$_2$" high	35.00	20.00
705.	Teapot (Cat-Litter), 5^1/$_4$" high	30.00	15.00

		U.S. $	British £
706.	Teapot (Cat-Nap), $5^1/2$" high	30.00	15.00
707.	Teapot (Cat Nap), $6^3/8$" high	35.00	20.00
708.	Teapot (Grapevine), $3^3/4$" high	20.00	10.00
709.	Teapot (Tetley "Sidney"), $5^3/4$" high	70.00	40.00
710.	Teapot (Pot Pouri), $4^1/8$" high	20.00	10.00
711.	Teapot (Blue Dresden), 4" high	20.00	10.00

PAGE 81

TEAPOTS AND MUGS

		U.S. $	British £
712.	Teapot (Cricket Match), 6" high	50.00	20.00
713.	Teapot (Genie), $8^1/4$" high	95.00	50.00
714.	Teapot (Wedding), 7" high	50.00	20.00
715.	Teapot (Helter Skelter), $7^1/4$" high	45.00	15.00
716.	Mug (Helter Skelter), $3^3/4$" high	15.00	8.00
717.	Teapot (Punch and Judy), $6^3/4$" high	45.00	15.00
718.	Mug (Punch and Judy), $3^3/4$" high	15.00	8.00
719.	Mug (La Bella Vista), $3^3/4$" high	15.00	8.00
720.	Teapot (La Bella Vista), $7^3/4$" high	50.00	20.00
721.	Teapot (Ringmaster), 5" high	45.00	15.00
722.	Mug (Ringmaster), $3^3/4$" high	10.00	5.00
723.	Mug (Noah's Ark), $3^3/4$" high	10.00	5.00
724.	Teapot (Noah's Ark), $5^1/4$" high	55.00	20.00
725.	Teapot (Jungle Fun), 5" high	45.00	15.00
726.	Teapot (Jungle Fun), 5" high	45.00	15.00
727.	Mug (Jungle Fun), $3^3/4$" high	10.00	5.00

PAGE 83

ENGLISH LIFE TEAPOTS, MUGS AND CADDIES 1988 - 1995

		U.S. $	British £
728.	Teapot (Post Office), $5^1/4$" high	35.00	12.00
729.	Mug (Post Office), $3^3/4$" high	10.00	5.00
730.	Tea Caddy (Post Office), $4^1/4$" high	10.00	4.00

		U.S. $	British £
731.	Teapot (Primrose Junction), $5^5/8$" high	35.00	12.00
732.	Mug (Primrose Junction), $3^3/4$" high	10.00	5.00
733.	Tea Caddy (Primrose Junction), $4^1/4$" high	10.00	4.00
734.	Teapot (Polly's Cafe), $4^1/2$" high	35.00	12.00
735.	Tea Caddy (Polly's Cafe), $4^1/2$" high	30.00	10.00
736.	Mug (Polly's Cafe), $3^5/8$" high	10.00	5.00
737.	Mug (T. Potts China Shop), $3^5/8$" high	10.00	5.00
738.	Teapot (T. Potts China Shop), 6" high	35.00	12.00
739.	Teapot (Florie's Flowers), $5^7/8$" high	35.00	12.00
740.	Mug (Florie's Flowers), $3^5/8$" high	10.00	5.00
741.	Teapot (Police Station), $6^1/4$" high	35.00	12.00
742.	Mug (Police Station), $3^5/8$" high	10.00	5.00

PAGE 83

		U.S. $	British £
743.	Tea Caddy (Antique Store), $5^1/4$" high	30.00	10.00
744.	Teapot (Antique Store), $5^7/8$" high	35.00	12.00
745.	Mug (Antique Store), $3^5/8$" high	10.00	5.00
746.	Tea Caddy (Antique Store), $4^1/4$" high	10.00	4.00
747.	Mug (Fish and Chip Shop), $3^5/8$" high	10.00	5.00
748.	Teapot (Fish and Chip Shop), $5^3/4$" high	35.00	12.00
749.	Teapot (Queen Victoria Pub), $5^5/8$" high	35.00	12.00
750.	Mug (Queen Victoria Pub), $3^1/2$" high	10.00	5.00
751.	Tea Caddy (Queen Victoria Pub), $5^1/4$" high	30.00	10.00
752.	Tea Caddy (Queen Victoria Pub), $4^1/4$" high	10.00	4.00
753.	Mug (Merry Christmas), $3^5/8$" high	10.00	5.00

		U.S. $	British £
754.	Teapot (Christmas Carol), 6" high	35.00	12.00
755.	Teapot (Christmas Tree, Light Green), $5^3/4$" high	45.00	15.00
756.	Teapot (Christmas Tree, White), $5^3/4$" high	35.00	10.00
757.	Teapot (Christmas Tree, Dark Green), $5^3/4$" high	35.00	10.00
758.	Teapot (Santa's Grotto), 6" high	35.00	12.00
759.	Mug (Conservatory), $3^5/8$" high	10.00	5.00
760.	Teapot (Conservatory), $5^1/4$" high	35.00	15.00
761.	Tea Caddy (Conservatory), $4^1/2$" high	30.00	10.00

PAGE 84

BOOTS TEAPOTS, MUGS AND COOKIE JARS 1991 - 1992

762.	Teapot (Drummer Boy), $6^3/4$" high	70.00	25.00
763.	Teapot (Gymkhana), $6^1/4$" high	70.00	25.00
764.	Teapot (White Rabbit), $8^1/4$" high	70.00	25.00
765.	Teapot (Dressage), $6^3/4$" high	70.00	25.00
766.	Mug (Fish), 4" high	10.00	5.00
767.	Mug (Cats), 4" high	10.00	5.00
768.	Teapot (Cats), $5^1/2$" high	60.00	20.00
769.	Teapot (Goose Fair), $6^1/2$" high	60.00	20.00
770.	Cookie Jar (Goose Fair), $10^1/2$" high	85.00	30.00
771.	Cookie Jar (Peasant), $10^1/2$" high	85.00	30.00
772.	Teapot (Peasant), $6^1/2$" high	70.00	25.00
773.	Teacup & Saucer (Fruits)	15.00	5.00
774.	Teapot (Fruits), $5^1/2$" high	35.00	12.00

NATIONAL TRUST TEAPOT 1989

775.	Teapot (Blaise Hamlet Cottage), 5" high	30.00	15.00
	Teapot (Alfriston Lodge, not illustrated), $5^7/8$" high	30.00	15.00

CLOWN TEAPOTS 1992 - 1995

		U.S. $	British £
776.	Teapot (Bow), $7^3/8$" high	35.00	15.00
777.	Teapot (Kipper), $7^5/8$" high	35.00	15.00

PAGE 85

MISCELLANEOUS TEAPOTS

778.	Teapot (Lighthouse), $7^1/2$" high	40.00	12.00
779.	Teapot (Pet Shop), $5^3/8$" high	25.00	10.00
	Mug (Pet Shop, not illustrated), $3^3/4$" high	10.00	5.00
780.	Teapot (Fishmongers), 6" high	25.00	10.00
781.	Teapot (Cockle Shell Pier Theatre), $6^3/8$" high	25.00	10.00
782.	Teapot (Santa's Christmas), $5^1/2$" high	13.00	15.00
783.	Teapot (Wadeland Fire Engine Company), 5" high	25.00	12.00
784.	Teapot (Apres Ski), $5^1/2$" high	30.00	15.00

TETLEY TEA TABLEWARE 1992

785.	Cookie Jar (Gaffer), $8^3/8$" high	50.00	30.00
786.	Toast Rack (Gaffer), $2^3/4$" h. x 6" l.	50.00	20.00
787.	Teapot (Gaffer & Sidney), 5" high	45.00	20.00

WILLIAMSON & MAGOR TEA CADDIES 1990 - 1993

788.	Tea Caddy (Earl Grey, matt gray), $7^1/4$" high	75.00	35.00
789.	Tea Caddy (English Breakfast, matt mid-blue), $7^1/4$" high	75.00	35.00
	Tea Caddy (English Breakfast, glossy dark blue), $7^3/4$" high *(See No.288 pg.60 of WPT)*	75.00	35.00

MISCELLANEOUS TABLEWARE

790.	Water Jug (The McCallum), $6^3/4$" high	150.00	70.00
791.	Flower Jug, $5^1/2$" high	35.00	20.00

		U.S. $	British £
792.	Covered Dish (Gothic), 2¹/₄" h. x 6" l.	90.00	40.00
793.	Money Box (Fried Green Tomatoes), 5¹/₄" h. x 6" dia.	140.00	75.00

PAGE 86

		U.S. $	British £
794.	Wall Plaque, 12¹/₂" dia.	180.00	100.00
795.	Bread & Butter Plate, 7³/₄" dia.	10.00	5.00
796.	Dinner Plate, 10³/₄" dia.	10.00	5.00
797.	Bowl, 2¹/₂" h. x 9" dia.	12.00	6.00
798.	Oval Pin Dish, 4¹/₄" long	12.00	6.00
799.	Honey Pot, 4¹/₈" high	45.00	25.00
800.	Cup & Saucer (Mode Shape)	20.00	10.00
801.	Cereal Bowl, 1¹/₂" h. x 6¹/₄" dia.	10.00	5.00
802.	Cup & Saucer (Rooster Decoration)	20.00	10.00
803.	Cheese Dish Cover (Rooster Decoration), 6³/₄" dia.	NPA	NPA
804.	Covered Box, 2¹/₈" high	35.00	15.00
805.	Covered Cameo Dish, 1¹/₂" h. x 3" dia.	75.00	35.00
806.	Covered Cameo Dish, 1¹/₂" high	75.00	35.00

FALSTAFF WARE CIRCA 1960 - 1970

		U.S. $	British £
807.	Claret Jug (Falstaff), 10" high	35.00	20.00

(See also Fig. 213 No.A pg. 248 of The W of W2)

MISCELLANEOUS TABLEWARE

		U.S. $	British £
808.	Ducor Storage Jar, 9³/₄" high	50.00	30.00
809.	Jug (Imperial Decoration), 5¹/₂" high	45.00	25.00
810.	Storage Jar, 3¹/₈" h. x 9¹/₂" l.	75.00	40.00
811.	Tray, 8¹/₂" l. x 4¹/₂" w.	115.00	60.00

PAGE 87

		U.S. $	British £
812.	Pitcher, 7¹/₄" high	65.00	50.00

(See also Fig. 79 pg. 121 of The W of W)

		U.S. $	British £
813.	Plate, 5³/₄" square	45.00	32.50

		U.S. $	British £
814.	Creamer, 3¹/₂" high	45.00	32.50
815.	Footed Sweet Dish, 2" h. x 6" dia.	75.00	40.00
816.	Cookie Jar, 6" high	115.00	60.00

BASKET WARE "1" AND BASKET WARE "2"

		U.S. $	British £
817.	Biscuit Barrel (Basket Ware "2"), 8¹/₂" high	60.00	35.00
818.	Biscuit Barrel (Basket Ware "1"), 6³/₄" high	55.00	30.00
819.	Basket, 5¹/₄" high	50.00	25.00
820.	Cruet Set (Basket Ware "1")	55.00	30.00

(See also Fig. 87 pg. 131 of The W of W)

		U.S. $	British £
821.	Creamer (Basket Ware "1"), 3¹/₈" high	30.00	17.50
822.	Sugar (Basket Ware "1"), 2" high	15.00	10.00
823.	Creamer (Basket Ware "1"), 3¹/₈" high	20.00	12.00
824.	Teapot (Basket Ware "1"), 6" high	60.00	35.00

QUACK QUACK CHILDREN'S DISHES 1947 - MID 1950'S

		U.S. $	British £
825.	Cereal Dish, 7¹/₄" dia.	55.00	40.00
826.	Plate, 6¹/₄" dia.	50.00	37.50

(See also Fig. 121 pg. 193 of The W of W2)

		U.S. $	British £
827.	Bowl, 6¹/₄" dia.	50.00	37.50
828.	Saucer, 5³/₄" dia.	20.00	15.00
829.	Cup, 2¹/₄" high	35.00	35.00

WALT DISNEY CHILDREN'S DISHES 1934 LATE 1950'S

		U.S. $	British £
830.	Plate (Mickey Mouse), 5³/₄" square	120.00	80.00
831.	Sugar Bowl, 1¹/₂" high	45.00	30.00
832.	Creamer, 2" high	50.00	35.00
833.	Saucer, 3³/₄" dia.	25.00	15.00
834.	Cup (Sleepy), 1⁷/₈" high	50.00	35.00
835.	Saucer, 3³/₄" dia.	25.00	15.00
836.	Cup (Happy), 1⁷/₈" high	50.00	35.00
837.	Teapot (Snow White), 3³/₈" high	105.00	70.00

		U.S. $	British £
838.	Butter Dish (Dopey), 4^1/$_2$" h. x 7" dia.	250.00	100.00
	(See also Fig.85 pg.129 of The W of W)		
839.	Sugar (Hiawatha), 1^1/$_2$" high	45.00	30.00
840.	Creamer (Funny Little Bunnies) 2" high	50.00	35.00
841.	Saucer (Ring o' Roses), 4" dia.	25.00	15.00
842.	Cup (Simple Simon Met A Pie Man), 1^7/$_8$" high	50.00	35.00
843.	Saucer (Little Jumping Joan), 4" dia.	25.00	15.00
844.	Cup (ABC Tumble Down D), 1^7/$_8$" high	50.00	35.00
845.	Teapot (What Are Little Girls Made Of), 3^3/$_8$" high	105.00	70.00

HONEY POTS AND TRAYS
CIRCA MID 1930'S - MID 1950'S

		U.S. $	British £
846.	Honey Pot (Bird Finial), 3^3/$_4$" high	45.00	25.00
847.	Honey Pot (Flower Finial), 4^1/$_4$" high	45.00	25.00
848.	Ashtray, 4" l. x 3" w.	20.00	15.00
849.	Ashtray, 4" l. x 3" w.	20.00	15.00
850.	Honey Pot (Beehive shape), 3^3/$_4$" high	45.00	25.00
851.	Honey Pot (Pear shape), 4^1/$_8$" high	45.00	25.00

PAGE 88
"RUBYTONE" TABLEWARE
1953 - CIRCA EARLY 1960'S

		U.S. $	British £
852.	Dinner Plate, 8^3/$_4$" dia.	35.00	18.00
853.	Dessert Plate, 6^3/$_4$" dia.	25.00	15.00
854.	Teapot - Large, 6^1/$_2$" high	85.00	45.00
855.	Cup & Saucer	35.00	20.00
856.	Covered Sugar with Handles, 3^1/$_2$" high	35.00	20.00
857.	Gravy Boat & Tray — Regal Green	40.00	25.00
858.	Gravy Boat & Tray	40.00	25.00
859.	Creamer, 3^1/$_2$" high	35.00	20.00
860.	Covered Sugar without Handles, 3^1/$_2$" high	35.00	20.00

		U.S. $	British £
861.	Platter, 11" long	45.00	25.00

REGENCY SHAPE COFFEE AND TEA SETS
EARLY 1950'S - 1961

		U.S. $	British £
862.	Coffee Pot, 6^3/$_4$" high	50.00	30.00
863.	Cup & Saucer	20.00	10.00
864.	Cup, 2^3/$_8$" high	12.00	5.00
865.	Saucer, 5" dia.	8.00	5.00
866.	Sugar, 1^3/$_4$" high	30.00	5.00
867.	Creamer, 1^7/$_8$" high	40.00	10.00
	(See also Fig.101 pg.140 of The W of W)		

MISCELLANEOUS TABLEWARE

		U.S. $	British £
868.	Milk Jug, 5^1/$_4$" high	50.00	35.00
869.	Vase — shape 3, 2^3/$_4$" high	20.00	10.00
870.	Vase — shape 1, 2^1/$_2$" high	20.00	10.00
871.	Demitass Creamer, 2" high	20.00	10.00
872.	Demitass Creamer, 2" high	20.00	10.00
873.	Demitass Covered Sugar, 2^1/$_4$" high	20.00	10.00
874.	Cup & Saucer	20.00	10.00

PAGE 89

		U.S. $	British £
875.	Plate (Hedgerow), 11" dia.	25.00	15.00
876.	Plate (Meadow), 8" dia.	25.00	15.00
877.	Saucer (Hedgerow), 5^1/$_2$" dia.	10.00	5.00
878.	Cup (Hedgerow), 2^1/$_4$" high	20.00	10.00
879.	Covered Candy Dish, 4^1/$_2$" high	25.00	15.00
880.	Dandy Milk Jug, 5^1/$_8$" high	65.00	40.00
881.	Plate, 6^3/$_4$" dia.	15.00	8.00
882.	Cup & Saucer	20.00	12.00
883.	Plate, 6^1/$_2$" square	20.00	12.00
884.	Cup & Saucer	20.00	12.00
885.	Plate, 6^3/$_4$" dia.	15.00	8.00
886.	Cup & Saucer	20.00	12.00
887.	Plate, 6^3/$_4$" dia.	15.00	8.00
888.	Sugar, 3" high	10.00	5.00
889.	Creamer, 3^1/$_2$" high	15.00	8.00
890.	Plate, 6^3/$_4$" dia.	15.00	8.00

	U.S. $	British £
891. Creamer, 3¹/₂" high	15.00	8.00
892. Cigarette Box, 1³/₄" h. x 5" l.	45.00	25.00
893. Ashtray, 4" l. x 3" w.	20.00	10.00
894. Cup, 2³/₄" high	10.00	5.00
895. Cup, 2³/₄" high	10.00	5.00
896. Dish (Lattice Ware), 6¹/₄" overall	35.00	20.00
897. Creamer (Lattice Ware), 2³/₄" high	35.00	20.00

PAGE 90
"CAMBRIDGE" TABLEWARE CIRCA MID 1950'S

	U.S. $	British £
898. Platter, 14¹/₄" overall	30.00	15.00
899. Saucer, 5¹/₂" dia.	4.00	2.00
900. Cup, 2⁵/₈" high	15.00	8.00
901. Platter, 11³/₄" overall	20.00	12.00
902. Dinner Plate, 10¹/₂" dia.	20.00	10.00
903. Bread & Butter Plate, 6¹/₂" dia.	15.00	8.00
904. Gravy Boat Tray	25.00	15.00
905. Creamer, 3" high	20.00	10.00
906. Fruit Bowl, 5¹/₄" dia.	10.00	5.00
907. Soup Bowl, 7¹/₂" dia.	10.00	5.00
908. Salad Plate, 8" dia.	15.00	8.00
909. Vegetable Bowl, 9" dia.	25.00	15.00
910. Gravy Boat, 3" high	10.00	5.00
911. Dinner Plate, 10" dia.	10.00	5.00
912. Dessert Plate, 9" dia.	10.00	5.00

PAGE 91
"MODE" TABLEWARE EARLY 1953

	U.S. $	British £
913. Teapot, 6" high	35.00	15.00
914. Creamer, 2¹/₂" high	10.00	4.00
915. Sugar, 2⁵/₈" high	8.00	4.00
916. Platter, 13¹/₂" dia.	20.00	8.00
917. Bread & Butter Plate, 6" dia.	8.00	4.00
918. Dinner Plate, 10¹/₄" dia.	15.00	5.00
919. Bowl, 6¹/₂" overall	10.00	4.00
920. Cup & Saucer	15.00	6.00

	U.S. $	British £
921. Dinner Plate, 10¹/₄" dia.	15.00	5.00
922. Cup & Saucer,	15.00	6.00
923. Bowl, 6¹/₂" overall	10.00	4.00

"ORB" TABLEWARE EARLY 1950'S

	U.S. $	British £
924. Dinner Plate, 8³/₄" dia.	15.00	5.00
925. Bread & Butter Plate, 6³/₈" dia.	10.00	4.00
926. Cup & Saucer,	10.00	4.00
927. Platter, 11" overall	20.00	8.00
928. Bowl, 6" dia.	10.00	4.00
929. Dinner Plate, 8³/₄" dia.	10.00	4.00
930. Cup & Saucer,	15.00	5.00
931. Bread & Butter Plate, 6³/₈" dia.	10.00	4.00
932. Cup & Saucer,	10.00	4.00
933. Bowl, 6" dia.	10.00	4.00

"MODE" WARE SNACK SET 1953

	U.S. $	British £
934. Snack Set (cup & plate),	25.00	15.00

PAGE 92
REGENCY TABLEWARE LATE 1940'S - 1960

	U.S. $	British £
935. Wall Plate — Somerset Cottage, 10¹/₂" dia.	75.00	40.00
936. Bread & Butter Plate — Somerset Cottage, 6³/₄" dia.	35.00	18.00
937. Cup — Somerset Cottage, 2⁵/₈" high	20.00	10.00
938. Saucer — Somerset Cottage, 5¹/₂" dia.	10.00	5.00
939. Plate — Springtime, 9" dia.	18.00	10.00

ROMANCE WALL PLATES 1951 - 1960

	U.S. $	British £
940. Wall Plate, 10¹/₂" dia.	75.00	40.00
941. Wall Plate, 10¹/₂" dia.	75.00	40.00
942. Wall Plate, 10¹/₂" dia.	75.00	40.00
943. Wall Plate, 10¹/₂" dia.	75.00	40.00

MISCELLANEOUS TABLEWARE

	U.S. $	British £
944. Nut Dish — Emerald Gold, 8" long	25.00	18.00

	U.S. $	British £
945. Dish — Emerald Gold, 12" long	35.00	20.00
946. Nut Dish — Gold Blush, 8" long	25.00	18.00
947. Nut Dish — Golden Turquoise, 9" dia.	22.00	12.00
948. Covered Sugar — Bramble, 3³/₄" high	25.00	18.00
949. Nut Dish, 8" long	25.00	18.00
950. Flower Pot, 2¹/₂" high	8.00	5.00

"FESTIVAL" WARE DECORATION MID 1952 - LATE 1950'S

951. Nut Dish, 6" dia.	40.00	35.00
952. Sugar, 2¹/₄" high	35.00	20.00
953. Creamer, 4¹/₄" high	50.00	45.00

PAGE 93
REGENCY WALL PLATES CIRCA 1952 LATE 1950'S

954. Wall Plate, 10¹/₂" dia.	45.00	25.00
955. Wall Plate, 10¹/₂" dia.	45.00	25.00
956. Wall Plate, 10¹/₂" dia.	45.00	25.00

DECORATION NO. 5091 CIRCA EARLY 1950'S

957. Platter, 14¹/₂" overall	25.00	14.00
958. Gravy Boat, 3⁷/₈" high	10.00	5.00
959. Platter, 12¹/₂" overall	20.00	10.00

"FLAIR" TABLEWARE CIRCA 1956 - EARLY 1960'S

960. Bread & Butter Plate — Carnival, 6¹/₂" dia.	10.00	4.00
961. Cup & Saucer — Carnival	25.00	6.00
962. Bread & Butter Plate — Sunflower, 6¹/₂" dia.	10.00	4.00
963. Cup & Saucer — Sunflower	25.00	6.00
964. Bread & Butter Plate, 6¹/₂" dia.	10.00	4.00
965. Bread & Butter Plate, 6¹/₂" dia.	10.00	4.00
966. Cup & Saucer	25.00	6.00
967. Bread & Butter Plate — Fern, 6¹/₂" dia.	10.00	4.00

	U.S. $	British £
968. Cup & Saucer — Fern	25.00	6.00

MISCELLANEOUS TABLEWARE

969. Ashtray — Niagara Falls, 5" square	12.00	7.00
970. Creamer, 2³/₄" high	10.00	6.00
971. Sugar Bowl — Darwin, 2¹/₂" high	10.00	6.00
972. Cup & Saucer	10.00	4.00
973. Cigarette Box — Veteran Car, 1³/₄" h. x 5" l.	40.00	18.00

PAGE 94
"TUTTI FRUITTI"— TABLEWARE 1990 - 1992

974. Covered Canister, 8" high	65.00	35.00
975. Covered Canister, 7¹/₄" high	55.00	30.00
976. Dinner Plate, 8¹/₂" dia.	22.00	12.00
977. Teapot, 6" high	75.00	40.00
978. Milk Jug, 5¹/₂" high	50.00	25.00
979. Coverd Sugar, 4¹/₄" high	30.00	15.00
980. Creamer, 3¹/₄" high	30.00	15.00
981. Teapot, 5" high	65.00	35.00
982. Covered Butter Dish, 4¹/₂" h. x 6¹/₄" l.	55.00	30.00
983. Salt, 3" high	15.00	8.00
984. Pepper, 3¹/₄" high	15.00	8.00
985. Mug, 4" high	20.00	10.00
986. Cup & Saucer	18.00	10.00
987. Fruit Bowl, 4¹/₄" h. x 9" dia.	55.00	30.00
988. Covered Cheese, 4¹/₂" high	75.00	40.00

PAGE 95
"CLASSIC LINEN" TABLEWARE 1989 - 1993

989. Coffee Pot, 9" high	30.00	10.00
990. Dinner Plate, 7³/₄" dia.	8.00	2.00
991. Coffee Cup, 2³/₈" high	8.00	3.00
992. Saucer, 5¹/₂" dia.	2.00	1.00
993. Tea Cup, 2⁷/₁₆" high	8.00	4.00
994. Saucer, 6⁷/₈" dia.	2.00	1.00
995. Creamer, 3³/₄" high	15.00	4.00

		U.S. $	British £
996.	Covered Sugar, 3⅞" high	18.00	6.00
997.	Teapot, 6" high	30.00	10.00

"MUSIC" TABLEWARE 1989 - 1991

		U.S. $	British £
998.	Covered Sugar, 3⅞" high	20.00	8.00
999.	Salt, 3⅝" high	15.00	7.00
1000.	Pepper, 3" high	15.00	6.00
1001.	Creamer, 4' high	18.00	5.00

BhS UTENSIL JAR LATE 1980'S

		U.S. $	British £
1002.	"Bon Appetit" Utensil Jar, 6⅛" high	20.00	5.00

"MEADOWLAND" TABLEWARE 1989 - 1993

		U.S. $	British £
1003.	Salt, 3⅝" high	15.00	5.00
1004.	Pepper, 3" high	15.00	5.00

"SUMMER FRUITS" TABLEWARE 1980 - 1993

		U.S. $	British £
1005.	Open Sugar, 2½" high	8.00	4.00
1006.	Gravy Boat, 3¼" high	18.00	8.00

"INDIAN TREE" TABLEWARE

		U.S. $	British £
1007.	Bowl, 9" dia.	20.00	12.00
1008.	Plate, 6¾" dia.	8.00	4.00
1009.	Cup & Saucer	20.00	8.00
1010.	Sugar Bowl, 2¾" high	10.00	5.00
1011.	Cereal Bowl, 6¼" dia.	18.00	8.00
1012.	Plate, 10" dia.	15.00	7.00

PAGE 96
ROYAL COMMEMORATIVES

		U.S. $	British £
1013.	Bell's Whisky Decanter, 75cl (Charles and Diana) full/boxed	1,000.00	600.00
	Bell's Whisky Decanter, 75cl (Charles and Diana) empty	250.00	150.00
1014.	Bell's Whisky Decanter, 75cl (Princess Beatrix) full/boxed	120.00	80.00
	Bell's Whisky Decanter, 75cl (Princess Beatrix) empty	40.00	25.00
1015.	Bell's Whisky Decanter, 75cl (Princess Eugenie) full/boxed	75.00	50.00
	Bell's Whisky Decanter, 75cl (Princess Eugenie) empty	30.00	20.00

		U.S. $	British £
1016.	Bell's Whisky Decanter, 75cl (Queen Mother) full/boxed	105.00	70.00
	Bell's Whisky Decanter, 75cl (Queen Mother) empty	40.00	25.00
1017.	Vase, 8¾" high *(See also Fig. 153 pg. 184 of The W of W)*	40.00	25.00
1018.	Bell's Whisky Decanter, 50cl (Prince Henry) full/boxed	480.00	320.00
	Bell's Whisky Decanter, 50cl (Prince Henry) empty	75.00	50.00
1019.	Teapot, 6⅜" high	120.00	75.00
1020.	Fruit Bowl, 9" dia.	45.00	25.00
1021.	Plate, 6" square	25.00	15.00
1022.	Tankard, ½ pt.	35.00	10.00
1023.	Beer Mug, 5" high	55.00	30.00
1024.	Tankard, ½ pt.	35.00	10.00
1025.	Baby's Cereal Dish, 6½" dia.	60.00	40.00
1026.	"Shell-Mex and B.P. Ltd." Coronation Dish, 4¾" dia.	30.00	18.00
1027.	Trinket Box, 1½" high	45.00	25.00
1028.	Trinket Box, 1¾" high	25.00	12.00
1029.	Pin Tray, 4⅜" dia.	18.00	8.00
1030.	"Burrows & Sturgess Ltd." Coronation Dish, 4¾" dia.	30.00	18.00
1031.	Coronation Fruit Bowl, 12" dia.	520.00	300.00
1032.	Coronation Fruit Bowl, 12" dia. *(See also Fig. 108 pg. 154 of The W of W)*	335.00	195.00

PAGE 97

		U.S. $	British £
1033.	Stein, 8½" high	120.00	80.00
1034.	Coach Decanter, 6½" high	390.00	200.00
1035.	Bell's Mini. Whisky Decanter, (Charles and Diana) 4" high, full/boxed	1,275.00	850.00
	Bell's Mini. Whisky Decanter (Charles and Diana) 4" high, empty	180.00	125.00

Records indicate that only 650/700 Royal Wedding miniature decanters were made rather than the 2,000 noted in *The W of W2*. These miniature decanters were originally made for employees of the distillery only and were not a retail item.

IRISH PORCELAIN

		U.S. $	British £
1036.	Eileen Oge, 8" high	350.00	275.00
1037.	Baby, 4¼" high	380.00	300.00

WALL PLAQUES EARLY - MID 1950'S

1038.	Wall Plaque — Horse, 8" h. x 11" l.	300.00	175.00
1039.	Wall Plaque — Abstract, 15" h. x 9½" l.	300.00	175.00
1040.	Wall Plaque — Fish, 7½" h. x 12" l.	300.00	175.00

WADE HEATH CHARACTER JUGS LATE 1950'S

1041.	Character Jug — Pirate, 6" high	200.00	120.00
1042.	Character Jug — Highwayman, 6" high	200.00	120.00

PAGE 98

IRISH GIFTWARE EARLY 1950'S - LATE 1980'S

1043.	One Pint Tankard, 6½" high	30.00	10.00
1044.	Killarney Urn, 8" high	65.00	45.00
1045.	Killarney Urn, 6¼" high	50.00	28.00
1046.	Killarney Urn, 4¼" high	30.00	12.00
1047.	Killarney Urn, 3" high	20.00	5.00
1048.	Stein Tankard, 6⅜" high	30.00	12.00
1049.	One Pint Tankard, 6½" high	30.00	10.00
1050.	One Pint "Tyrone" Tankard, 6½" high	30.00	20.00
1051.	Half Pint "Tyrone" Tankard, 5½" high	20.00	12.00
1052.	Miniature "Tyrone" Tankard, 3" high	15.00	5.00
1053.	Musical Tankard, 5½" high	65.00	20.00
1054.	Child's Tankard, 3" high	20.00	5.00
1055.	Vinegar Bottle, 6¾" high	50.00	30.00

MOURNE RANGE 1971 - MID 1970'S

1056.	Vase, 6¾" high	60.00	30.00
1057.	Cream Jug, 4¼" high	60.00	30.00
1058.	Covered Preserve Jar, 3¾" high	75.00	35.00

		U.S. $	British £
1059.	Half Pint Tankard, 4" high	45.00	25.00
1060.	One Pint Tankard, 5" high	60.00	30.00
1061.	Dish, 7" l. x 5" w.	60.00	35.00
1062.	Covered Candy Box, 5" l. x 3¾" w.	60.00	35.00

MISCELLANEOUS GIFTWARE

1063.	Covered Jar, 5¼" high	75.00	35.00
1064.	Covered Sugar — Shamrock, 4¼" high	50.00	25.00
	Coffee Pot — Shamrock	80.00	40.00
	Open Sugar — Shamrock	25.00	10.00
	Cream Jug — Shamrock	25.00	10.00
	Covered Hot Milk Jug — Shamrock	50.00	25.00
	One Pint Jug — Shamrock	45.00	20.00
	Cup & Saucer — Shamrock	20.00	10.00

PAGE 99

1065.	Teapot Stand, 5½" square	65.00	25.00
1066.	Coffee Pot, 10½" high	90.00	40.00
1067.	Teapot Stand, 5½" square	65.00	25.00
1068.	Plate, 7" dia.	50.00	25.00

WALL PLATES LATE 1980'S

1069.	Blarney Castle, 7¾" dia.	35.00	20.00
1070.	"Wolseley" Veteran Car, 7¾" dia.	45.00	28.00
1071.	"Fiat" Veteran Car, 7⅛" dia.	35.00	20.00
1072.	"Duesenberg" Veteran Car, 7⅛" dia.	35.00	20.00
1073.	"Wolseley" Veteran Car, 7⅛" dia.	35.00	20.00
1074.	"Austin Seven" Veteran Car, 7⅛" dia.	35.00	20.00

RAINDROPS GIFTWARE

1075.	Teapot, 4¾" high	80.00	40.00
1076.	Creamer, 2¾" high	25.00	10.00
1077.	Sugar, 2" high	20.00	10.00
1078.	Table Lighter, 3¼" high	45.00	15.00

	U.S. $	British £
1079. One Pint Jug, 4½" high	45.00	20.00
Three Quarter Pint Jug (not illustrated)	40.00	18.00
Half Pint Jug (not illustrated)	35.00	12.00
1080. Coffee Pot, 6¼" high	80.00	40.00

SELF STANDING PICTURES

	U.S. $	British £
1081. Picture, 4" square	65.00	25.00
1082. Oval Picture Frame, 4" high	50.00	15.00

LUCKY LEPRECHAUNS CIRCA 1956 - 1986

	U.S. $	British £
1083. Pintray — Pot of Gold, 1⅝" high	25.00	5.00
1084. Pintray — Tailor, 1⅞" high	25.00	5.00
1085. Dish — Leprechaun on Acorn, 2½" h. x 3¼" dia.	75.00	35.00
1086. Leprechaun on Acorn, 1½" high (See also Fig. 125 pg. 165 of The W of W)	75.00	30.00
1087. Leprechaun on Rabbit, 1½" high (See also Fig. 125 pg. 165 of The W of W)	75.00	35.00
1088. Lucky Irish Leprechaun, 2⅛" high	45.00	15.00

IRISH CHARACTER FIGURES EARLY 1990'S

	U.S. $	British £
1089. Danny Boy, 4" high	30.00	16.00
1090. Mother MacCree, 2½" high	30.00	14.00
1091. Molly Malone, 3¼" high	30.00	25.00
1092. Kathleen, 3½" high	30.00	15.00
1093. Eileen Oge, 3¾" high	30.00	16.00
1094. Phil the Fluter, 3¾" high	30.00	30.00
1095. Paddy Reilly, 3¾" high	30.00	25.00
1096. Rose of Tralee, 4" high	30.00	18.00
1097. Paddy Maginty, 3¼" high	30.00	18.00

PAGE 100

IRISH SONG FIGURES 1962 - 1986

Modelling of Eileen Oge (No. 1098), Dan Murphy (No. 1101) and Mother MacCree (No. 1102) was done by Raymond Piper and not by Phoebe Stabler as reported in *The W of W2*. It is interesting to note that Felicity Carryer Grahamn sat for the EileenOge figure.

	U.S. $	British £
1098. Eileen Oge, 8" high	350.00	275.00
1099. Widda Cafferty, 6¼" high	350.00	300.00
1100. The Bard of Armagh, 5⅛" high	350.00	300.00
1101. Dan Murphy, 8¼" high	350.00	250.00
1102. Mother MacCree, 8¼" high	450.00	250.00

MISCELLANEOUS IRISH GIFTWARE

	U.S. $	British £
1103. "Larry" Bookend, 4½" high	75.00	65.00
1104. "Lester" Bookend, 4½" high	75.00	65.00
1105. Lucky Leprechaun, 2¾" high	25.00	20.00
1106. Inkwell, 1⅞" high	45.00	30.00
1107. Leprechaun & Cottage, 2¼" h. x 5⅜" across (See also Fig. 126 pg. 165 of The W of W)	100.00	85.00
1108. Single Egg Coddler, 3" high	15.00	8.00
1109. Lucky Leprechaun, 2¾" high	25.00	20.00
1110. Flower Pot Holder, 4" high	55.00	25.00
1111. Cup & Saucer — Shamrock	45.00	25.00
1112. Duck Posy Bowl, 4½" h. x 7½" l.	165.00	150.00
1113. Celtic Porcelain Dish, 4½" dia.	35.00	20.00
1114. Celtic Porcelain Covered Box, 4½" high	50.00	28.00
1115. "Rose" Ashtray, 6¾" across	20.00	10.00
1116. Miniature Traditional Tankard, 3" high	16.00	15.00
1117. "Paddy Maginty" Pipe Rest, 3⅝" high	90.00	35.00
1118. Pipe Rest, 2" high	15.00	10.00
1119. "Phil Fluter" Pipe Rest, 3¾" high	90.00	35.00
1120. Cruet Set & Stand	55.00	25.00

YACHT WALL PLAQUES 1955

	U.S. $	British £
1121. Yacht Wall Plaque, 4½" high	40.00	35.00
1122. Yacht Wall Plaque, 4⅛" high	40.00	35.00
1123. Yacht Wall Plaque, 3⅜" high	40.00	35.00

PINK ELEPHANTS 1959

	U.S. $	British £
1124. "Never Mix'em!" — Pink Elephant, 1½" h. x 3" l.	65.00	25.00

POGO 1959

		U.S. $	British £
1125.	Pogo, 3¹/₄" high	600.00	450.00

PINK ELEPHANTS 1959

		U.S. $	British £
1126.	"Stick to Water!" — Pink Elephant, 1¹/₂" h. x 3" l.	65.00	25.00

FLYING BIRDS SET 1 CIRCA 1956 - 1959

		U.S. $	British £
1127.	Flying Bird — Green, 1" h. x 2³/₄" across	15.00	5.00
1128.	Flying Bird — Yellow, 1" h. x 2³/₄" across	15.00	10.00
1129.	Flying Bird — Blue, 1" h. x 2³/₄" across	15.00	5.00

(See also Fig. 123 pg. 164 of The W of W)

<u>PAGE 101</u>

BELLS WHISKY DECANTERS

		U.S. $	British £
1130.	Bell's Old Scotch Whisky, 75cl (full/boxed)	95.00	55.00
	Bell's Old Scotch Whisky, 75cl (empty)	35.00	20.00
1131.	Bell's Old Scotch Whisky — Christmas 1989, 75cl (full/boxed)	105.00	60.00
	Bell's Old Scotch Whisky — Christmas 1989, 75cl (empty)	60.00	35.00
1132.	Bell's Old Scotch Whisky — Christmas 1990, 75cl (full/boxed)	85.00	50.00
	Bell's Old Scotch Whisky — Christmas 1990, 75cl (empty)	60.00	35.00
1133.	Bell's Old Scotch Whisky — Christmas 1991, 75cl (full/boxed)	85.00	50.00
	Bell's Old Scotch Whisky — Christmas 1991, 75cl (empty)	60.00	35.00
1134.	Bell's Fine Old Scotch Whisky, 75cl (full/boxed)	95.00	55.00
	Bell's Fine Old Scotch Whisky, 75cl (empty)	60.00	35.00
1135.	Bell's Old Scotch Whisky — Hawaii, 75cl (full/boxed)	510.00	300.00
	Bell's Old Scotch Whisky — Hawai, 75cl (empty)	105.00	60.00
1136.	Bell's Old Scotch Whisky — Wedding, 75cl (full/boxed)	510.00	300.00

		U.S. $	British £
	Bell's Old Scotch Whisky — Wedding, 75cl (empty)	105.00	60.00
1137.	Bell's Old Scotch Whisky, 5cl (full/boxed)	35.00	22.00
	Bell's Old Scotch Whisky, 5cl (empty)	20.00	15.00
1138.	Bell's Old Scotch Whisky — Year of the Sheep 1991, 75cl (full/boxed)	190.00	110.00
	Bell's Old Scotch Whisky — Year of the Sheep 1991, 75cl (empty)	45.00	25.00
1139.	Bell's Old Scotch Whisky — Year of the Monkey 1992, 75cl (full/boxed)	220.00	130.00
	Bell's Old Scotch Whisky — Year of the Monkey 1992, 75cl (empty)	45.00	25.00

FINDLATER'S WHISKY DECANTERS 1986 - 1990

		U.S. $	British £
1140.	Findlater's First XI, 750ml (empty)	75.00	40.00
1141.	Findlater's Fist XI World Cup Italy 1990, 750ml (empty)	80.00	45.00

MISCELLANEOUS DECANTERS

		U.S. $	British £
1142.	John Jameson & Son Irish Whisky, 750ml (empty)	75.00	40.00
1143.	Beneagles Scotch Whisky — Brown Bear, 4³/₄" high (empty)	75.00	40.00
1144.	Glen Turret 25 Year Old Scotch Whisky, 70cl (empty)	80.00	45.00

TAUNTON'S CIDER

		U.S. $	British £
1145.	Taunton's "Autumn Gold" Cider, 6¹/₄" high	35.00	20.00
1146.	Taunton's "Dry Blackthorn" Cider, 6¹/₄" high	35.00	20.00

PUSSER'S RUM DECANTERS

		U.S. $	British £
1147.	"Nelson's Ship" Miniature Decanter, 3¹/₂" high (empty)	25.00	15.00
1148.	British Navy Rum "West Indies" Hip Flask, 5³/₄" high (empty)	30.00	18.00

(See also Fig.177 pg.228 of The W of W2)

		U.S. $	British £
1149.	"British Navy" Rum Miniature Flagon, 2¹/₂" high (empty)	20.00	10.00

PAGE 102

MISCELLANEOUS DECANTERS AND LIQUOR BOTTLES

		U.S. $	British £
1150.	Beneagles Scotch Whisky — Curling Stone, $2^3/4$" high (empty)	45.00	25.00
1151.	Whyte & MacKay Scotch Whisky, $9^3/4$" high (empty)	50.00	35.00
1152.	Glenfiddich® Ancient Reserve Scotch Whisky, 700ml (empty)	35.00	20.00
1153.	Glenfiddich® Ancient Reserve Scotch Whisky, 700ml (empty)	35.00	20.00
1154.	Glenfiddich® Ancient Reserve Scotch Whisky, 700ml (empty)	35.00	20.00
1155.	Abbot's Choice Scotch Whisky, 10" high (empty)	110.00	60.00
1156.	Villa Colonna®, $9^1/2$" high (empty)	80.00	45.00
1157.	Old Parr Tribute, 7" high (empty)	260.00	150.00
1158.	Carlton Special Scotch Whisky, 750ml (empty)	50.00	35.00

FINDLATER'S WHISKY DECANTERS 1986 - 1990

		U.S. $	British £
1159.	Findlater's First XV, 750ml (empty)	75.00	40.00
1160.	Findlater's First XV, 750ml (empty)	80.00	45.00

DIMPLE SCOTCH WHISKY LIQUOR BOTTLES 1987 - 1990

		U.S. $	British £
1161.	Dimple Scotch Whisky — Hawaii, 75cl (empty)	110.00	65.00
1162.	Dimple Scotch Whisky — 1990 Year of the Horse, 75cl (full/boxed)	510.00	300.00
	Dimple Scotch Whisky — 1990 Year of the Horse, 75cl (empty)	100.00	35.00
1163.	Dimple Scotch Whisky — 1989 Year of the Snake, 75cl (full/boxed)	510.00	300.00
	Dimple Scotch Whisky — 1989 Year of the Snake, 75cl (empty)	100.00	35.00

THE THISTLE AND THE ROSE CHESS SET 1980

		U.S. $	British £
1164.	Norman English Tower, 4" high	30.00	12.00
1165.	Sir Francis Drake, $5^1/8$" high	30.00	12.00
1166.	Thomas A'Becket, $5^1/4$" high	30.00	12.00
1167.	Queen Elizabeth I, $5^1/4$" high	30.00	12.00
1168.	King Henry VIII, $5^1/4$" high	30.00	12.00
1169.	Pawn - Rose, $3^5/8$" high	35.00	18.00
1170.	Pawn - Thistle, $3^5/8$" high	35.00	18.00
1171.	King Robert the Bruce, $5^1/8$" high	30.00	12.00
1172.	Mary Queen of Scots, $4^7/8$" high	30.00	12.00
1173.	John Knox, 5" high	30.00	12.00
1174.	Sir William Wallace, $5^3/8$" high	30.00	12.00
1175.	Scottish Tower House, $4^1/8$" high	30.00	12.00

PAGE 103

BLACK & WHITE SCOTCH WHISKY DECANTER 1972 - 1986

		U.S. $	British £
1176.	Black & White "Dog" Gift Decanter, $7^1/2$" high (full/boxed)	300.00	150.00
	Black & White "Dog" Gift Decanter, $7^1/2$" high (empty)	175.00	85.00

CHIVAS ROYAL SALUTE LIQUOR BOTTLES 1982 - PRESENT

		U.S. $	British £
1177.	Chivas Scotch Whisky, 750ml (empty)	25.00	15.00
1178.	Chivas Scotch Whisky, 375ml (empty)	20.00	10.00
1179.	Chivas Scotch Whisky, 750ml (empty)	25.00	15.00
1180.	Chivas Scotch Whisky, 375ml (empty)	25.00	15.00
1181.	Chivas Scotch Whisky, 750ml (empty)	25.00	15.00
1182.	Chivas Scotch Whisky, 200ml (empty)	25.00	15.00
1183.	Chivas Scotch Whisky, 50ml (empty)	20.00	10.00
1184.	Water Jug — Chivas Regal 12 Year Old Whisky, 8" high	25.00	15.00

GILBEY'S WINE BARRELS 1953

The height of these two barrels was incorrectly noted in *The W of W2*. The correct dimensions are shown below. For further information on Gilbey's wine barrels see pg. 174 of *The W of W*.

		U.S. $	British £
1185.	Cognac Barrel, 5³/₄" high	25.00	15.00
1186.	Rum Barrel, 5³/₄" high	25.00	15.00

MISCELLANEOUS WATER JUGS, ASHTRAYS AND WAITER TRAYS

		U.S. $	British £
1187.	Water Jug — Nicholson's Lamplighter Gin, 6" high	30.00	15.00
1188.	Ashtray — Long John Scotch Whisky, 6" dia.	15.00	7.00
1189.	Water Jug — Pussers British Navy Rum, 5³/₄" high	30.00	12.00
1190.	Ashtray — Keg Harp Lager, 7" dia.	10.00	5.00
1191.	Water Jug — Imperial Vodka, 6¹/₂" high	30.00	15.00
1192.	Water Jug — Crawford's Old Scotch Whisky, 4" high	45.00	20.00
1193.	Water Jug — John Begg Scotch Whisky, 5" high	30.00	18.00
1194.	Ashtray — John Begg Scotch Whisky, 6" across	15.00	6.00
1195.	Water Jug "Quantas" Australia's Overseas Airlines, 4¹/₂" high	30.00	20.00

PAGE 104

		U.S. $	British £
1196.	Waiter Tray — Johnnie Walker Scotch Whisky, 12³/₄" square	15.00	8.00
1197.	Water Jug — Johnnie Walker Scotch Whisky, 6¹/₂" high	20.00	12.00
1198.	Ashtray — Johnnie Walker Scotch Whisky, 6³/₄" square	15.00	4.00
1199.	Ashtray — Johnnie Walker Scotch Whisky, 4³/₄" square	12.00	4.00
1200.	Water Jug — Johnnie Walker Red Label, 7¹/₂" high	45.00	30.00
1201.	Ashtray — Bell's Old Scotch Whisky, 9" long	20.00	8.00
1202.	Ashtray — Bell's Old Scotch Whisky, 7" dia.	15.00	4.00
1203.	Water Jug — Bell's Old Scotch Whisky, 8" high	30.00	12.00
1204.	Water Jug, Arthur Bell & Sons Ltd. Scotch Whisky, 5" high	40.00	25.00

		U.S. $	British £
1205.	Water Jug, Bell's Scotch Whisky, 5¹/₂" high	28.00	20.00
1206.	Water Jug — Black & White Scotch Whisky, 5" high	28.00	20.00
1207.	Ashtray — Black & White Scotch Whisky, 5" dia.	15.00	4.00
1208.	Sherry Container — Bertola Cream Sherry, 9" high	35.00	18.00
1209.	Water Jug — John Player Special Cigarettes, 6¹/₄" high	20.00	12.00
1210.	Water Jug — Jubilee Stout, 4³/₄" high	20.00	10.00
1211.	Water Jug — Vat 69 Scotch Whisky, 4¹/₂" high	20.00	12.00
1212.	Ashtray — Vat 69 Scotch Whisky, 4¹/₈" dia.	10.00	4.00
1213.	Ashtray — The Abbot's Choice Scotch Whisky, 5" dia.	10.00	6.00
1214.	Ashtray — Canada Dry, 5" across	10.00	6.00
1215.	Water Jug — Old Rarity Delux Scotch Whisky, 5" high	30.00	14.00

PAGE 105

		U.S. $	British £
1216.	Water Jug — Johnnie Walker Scotch Whisky, 5³/₄" high	25.00	25.00
1217.	Water Jug — Dewar's Special Scotch Whisky, 6¹/₄" high	30.00	20.00
1218.	Water Jug — The Dewar Highlander, 5³/₄" high	25.00	25.00
1219.	Water Jug — Grand MacNish Scotch Whisky, 5¹/₂" high	30.00	14.00
1220.	Waiter Tray — Grand MacNish Scotch Whisky, 12¹/₂" square	15.00	8.00
1221.	Toby Jug — Charrington's Beers, 7³/₈" high	145.00	85.00
1222.	Water Jug — Toby Jim Jug, 4³/₈" high	112.00	65.00
1223.	Ashtray — Dewar's® Deluxe Ancestor® Scotch Whisky, 5¹/₂" square	8.00	2.00
1224.	Water Jug — Dewar's "White Label" Scotch Whisky, 5³/₄" high	25.00	20.00
1225.	Water Jug — The Famous Grouse, 4¹/₂" high	28.00	14.00

	U.S. $	British £
1226. Ashtray — The Famous Grouse, 5^1/$_2$" dia.	10.00	4.00
1227. Water Jug — The Buchanan Blend, 6" high	30.00	14.00
1228. Water Jug — Beefeater Gin, 6" high (PDM Mark)	30.00	14.00
For Beefeater Jugs with Regicor Mark, add 30%		
1229. Ashtray — Beefeater Dry Gin, 4^1/$_4$" square	10.00	6.00
1230. Ashtray — Beefeater London Gin, 8" long	15.00	8.00
1231. Water Jug — Beefeater Gin, 6" high	35.00	14.00
For Beefeater Jugs with Regicor Mark, add 30%		
1232. Water Jug — McCallum's Scotch Whisky, 5" high	30.00	14.00
1233. Ashtray — Double Diamond, 4" square	10.00	4.00
1234. Salt Shaker — Jubilee Stout, 3^1/$_8$" high	18.00	10.00
1235. Pepper Shaker — Jubilee Stout, 3^1/$_8$" high	18.00	10.00
1236. Mustard Pot — Jubilee Stout, 3^1/$_8$" high	18.00	10.00
1237. Salt Shaker — Welcome, 4^5/$_8$" high	15.00	4.00
1238. Pepper Shaker — Welcome, 4^5/$_8$" high	15.00	4.00

PAGE 106

BASS PROMOTIONAL ITEMS

1239. Ashtray — Bass, 5^1/$_4$" dia.	15.00	8.00
1240. Waiter Tray — Bass The Great Ale of England, 12^1/$_2$" square	20.00	10.00
1241. Ashtray — You're Twice the Man on Worthington, 5^1/$_2$" dia.	10.00	6.00

MISCELLANEOUS ASHTRAYS AND WATER JUGS

1242. Water Jug — Grant's Scotch Whisky, 6" high	30.00	15.00
1243. Ashtray — Grant's Scotch Whisky, 4" triangle	10.00	6.00

	U.S. $	British £
1244. Water Jug — Grant's Scotch Whisky, 6^1/$_2$" high	30.00	15.00
1245. Water Jug — Gordon's Special London Dry Gin, 5^1/$_8$" high	20.00	10.00
1246. Ashtray — Gordon's Special Dry Gin, 6^1/$_4$" square	10.00	6.00
1247. Ashtray — Cavalier Panatellas, 9" long	20.00	10.00
1248. Water Jug — Catto's Scotch Whisky, 6^3/$_4$" high	34.00	18.00
1249. Water Jug — Kentucky Tavern, 7^1/$_2$" high	30.00	15.00
1250. Water Jug — Something Special, 5^3/$_4$" high	25.00	12.00
1251. Ashtray - Benson & Hedges, 9^1/$_2$" long	10.00	6.00
1252. Cigarette Lighter — Benson & Hedges, 4^1/$_2$" high	40.00	18.00
1253. Water Jug — Chequers Scotch Whisky, 6" high	35.00	12.00
1254. Water Jug — Black Bush Irish Whisky, 6^5/$_8$" high	35.00	12.00
1255. Ashtray — Kronenbourg, 5" square	10.00	4.00
1256. Ashtray — Kronenbourg, 6" dia.	20.00	10.00
1257. Ashtray — Morland, 5^1/$_2$" square	10.00	4.00

WHITBREAD HOPPER 1987

1258. Pin Badge and Ceramic Frog, 2^1/$_4$" dia. (complete)	40.00	25.00
Ceramic Frog only	20.00	12.50

MISCELLANEOUS ASHTRAYS, WATER JUGS AND WAITER TRAYS

1259. Ashtray — Austin, 5^1/$_2$" square	15.00	8.00
1260. Beer Display Sign — Marston's Burton Bitter, 2^1/$_4$" high	30.00	10.00

PAGE 107

1261. Plate — Mansfield Ales, 8" square	15.00	8.00

	U.S. $	British £
1262. Hors d'oeuvres Dish — Celebration Ale, 8¹/₂" dia.	14.00	18.00
1263. Waiter Tray — Marston's Low C, 10¹/₂" dia.	15.00	8.00
1264. Waiter Tray — Allbright A Great Bitter, 12¹/₂" square	15.00	8.00
1265. Ashtray — Senior Service Cigarettes, 9¹/₂" across	15.00	8.00
1266. Water Jug — Dunhill International, 6" high	25.00	12.00
1267. Ashtray — Dunhill International, 4¹/₄" square	10.00	6.00
1268. Water Jug — Dunhill International, 5¹/₂" high	25.00	12.00
1269. Ashtray — Samuel Webster 1838, 10" long	10.00	6.00
1270. Ashtray — Badger Beer, 5¹/₄" square	15.00	8.00
1271. Ashtray — Badger Beer, 8¹/₂" long	10.00	7.00
1272. Ashtray — Booth's Gin, 5³/₄" dia.	10.00	6.00
1273. Ashtray — Carling Black Label, 8¹/₂" long	15.00	8.00
1274. Water Jug — Carling Black Label, 6¹/₂" high	20.00	10.00

BOTTLE POURERS

	U.S. $	British £
1275. Bird, 5" long	90.00	30.00
1276. Eagle, 5¹/₂" long	100.00	30.00
1277. Bush Baby, 5" long	90.00	35.00
1278. Beefeater, 3" long	45.00	30.00
1279. Captain Morgan, 4¹/₂" long	25.00	10.00
1280. J & B Whisky, 3" long	20.00	8.00
1281. White Horse, 5" long	35.00	12.00

MISCELLANEOUS ASHTRAYS, WATER JUGS AND WAITER TRAYS

	U.S. $	British £
1282. Ashtray — Greene King, 5" dia.	10.00	2.00
1283. Dish, 4³/₄" across	10.00	6.00
1284. Ashtray — Greene King, 5¹/₂" square	10.00	5.00

PAGE 108

	U.S. $	British £
1285. Waiter Tray — Wm. Younger's Tartan, 12¹/₂" square	15.00	8.00
1286. Waiter Tray — Tetley Mild, 12¹/₂" square	15.00	8.00
1287. Waiter Tray — The Northern Clubs, 12¹/₂" square	15.00	8.00
1288. Waiter Tray — Tennent's Lager, 12¹/₂" square	15.00	8.00
1289. Ashtray — Down with Marksman, 8¹/₂" dia.	10.00	4.00

GUINNESS DISHES EARLY 1960'S

	U.S. $	British £
1290. "Kangaroo" Bon Bon Dish, 4" dia.	45.00	25.00
1291. "Toucan" Bon Bon Dish, 4" dia.	45.00	25.00
1292. Plate — Guinness Stout, 8" dia.	45.00	25.00
1293. "Pelican" Bon Bon Dish, 4" dia.	45.00	25.00
1294. "Seal" Bon Bon Dish, 4" dia.	45.00	25.00

MISCELLANEOUS ASHTRAYS AND WATER JUGS

	U.S. $	British £
1295. Ashtray — Breaker Real Malt Liquor, 8" dia.	10.00	4.00
1296. Water Jug — Black Bottle® Scotch Whisky, 5¹/₂" high	30.00	18.00
1297. Ashtray — Carrolls No.1 Virginia Cigarettes, 9" overall	10.00	5.00
1298. Ashtray — White Horse Scotch Whisky, 8" long	20.00	5.00
1299. Ashtray — White Horse Scotch Whisky, 5³/₄" long	15.00	6.00
1300. Ashtray — Treble Gold, 9" long	15.00	8.00
1301. Water Jug — Usher's Scotch Whisky, 5" high	40.00	25.00
1302. Ashtray — Romanoff Vodka, 5¹/₂" square	6.00	2.00
1303. Glass Ashtray — Tennent's Lager and Stout, 5¹/₂" dia.	6.00	2.00
1304. Ashtray — John Bull Bitter, 6¹/₂" dia.	6.00	3.00
1305. Water Jug — Whitehall London Dry Gin, 4⁵/₈" high	20.00	12.00

	U.S. $	British £
1306. Ashtray — Old Parr Scotch Whisky, $6^1/4$" dia.	10.00	4.00
1307. Ashtray — Booth's Gin, $6^1/4$" square	10.00	6.00

PAGE 109
VAUX BREWERIES TANKARDS

	U.S. $	British £
1308. A - Gold Tankard	60.00	25.00
B - Sunderland Draught Bitter	60.00	25.00
C - Lorimer's	55.00	22.00
D - Group Logos	55.00	22.00
E - Double Maxim	65.00	22.00
F - School of Sport	65.00	22.00
G - Vehicles	50.00	22.00
H - Vaux Group	50.00	22.00
I - Old Brewers Shot	50.00	22.00
J - Vaux Breweries	50.00	22.00
K - Double Maxim	50.00	22.00
L - Maxim Light	50.00	22.00
M - Ward's	50.00	22.00
N - Brand Logos	50.00	22.00

TAUNTON CIDER MUGS

	U.S. $	British £
1309. A - 1981	100.00	45.00
B - 1976	100.00	45.00
C - 1982	100.00	45.00
D - 1989	100.00	45.00
E - 1980	100.00	45.00
F - 1983	100.00	45.00
G - 1977	100.00	45.00
H - 1988	100.00	45.00
I - 1980	35.00	16.00
J - pre 1980	45.00	20.00
K - pre 1980	55.00	25.00
L - 1990	35.00	16.00
M - 1987	35.00	15.00
1310. Tankard - Vaux Breweries, $4^1/4$" high	45.00	20.00
1311. Tankard - Vaux Breweries, $4^1/4$" high	55.00	25.00

	U.S. $	British £
1312. Taunton Cider Mug, 5" high	130.00	60.00
1313. Taunton Cider Mug, $4^7/8$" high	130.00	60.00

PAGE 110
MISCELLANEOUS DECANTERS, WATER JUGS AND ASHTRAYS

	U.S. $	British £
1314. Decanter — The English Gentlemen's Choice, 10" high (empty)	130.00	60.00
1315. Decanter — Irish Mist, 9" high (empty)	30.00	25.00
1316. Liquor Bottle — British Airways, $2^1/4$" high (empty)	120.00	50.00
1317. Decanter — John Paul Jones Ships, $8^3/4$" high (empty) *(See also No. 347 pg. 44 of the WPT)*	85.00	50.00
1318. Bell's Scotch Whisky Decanter — Christmas 1988, 75cl (full/boxed)	490.00	290.00
Bell's Scotch Whisky Decanter — Christmas 1988, 75cl (empty)	260.00	100.00
1319. Water Jug — Canadian Club, $5^1/2$" high	30.00	15.00
1320. Ashtray — Canadian Club, 4" square	10.00	5.00
1321. Water Jug — Canadian Club, $6^3/4$" high	35.00	25.00
1322. Water Jug — Royal Salute Scotch Whisky, $4^3/4$" high	25.00	14.00
1323. Ashtray — Keg Harp Lager, 3" h. x $5^3/4$" across	12.00	8.00
1324. Ashtray — Cream of the Barley, $5^1/4$" across	20.00	12.00
1325. Water Jug — Bell's Finest Old Scotch Whisky, 6" high	20.00	12.00
1326. Water Jug — Bass & Co's Pale Ale, $6^1/4$" high	35.00	25.00
1327. Water Jug — Imperial, 6" high	30.00	16.00
1328. Cigarette Lighter — Imperial, $4^1/4$" high	40.00	18.00
1329. First Camp of the Scouts — Anniversary Loving Cup, $3^1/4$" high	45.00	20.00
1330. First Camp of the Scouts — Anniversary Tankard, $4^3/4$" high	35.00	15.00

		U.S. $	British £
1331.	Tankard — Vaux Breweries, 4^1/$_8$" high	55.00	25.00
1332.	Tankard — Vaux Breweries, 4^1/$_8$" high (Reverse Side of No. 1331)	55.00	25.00

		U.S. $	British £
1333.	Decanter — Leaping Trout, 10^3/$_4$" high (prototype)	NPA	NPA

At the time of publication of the *WPT*, the Trout decanter has not been produced commercially.

ANIMALS FIGURES, CARTOON, WHIMSIES AND NOVELTY FIGURES
by George Wade & Son Ltd. and Wade Heath & Company Ltd.

PAGE 114
FIG. 18. MR. PENGUIN LATE 1940'S MID - 1950'S

	U.S. $	British £
Pepper Shaker, 3^1/$_2$" high	120.00	90.00

PAGE 117
FIG. 19. DRUM BOX SERIES 1956 - 1959

	U.S. $	British £
Jem, 2" high	85.00	35.00

(See also No. 48 pg. 34 of The W of W)

PAGE 118
FIG. 20. WHIMSIES 1971 - 1984

		U.S. $	British £
A.	Hippo, ^{15}/$_{16}$" h. x 1^1/$_2$" l.	4.00	1.50
B.	Hippo, 1" h. x 1^5/$_8$" l.	8.00	2.50
C.	Hippo, 1^1/$_{16}$" h. x 1^3/$_4$" l.	5.00	1.50

(See also No. 158-20 pg. 40 of The W of W)

PAGE 119
FIG. 21. WHIMSIES 1971 - 1984

		U.S. $	British £
A.	Bison, 1^1/$_8$" h. x 1^5/$_8$" l.	10.00	4.00
B.	Bison, 1^3/$_8$" h. x 1^3/$_4$" l.	5.00	2.00

(See also No. 165-51 pg. 40 of The W of W)

FIG. 22. WHIMSIES 1971 - 1984

		U.S. $	British £
A.	Pig, ^{13}/$_{16}$" h. x 1^1/$_2$" l.	25.00	4.00

		U.S. $	British £
B.	Pig, 1" h. x 1^3/$_4$" l.	18.00	2.50

(See also No. 160-28 pg. 40 of The W of W)

FIG. 23. BABY POLAR BEAR BLOW-UP CIRCA 1962

	U.S. $	British £
Baby Polar Bear Blow-up (left), 3^3/$_4$" h. x 4" l.	270.00	160.00
Baby Polar Bear — Whimsies 1953-1959 (right), ^{7}/$_8$" high	34.00	16.00

(See also No. 150-29 pg. 39 of The W of W)

PAGE 120
FIG. 24. BABY SEAL BLOW-UP CIRCA 1962

	U.S. $	British £
Baby Seal Blow-up, (left) 4^3/$_4$" h. x 5" l.	300.00	180.00
Baby Seal-Whimsies 1953-1959 (right), ^{7}/$_8$" high	28.00	12.00

(See also No. 150-28 pg. 39 of The W of W)

FIG. 25. PROTOTYPE MONKEY

		U.S. $	British £
A.	Monkey and Baby, 3^1/$_4$" high	250.00	150.00
B.	Monkey and Baby — Whimsies 1953 - 1959, 1^7/$_8$" high	30.00	20.00

(See also No. 148-18 pg. 39 of The W of W)

BIRDS, ANIMALS AND PREMIUMS *by George Wade & Son Ltd. and Wade Heath & Company Ltd.*

PAGE 122
FIG. 26. THE TORTOISE FAMILY 1958 - 1988

	U.S. $	British £
Rectangular Tortoise Ashbowl, 6" l. x 4^1/$_4$" w.	60.00	30.00

FIG. 27. BIRD VASES 1936 - 1939

		U.S. $	British £
A.	Small Birdvase, 3^1/$_2$" high	60.00	30.00
B.	Large Birdvase, 6^3/$_4$" high	170.00	90.00

PAGE 127				PAGE 128		

PAGE 127
FIG. 32. ANIMAL FIGURINES

	U.S. $	British £
Sitting Pup, 4¼" high	175.00	50.00

PAGE 128
FIG. 34. ST. JOHNS AMBULANCE BADGER 1990

	U.S. $	British £
Standing Badger, 4" high	130.00	150.00

MISCELLANEOUS ITEMS *by George Wade & Son Ltd. and Wade Heath & Company Ltd.*

PAGE 136
FIG. 36. ASCOT BOWL LATE 1950'S

	U.S. $	British £
Ascot Bowl, 2¼" h. x 3¼" dia.	95.00	50.00

PAGE 138
FIG. 37. MISCELLANEOUS ITEMS

	U.S. $	British £
Bunny Night Light, 4½" h. x 5½" l.	85.00	50.00

PAGE 139
FIG. 39. MISCELLANEOUS ITEMS

	U.S. $	British £
Tree Trunk Covered Dish, 2" h. x 3" dia.	25.00	10.00

FIG. 40. MISCELLANEOUS ITEMS

	U.S. $	British £
Bird Bath Bowl, 3⅛" h. x 4½" dia.	30.00	15.00

PAGE 140
FIG. 41. ZOO LIGHTS 1959

	U.S. $	British £
Alsatian	40.00	14.00

PAGE 141
FIG. 42. ANGEL CANDLEHOLDER

	U.S. $	British £
Standing Angel	100.00	45.00

FIG. 43. BOULDRAY TRAYS

	U.S. $	British £
A. Pelican, 2¼" high	26.00	8.00
B. Horse, 2¾" high	26.00	8.00

PAGE 142
FIG. 44. PEERAGE TRAYS

	U.S. $	British £
A. Girl with Basket, 2¾" high	26.00	8.00
B. Knight in Armour, 2¾" high	26.00	8.00

	U.S. $	British £
C. Elf, 2" high	26.00	8.00

FIG. 45. WHIMTRAYS

	U.S. $	British £
Swan Whimtray	145.00	40.00

FIG. 46. TEENAGE POTTERY EARLY 1960'S

	U.S. $	British £
A. Marty Wilde Casket, 1⅝" high *(See also No.368 pg.63 of The W of W2)*	130.00	85.00
B. Tommy Steele Casket, 1⅝" high	130.00	85.00
C. Cliff Richards Casket, 1⅝" high	130.00	85.00
D. Cliff Richards Brooch, 2⅜" long	150.00	150.00
E. Tommy Steele Brooch, 2⅜" long	150.00	150.00
F. Frankie Vaughan Brooch, 2⅜" long	150.00	150.00
G. Marty Wilde Brooch, 2⅜" long	150.00	150.00
H. Marty Wilde Plaque, 3¾" long	280.00	175.00
I. Frankie Vaughan Casket, 1⅝" high *(See also No.367 pg.63 of The W of W2)*	130.00	85.00
J. Cliff Richards Plaque, 3¾" long	280.00	175.00

PAGE 144
FIG. 48. CANDLEHOLDERS

	U.S. $	British £
Christmas Candleholders (boxed set of two)	50.00	30.00

FIG. 49. PRICE'S CANDLEHOLDERS 1963 - 1982

	U.S. $	British £
A. Tulip Holder (small), 1¾" high *(See also Nos. 386 and 387 pg.64 of The W of W2)*	12.00	3.00
B. Tulip Holder (large), 2¼" high	18.00	6.00

MONEY BANKS AND PROTOTYPE MODELS
by George Wade & Son Ltd. and Wade Heath & Company Ltd.

PAGE 146
FIG. 50.MONEY BANKS EARLY 1960'S - 1993

	U.S. $	British £
A. Fawn Money Bank (1987), 5¼" high *(See also No.391 pg.64 of The W of W2)*	45.00	25.00
B. Bambi Money Box (1960's)	60.00	40.00
C. Blow-up Disney Bambi (1961 - 1965), 4½" high *(See also No.167 pg.55 of The W of W2)*	150.00	85.00

PAGE 147
FIG. 51. PIGGY MONEY BANKS

	U.S. $	British £
Piggy Money Bank with Flower Decoration, 5" high	65.00	40.00

TANKARDS AND SOUVENIRS *by Wade Heath & Company Ltd. and Wade (Ireland) Ltd.*

PAGE 151
FIG. 57. WALL PLATE

	U.S. $	British £
Isle of Wight Wall Plate, 9½" dia.	15.00	20.00

FIG. 58. DOGHOUSE TANKARD

	U.S. $	British £
One Pint Doghouse Tankard, 4¾" high	25.00	10.00

FIG. 59. "PUNK PIG" TANKARD

	U.S. $	British £
"Punk Pig" Tankard, 4¼" high	40.00	30.00

PAGE 152
FIG. 60. TYRE DISHES

	U.S. $	British £
"Brightlingsea" Tyre Dish, 5" dia.	15.00	10.00

FIG. 61. POTTERY TRAYS

	U.S. $	British £
A. "Stockport" Pottery Tray, 4½" dia.	10.00	6.00
B. "Remember Aberdobey" Pottery Tray, 4½" dia.	10.00	6.00

PAGE 153
FIG. 62. LESNEY TRAYS CIRCA 1968 - 1975

	U.S. $	British £
A. "Double Decker Bus" Tray, 2¼" h. x 6" l.	50.00	25.00
B. "Open Double Decker Bus" Tray, 2½" h. x 6" l.	50.00	25.00

FIG. 63. LESNEY TRAYS CIRCA 1968 - 1975

	U.S. $	British £
A. "Duke of Connaught" Tray, 2½" h. x 6" l.	50.00	25.00
B. "Santa Fe" Tray, 2¼" h. x 6" l.	50.00	25.00

FIG. 64. LESNEY TRAY CIRCA 1968 - 1975

	U.S. $	British £
"Pike" Tray, 3½" w. x 6" l.	50.00	30.00

PAGE 154
FIG. 65. SOUVENIR DISHES

	U.S. $	British £
A. "Scottish Piper" Dish, 4½" l. x 4" w.	45.00	20.00
B. "City of London" Dish, 4½" l. x 4" w.	45.00	20.00

FIG. 66. SOUVENIR DISH

	U.S. $	British £
"Mermaid" Dish, 4½" l. x 4" w.	45.00	20.00

PAGE 155
FIG. 67. SOUVENIR DISHES

	U.S. $	British £
A. "City of Stoke-on-Trent" Dish, 4⅜" dia.	25.00	10.00
B. "The Yorkshire Insurance Company Ltd." Dish, 4⅜" dia.	25.00	10.00

FIG. 68. SOUVENIR DISHES

	U.S. $	British £
"Male Costume" Nut Dish (left), 4" dia.	25.00	10.00

	U.S. $	British £
"Female Costume" Nut Dish (right), 4" dia.	25.00	10.00

FIG. 69. ROLL OUT THE BARREL TANKARD CIRCA 1940

"Soldier" Tankard, 6" high	100.00	55.00

FIG. 70. "ROOSEVELT AND CHURCHILL" TANKARD CIRCA 1942

Tankard, $5^1/2$" high	290.00	160.00

FIG. 71. TRADITIONAL TANKARD

"Honi Soit Qui Mal Y Pense" Tankard, $4^1/2$" high	25.00	15.00

PAGE 156

FIG. 72. TOBY JUG

Miniature Toby Jug, $2^7/8$" high	55.00	35.00

FIG. 73. CRANKY TAKARDS LATE 1930'S

A.	"The Hangovah" Tankard, $4^3/4$" high	30.00	8.00
B.	"The Hyperfloogie" Tankard, $3^3/4$" high	30.00	8.00

PAGE 157

FIG. 74. POTTERY TRAYS

A.	"Ready Mix Concrete" Tray, $4^1/2$" overall	15.00	12.00
B.	"Ready Mix Concrete" Tray, $4^1/2$" high	15.00	12.00

FIG. 75. CIGARETTE BOX

Ready Mix Concrete Cigarette Box	55.00	35.00

PAGE 158

FIG. 76. MISCELLANEOUS ITEMS

"Mrs. Gamp" Pottery Tray, $4^3/8$" overall	25.00	10.00

FIG. 77. MISCELLANEOUS ITEMS

"Pears" Soap Dish, $5^3/4$" l. x $4^1/2$" w.	25.00	10.00

FIG. 78. JUGS

		U.S. $	British £
A.	Balmoral Castle, $3^1/4$" high	20.00	8.00
B.	Truro, 5" high	20.00	8.00

FIG. 79. NATIONAL WESTMINSTER BANK MUG 1987 - 1988

Piggy Bank Mug, $3^5/8$" high	65.00	45.00

PAGE 159

FIG. 80. VETERAN CAR SERIES

Veteran Car Ashtray, $1^1/2$" h. x $5^7/8$" dia.	25.00	15.00

FIG. 81. DECORATIVE GIFTWARE

		U.S. $	British £
A.	Bowl, $4^1/2$" high	30.00	12.00
B.	Bud Vase, $5^3/4$" high	20.00	10.00
C.	Bud Vase, $6^3/4$" high	15.00	6.00
D.	Bowl, $4^1/2$" high	30.00	12.00
E.	Jug, $5^3/4$" high	20.00	8.00
F.	Bud Vase, $4^3/4$" high	15.00	5.00
G.	Pottery Tray, 4" dia.	15.00	5.00
H.	Pottery Tray, 4" dia.	15.00	5.00
I.	Jug, $5^3/4$" high	20.00	8.00
J.	Jug, $5^3/4$" high	20.00	8.00

PAGE 161

FIG. 82. DECORATIVE GIFTWARE

Barrel Ashtray, $2^1/2$" h. x 6" dia.	20.00	12.00

FIG. 83. DECORATIVE GIFTWARE

"Captain Kidd's Treasure Chest" Candy Box	35.00	14.00

PAGE 163

FIG. 84. BUD VASE

"Little Nell" Bud Vase, $4^1/2$" high	35.00	15.00

FIG. 85. SHAVING MUGS

Boxed Naval Set	20.00	14.00

FIG. 86. AIRLINER SERIES

	U.S. $	British £
A. Pottery Tray, 4¼" square	20.00	12.00
B. One Pint Tankard, 4¾" high	35.00	20.00

PAGE 164

FIG. 87. LOVING CUP

"William Walker" Retirement Loving Cup, 5" high	NPA	NPA

FIG. 88 LOVING CUP

"Year of the Scout 1907 - 1982" Loving Cup, 3¼" high	35.00	20.00

PAGE 165

FIG. 90. POTTERY ACCESSORIES

	U.S. $	British £
A. "Horses" Ashtray, 2⅝" h. x 2¾" square	35.00	15.00
B. "Horses" Wall Plate, 8" dia.	35.00	20.00
C. "Horses" Half Pint Tankard, 3¾" high	20.00	8.00

PAGE 166

FIG. 91. MY FAIR LADY TRAYS 1958

A. My Fair Lady Sweet Dish, 4¼" square	20.00	6.00
B. My Fair Lady Sweet Dish, 4¼" square	20.00	6.00

FLOWER JUGS AND VASES *by Wade Heath & Company, Ltd.*

PAGE 172

FIG. 94. FLOWER JUG

	U.S. $	British £
"Castile 15" Flower Jug, 8¾" high *(See also No. 584 pg. 75 of The W of W2)*	120.00	75.00

TEAPOTS, TEACADDIES AND CREAM & SUGARS

by Wade Heath & Company, Ltd. and Wade Ceramics Ltd.

PAGE 177

FIG. 95. COOKIE JAR

	U.S. $	British £
Cookie Jar, 8½" high	45.00	25.00

PAGE 178

FIG. 96. COOKIE JAR AND COFFEE POT LATE 1930'S

	U.S. $	British £
Cookie Jar (left), 6" high *(See also No. 646 pg. 77 of The W of W2)*	115.00	60.00
Coffee Pot (right), 7½" high	120.00	65.00

PAGE 179

FIG. 97. TEAPOT

Old English Castle Teapot, 5" high *(See also No. 256 pg. 58 of the WPT)*	120.00	65.00

PAGE 181

FIG. 102. TEA CADDY 1991

	U.S. $	British £
Ringtons Ltd. Tea Caddy, 5½" high	60.00	35.00

FIG. 103. TEA CADDY 1993

Ringtons Ltd. Tea Caddy, 5½" high	60.00	35.00

PAGE 182

FIG. 104. TEAPOT 1989

"RSPB" Teapot, 4⅜" high	55.00	30.00

FIG. 105. TEAPOT AND CREAMER LATE 1930

Creamer (left), 2" high	15.00	6.00
Teapot (right), 3¼" high	45.00	20.00

FIG. 106. KEY RING

	U.S. $	British £
"Ridgeways" Teapot Key Ring, 1" high	45.00	35.00

FIG. 107. TEAPOT LATE 1980'S

	U.S. $	British £
Tetley Teapot, 4^1/$_2$" high	30.00	20.00

TABLEWARE *by Wade Heath & Company, Ltd. and Wade Ceramics Ltd.*

PAGE 189
FIG. 112. MISCELLANEOUS TABLEWARE

	U.S. $	British £
Covered Box, 1^3/$_4$" h. x 4" dia.	60.00	35.00

PAGE 190
FIG. 113. FALSTAFF WARE CIRCA 1960 - 1970

	U.S. $	British £
Claret Jug, 10" high	120.00	70.00

FIG. 114. FALSTAFF WARE CIRCA 1960 - 1970

	U.S. $	British £
A. Sugar Bowl, 3" high	25.00	15.00
B. Posy Bowl, 3^1/$_4$" h. x 5^1/$_4$" dia.	35.00	20.00
C. Footed Jug (not Falstaff), 5^3/$_4$" high	45.00	25.00

FIG. 116. DUCOR WARE CIRCA MID 1950'S

	U.S. $	British £
A. Cup and Saucer	18.00	10.00
B. Coffee Pot, 9^3/$_4$" high	80.00	45.00
C. Sugar Bowl, 2" high	18.00	10.00
D. Creamer, 5^3/$_4$" high	45.00	25.00

PAGE 192
FIG. 120. FRUIT BOWL AND NAPPY CIRCA EARLY 1920'S

	U.S. $	British £
A. Fruit Bowl, 9^3/$_4$" wide	25.00	16.00
B. Nappy, 6^1/$_2$" wide	10.00	5.00

PAGE 193
FIG. 121. "QUACK QUACK" DISHES

	U.S. $	British £
Plate, 6^1/$_4$" dia.	50.00	37.50

PAGE 194
FIG. 122. WALT DISNEY CHILDREN'S DISHES 1934 - LATE 1950'S

	U.S. $	British £
A. Creamer, 2" high	50.00	35.00

	U.S. $	British £
Teapot, 3^3/$_8$" high	105.00	70.00
Sugar, 1^1/$_2$" high	45.00	30.00
B. Cup and Saucer Set, per set	75.00	50.00
C. Plate, 5^1/$_8$" dia., each	75.00	50.00

PAGE 197
FIG. 123. MISCELLANEOUS TABLEWARE

	U.S. $	British £
Bowl, 6^1/$_4$" dia.	19.00	8.00

FIG. 124. MISCELLANEOUS TABLEWARE

	U.S. $	British £
Saucer, 4^1/$_2$" dia.	5.00	2.00
Cup, 2^1/$_4$" high	10.00	4.00

PAGE 198
FIG. 125. COPPER LUSTRE WARE 1935 - EARLY 1980'S

	U.S. $	British £
1. Candy Box, 6^3/$_4$" l. x 5" w.	65.00	40.00
2. Cigarette Box, 5" l. x 3^3/$_4$" w.	50.00	25.00
3. Ashtray, 4" l. x 3" w.	20.00	10.00
4. Finger Bowl, 4" dia.	30.00	18.00
5. Dandy Jug, 3" high *(See also No.524 pg.56 of The W of W)*	15.00	20.00
6. Dandy Jug, 3^1/$_2$" high	15.00	20.00
7. Dandy Jug, 4^1/$_2$" high	20.00	20.00
8. Dandy Jug, 5^1/$_4$" high	25.00	30.00
9. Dandy Jug, 6^1/$_4$" high *(See also No.508 pg.56 of The W of W)*	35.00	30.00
10. Dandy Jug, 5^3/$_4$" high	25.00	30.00
11. Beer Mug, 5" high	35.00	25.00
12. Eagle Teapot, 6" high and Stand	120.00	75.00
13. Dandy Sugar, 1^3/$_4$" high *(See also No.523 pg.56 of The W of W)*	15.00	8.00

		U.S. $	British £
14.	Dandy Sugar, 2" high	15.00	8.00
15.	Toby Jug (Pirate), 5" high	125.00	80.00
16.	Toby Jug (Highwayman), 5" high	125.00	80.00
17.	Lattice Jug, 6" high	45.00	35.00
	(See also No.506 pg.56 of The W of W)		
18.	Lattice Jug, 5" high	45.00	35.00
19.	Nelson Teapot, $5^1/_2$" high	70.00	60.00
20.	Nelson Teapot, $5^3/_4$" high	80.00	60.00
21.	Dutch Jug, $4^1/_2$" high	60.00	35.00
22.	Dutch Jug, $5^1/_2$" high	50.00	25.00
23.	Dutch Jug, $5^3/_4$" high	60.00	35.00
24.	Diamond Jug, 6" high	50.00	35.00
25.	Diamond Jug, $5^1/_2$" high	40.00	35.00
26.	Stag Bowl,	45.00	35.00
27.	Console Bowl, 4" h. x $11^1/_4$" l.	75.00	50.00
	(See also No.516 pg.56 of The W of W)		
28.	Stag Jug, 5" high	45.00	35.00
29.	Polka Jug, 6" high	60.00	35.00
30.	Stag Jug, 6" high	50.00	35.00

FIG. 126. MEADOW TABLEWARE

	Covered Vegetable Dish, $9^3/_4$" across	30.00	18.00

PAGE 199

FIG. 127. ORB SHAPE TABLEWARE

	Cup and Saucer Set, each	15.00	5.00

FIG. 128. MISCELLANEOUS TABLEWARE

A.	Plate, $9^1/_2$" dia.	20.00	12.00
B.	Veteran Car Cigarette Box,	40.00	18.00
	(See also No.973 pg.93 of The W of W2)		
C.	Tankard, 5" high	20.00	12.00
D.	Tankard, 5" high	20.00	12.00
E.	Dish, 10" l. x $6^3/_4$" w.	25.00	18.00
F.	Plate, $9^1/_2$" dia.	20.00	12.00
G.	Jug, 5" high	20.00	8.00
	(See also Fig.78 No.B pg.158 of The W of W2)		
H.	Plate, $9^1/_2$" dia.	20.00	12.00

PAGE 200

FIG. 129. FRUIT BOWLS LATE 1930'S

		U.S. $	British £
A.	Bowl, $3^1/_4$" h. x $8^1/_4$" dia.	25.00	16.00
B.	Bowl, 3" h. x $7^1/_4$" dia.	10.00	5.00

FIG. 130. "ROSETTA" TABLEWARE MID-1950'S

	Plate, $7^3/_4$" dia.	18.00	10.00

PAGE 201

FIG. 131. DINNERWARE

A.	Tab Handled Plate, $9^1/_2$" dia.	15.00	8.00
B.	Cup and Saucer Set, per set	12.00	6.00
C.	Plate, $6^1/_2$" dia.	12.00	6.00
D.	Creamer, $2^3/_4$" high	15.00	8.00
E.	Sugar, $2^3/_4$" high	12.00	6.00
F.	Oval Tab Handled Platter, 11" long	18.00	10.00

FIG. 132. MODE WARE 1953

	"Carnival" Snack Set,	25.00	15.00
	(See also No.934 pg.91 of The W of W2)		

PAGE 202

FIG. 134. REGENCY TABLEWARE

	Handled Sandwich Plate, $10^1/_2$" dia.	25.00	15.00

PAGE 203

FIG. 135. BRAMBLE WARE

	Milk Jug, 5" high	30.00	28.00

PAGE 204

FIG. 136. MISCELLANEOUS TABLEWARE

	"Parasol" Nut Dish, 7" dia.	22.00	12.00

PAGE 207

FIG. 143. DECORATION NO. 6136

A.	Nut Dish, $4^1/_8$" dia.	20.00	12.00
B.	Dandy Jug, $5^3/_4$" high	35.00	25.00

FIG. 144. "DARWIN" TABLEWARE

	U.S. $	British £
Plate, 9¹/₂" dia.	15.00	6.00

FIG. 145. MISCELLANEOUS TABLEWARE

	U.S. $	British £
Plate, 6¹/₂" dia.	15.00	6.00

PAGE 208
FIG. 146. "RIBBON AND BOW" TABLEWARE

	U.S. $	British £
Saucer, 5⁵/₈" dia.	4.00	2.00

ROYAL COMMEMORATIVES *by Wade Heath & Company, Ltd.*

PAGE 214
FIG. 157. MISCELLANEOUS ITEMS

	U.S. $	British £
A. "Edward VIII" Musical Loving Cup, 5" high	300.00	145.00
B. "Queen Elizabeth II" Mug, 2¹/₄" high	35.00	12.00
C. Fruit Bowl, 9" across *(See also No.1020 pg.96 of The W of W2)*	45.00	25.00
D. "Charles and Diana" Loving Cup, 3¹/₄" high	55.00	30.00

PAGE 215
FIG. 158. MISCELLANEOUS ITEMS

	U.S. $	British £
A. "Queen Elizabeth II" Cup and Saucer Set,	28.00	10.00
B. "Queen Elizabeth II" Plate, 7" dia.	28.00	10.00

	U.S. $	British £
C. "Charles and Diana" Napkin Ring, 2³/₄" dia.	40.00	35.00
D. "George VI and Queen Elizabeth" Mug, 3" high	40.00	25.00

FIG. 159. TAUNTON CIDER MUG 1977

	U.S. $	British £
Queen's Silver Jubilee Mug, 3¹/₄" high	65.00	30.00

PAGE 216
FIG. 160. CORONATION BOWL

Bowl, 7¹/₂" dia.	25.00	16.00

FIG. 161. COMMEMORATIVE TANKARD

Tankard, 4¹/₈" high	25.00	20.00

WADE (ULSTER) LTD. AND WADE IRELAND LTD.

PAGE 219
FIG. 162. IRISH GIFTWARE

	U.S. $	British £
A. Hot Plate, 5¹/₂" square *(See also Nos.1065 & 1067 pg.99 of The W of W2)*	65.00	25.00
B. Tankard, 4¹/₄" high	25.00	12.00
C. Lamp Base, 6" dia.	50.00	25.00
D. Shamrock Dish, 4¹/₂" across	55.00	15.00
E. Duck Planter, 4¹/₄" h. x 7" l. *(See also No.1112 pg.100 of The W of W2)*	165.00	150.00
F. Donkey and Side Panniers, 4" high	55.00	20.00
G. Self-standing Picture, 3⁵/₈" h. x 4¹/₂" l. *(See also No.1081 pg.99 of The W of W2)*	65.00	25.00

FIG. 163. IRISH GIFTWARE

	U.S. $	British £
Cup and Saucer Set	40.00	20.00

PAGE 220
FIG. 164. PROTOTYPE TEAPOTS

Teapot (left), 6¹/₂" high	NPA	NPA
Teapot (right), 6¹/₂" high *(See also No. 158 pg.54 of theWPT)*	NPA	NPA

PAGE 222
FIG. 165. MISCELLANEOUS GIFTWARE

"Kingsford's" Decanter, 6³/₄" high	75.00	40.00

FIG. 166. MISCELLANEOUS GIFTWARE

	U.S. $	British £
"Pheasant" Decanter, 5¹/₂" high	75.00	40.00

PAGE 223
FIG. 167. RHINOCEROS ASHTRAYS 1962

Rhino Ashtray (left), 5¹/₂" h. x 6" l.	150.00	250.00
Rhino Ashtray (right), 8¹/₄" h. x 9" l.	200.00	255.00

FIG. 168. OINTMENT JAR 1976

"Glaxo" Jar, 7" high	35.00	35.00

FIG. 169. CANDLEHOLDER MID 1950'S

Candleholder, 6¹/₂" dia.	50.00	30.00

FIG. 170. CANDLEHOLDER/ASHTRAY EARLY 1960'S

Ashtray, 8" dia.	50.00	30.00

PAGE 224
FIG. 171. PADDY MCGREDY FLORIBUNDA SET

	U.S. $	British £
A. Half Pint Tankard, 4¹/₄" high	25.00	12.00
B. Ashtray	20.00	10.00
C. Cigarette Box, 1³/₄" h. x 5" l.	40.00	25.00

FIG. 172. "PEX" FAIRY 1948 - 1950

Pex Fairy Figurine, 2³/₈" high	500.00	250.00

(See also Nos. 11 & 12 pg. 49 of the WPT)

FIG. 173. "PEX" FAIRY CANDLEHOLDER

Pex Fairy Candleholder, 3" high	600.00	350.00

PAGE 225
FIG. 174. FLYING BIRDS SET 2 LATE 1950'S

Bird, each	28.00	20.00
Birds, set of three	75.00	50.00

FIG. 175. ANIMAL FIGURES

Walrus, 4" high	645.00	375.00

WADE (PDM) LTD.

PAGE 227
FIG. 176. NOVELTY ITEMS

	U.S. $	British £
Reginald Corfield Dish (left), 4³/₄" dia.	30.00	18.00
London Zoo Dish (right), 4³/₄" dia.	30.00	18.00

PAGE 228
FIG. 177. PUSSER'S RUM DECANTER 1983

Hip Flask, 5³/₄" high	30.00	18.00

(See also No. 1148 pg. 101 of The W of W2)

FIG. 178. "BRONTE" DECANTERS

Decanter Jug, 7¹/₂" high	75.00	40.00

FIG. 179. "BRONTE" DECANTERS

Liquor Bottle (left), 2³/₄" high	10.00	5.00
Liquor Bottle (right), 6¹/₄" high	25.00	10.00

PAGE 229
FIG. 181. THORNTON & FRANCE SHERRY BARREL

	U.S. $	British £
Sherry Barrel, 8³/₄" h. x 11¹/₄" l.	300.00	175.00

PAGE 230
FIG. 182. WATER JUGS

Black & White Whisky Water Jug (left), 2¹/₈" high	15.00	10.00
Black & White Whisky Water Jug (right), 4⁷/₈" high	28.00	20.00

PAGE 231
FIG. 183. M & B CENTENARY JUG 1979

Water Jug, 5³/₈" high	30.00	20.00

FIG. 184. COFFEE MUG

Mug, 2¹/₂" high	20.00	10.00

FIG. 185.NELSON CIGARETTES

Ashtray, 1³/₄" h. x 7" l.	20.00	8.00

FIG. 186.BOMBAY DRY GIN

Miniature Water Jug, 2¹/₂" high	15.00	10.00

FIG. 187.MARSTON'S GOOD FOOD

Salt Shaker (left), 4⁵/₈" high	15.00	4.00
Pepper Shaker (right), 4⁵/₈" high	15.00	4.00

FIG. 188. KRONENBOURG TANKARD

Tankard, 4⁷/₈" high	25.00	12.00

FIG. 189.PICON - PICON CONTAINER

Desk Tidy, 3¹/₄" high	15.00	8.00

FIG. 190.WAITER TRAY

McCallum's Whisky Waiter Tray, 12³/₄" square	15.00	8.00

FIG. 191.BELL'S WHISKY DECANTER

This decanter was incorrectly identified in *The W of W2* as being issued for the U.K. market. It was in fact issued for the South African market.

	U.S. $	British £
Christmas 1993 Decanter, 75cl, full and boxed	490.00	285.00
Christmas 1993 Decanter, 75cl, empty	200.00	150.00

FIG. 192.BELL'S WHISKY DECANTER

This decanter was incorrectly identified in *The W of W2* as being issued for the South African market. It was in fact issued for the U.K. market.

Christmas 1993 Decanter, 75cl, full and boxed	80.00	45.00
Christmas 1993 Decanter, 75cl, empty	35.00	20.00

FIG. 193A.PETER ENGLAND ASHTRAY

Lion Ashtray, 7¹/₄" wide	90.00	50.00

FIG. 194.BACARDI RUM

Ashtray, 1³/₄" h. x 7¹/₂" l.	10.00	5.00

INDEX